Computer Test Bank

Test Bank CD-ROM Inside!

A HISTORY OF
THE UNITED STATES

BOORSTIN · KELLEY

PRENTICE HALL

Prentice
Hall

Needham, Massachusetts
Upper Saddle River, New Jersey
Glenview, Illinois

ISBN 0-13-410838-8

1 2 3 4 5 6 7 8 9   05 04 03 02 01

TABLE OF CONTENTS

EXAMVIEW® PRO 3.0 TEST GENERATOR USER'S GUIDE

QUESTION BANK

SECTION 1 — INTRODUCTION

This user's guide accompanies a test generator program called *ExamView® Pro 3.0*–an application that enables you to quickly create printed tests, Internet tests, and computer (LAN-based) tests. You can enter your own questions and customize the appearance of the tests you create. The *ExamView Pro* test generator program offers many unique features. Using the QuickTest wizard, for example, you are guided step-by-step through the process of building a test. Numerous options are included that allow you to customize the content and appearance of the tests you create.

As you work with the *ExamView* test generator, you may use the following features:

- **an interview mode or "wizard" to guide you through the steps to create a test in less than five minutes**
- **five methods to select test questions**
  - random selection
  - from a list
  - while viewing questions
  - by criteria (difficulty code, objective, topic, etc.–if available)
  - all questions
- **the capability to edit questions or to add an unlimited number of questions**
- **online (*Internet-based*) testing**
  - create a test that students can take on the Internet using a browser
  - receive instant feedback via email
  - create online study guides with student feedback for incorrect responses
  - include any of the twelve (12) question types
- **Internet test-hosting ***
  - instantly publish a test to the *ExamView* website
  - manage tests online
  - allow students to access tests from one convenient location
  - receive detailed reports
  - download results to your gradebook or spreadsheet
- **online (*LAN-based*) testing**
  - allow anyone or selected students to take a test on your local area network
  - schedule tests
  - create online study guides with student feedback for incorrect responses
  - incorporate multimedia links (movies and audio)
  - export student results to a gradebook or spreadsheet
- **a sophisticated word processor**
  - streamlined question entry with spell checker
  - tabs, fonts, symbols, foreign characters, and text styles
  - tables with borders and shading
  - full-featured equation editor
  - pictures or other graphics within a question, answer, or narrative
- **numerous test layout and printing options**
  - scramble the choices in multiple choice questions
  - print multiple versions of the same test with corresponding answer keys
  - print an answer key strip for easier test grading
- **link groups of questions to common narratives**

* The Internet test-hosting service must be purchased separately. Visit www.examview.com to learn more.

SECTION 2 — INSTALLATION AND STARTUP INSTRUCTIONS

The *ExamView Pro 3.0* test generator software is provided on a CD-ROM or floppy disks. The disc includes the program and all of the questions for the corresponding textbook. The *ExamView Test Player,* which can be used by your students to take online (computerized or LAN-based) tests, is also included.

Before you can use the test generator, you must install it on your hard drive. The system requirements, installation instructions, and startup procedures are provided below.

SYSTEM REQUIREMENTS

To use the *ExamView Pro 3.0* test generator or the online test player, your computer must meet or exceed the following minimum hardware requirements:

Windows

- Pentium computer
- Windows 95, Windows 98, Windows 2000 (or a more recent version)
- color monitor (VGA-compatible)
- CD-ROM and/or high-density floppy disk drive
- hard drive with at least 7 MB space available
- 8 MB available memory *(16 MB memory recommended)*
- an Internet connection to access the Internet test-hosting features

Macintosh

- PowerPC processor, 100 MHz computer
- System 7.5 (or a more recent version)
- color monitor (VGA-compatible)
- CD-ROM and/or high-density floppy disk drive
- hard drive with at least 7 MB space available
- 8 MB available memory *(16 MB memory recommended)*
- an Internet connection with System 8.6 (or more recent version) to access the Internet test-hosting features

INSTALLATION INSTRUCTIONS

Follow these steps to install the *ExamView* test generator software. The setup program will automatically install everything you need to use *ExamView*. **Note:** A separate test player setup program is also included for your convenience. [See *Online (LAN-based) Testing* on page 9 for more information.]

Windows

Step 1
Turn on your computer.

Step 2
Insert the *ExamView* disc into the CD-ROM drive. If the program is provided on floppy disks, insert Disk 1 into Drive A.

Step 3
Click the **Start** button on the *Taskbar* and choose the *Run* option.

Step 4

If the *ExamView* software is provided on a CD-ROM, use the drive letter that corresponds to the CD-ROM drive on your computer (e.g., **d:\setup.exe**). The setup program, however, may be located in a subfolder on the CD-ROM if the *ExamView* software is included on the disc with other resources. In which case, click the **Browse** button in the Run dialog box to locate the setup program (e.g., **d:\evpro\setup.exe**).

If you are installing the software from floppy disks, type **a:\setup** and press **Enter** to run the installation program.

Step 5

Follow the prompts on the screen to complete the installation process.

If the software and question banks are provided on more than one floppy disk, you will be prompted to insert the appropriate disk when it is needed.

Step 6

Remove the installation disc when you finish.

Macintosh

Step 1

Turn on your computer.

Step 2

Insert the *ExamView* installation disc into your CD-ROM drive. If the program is provided on floppy disks, insert Disk 1 into a disk drive.

Step 3

Open the installer window, if necessary.

Step 4

Double-click the installation icon to start the program.

Step 5

Follow the prompts on the screen to complete the installation process.

If the software and question banks are provided on more than one floppy disk, you will be prompted to insert the appropriate disk when it is needed.

Step 6

Remove the installation disc when you finish.

GETTING STARTED

After you complete the installation process, follow these instructions to start the *ExamView* test generator software. This section also explains the options used to create a test and edit a question bank.

Startup Instructions

Step 1
Turn on the computer.

Step 2

Windows: Click the **Start** button on the *Taskbar*. Highlight the **Programs** menu and locate the *ExamView Test Generator* folder. Select the *ExamView Pro* option to start the software.

Macintosh: Locate and open the *ExamView* folder. Double-click the *ExamView Pro* program icon.

Step 3
The first time you run the software, you will be prompted to enter your name, school/institution name, and city/state. You are now ready to begin using the *ExamView* software.

Step 4
Each time you start *ExamView,* the **Startup** menu appears. Choose one of the options shown in Figure 1. **Note:** All of the figures shown in this user's guide are taken from the Windows software. Except for a few minor differences, the Macintosh screens are identical.

Step 5
Use *ExamView* to create a test or edit questions in a question bank.

ExamView includes three components: Test Builder, Question Bank Editor, and Test Player. The **Test Builder** includes options to create, edit, print, and save tests. The **Question Bank Editor** lets you create or edit question banks. The **Test Player** is a separate program that your students can use to take online (LAN-based) tests/study guides.

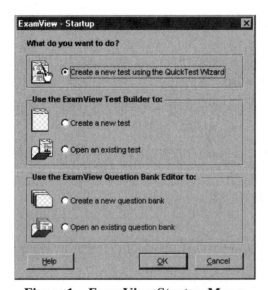

Figure 1 – ExamView Startup Menu

Using The Help System

Whenever you need assistance using *ExamView,* access the extensive help system. Click the **Help** button or choose the **Help Topics** option from the *Help* menu to access step-by-step instructions from more than 150 help topics. If you experience any difficulties while you are working with the software, you may want to review the troubleshooting tips in the user-friendly help system.

Test Builder

The Test Builder allows you to create tests using the QuickTest Wizard, or you can create a new test on your own. (See the sample test in Figure 2.) Use the Test Builder to prepare both printed and online tests/study guides.

- *If you want ExamView to select questions randomly from one or more question banks,* choose the *QuickTest Wizard* option to create a new test. (Refer to Figure 1 on page 4.) Then, follow the step-by-step instructions to (1) enter a test title, (2) choose one or more question banks from which to select questions, and (3) identify how many questions you want on the test. The QuickTest Wizard will automatically create a new test and use the Test Builder to display the test on screen. You can print the test as is, remove questions, add new questions, or edit any question.

- *If you want to create a new test on your own,* choose the option to create a new test. (Refer to Figure 1 on page 4.) Then, identify a question bank from which to choose questions by using the *Question Bank* option in the **Select** menu. You may then add questions to the test by using one or more of the following selection options: *Randomly, From a List, While Viewing, By Criteria,* or *All Questions.*

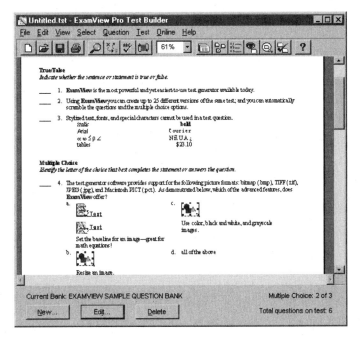

Figure 2 – Sample Test

IMPORTANT: The Test Builder and the Question Bank Editor systems are integrated in one program. As you work with *ExamView*, you can easily switch between the Test Builder and Question Bank Editor components using the *Switch to...* option in the **File** menu.

To create a new test:

Step 1

Start the *ExamView* software.

Step 2

At the Startup window, choose the *Create a new test* option.

Step 3

Enter a title for the new test.

    After you enter the title, the program will automatically display the option for you to select a question bank.

Step 4

Choose a question bank.

Step 5

Select the questions you want to include on the test.

    Use the question selection options that appear in the **Select** menu. Or, click the corresponding buttons on the toolbar. A description for each of the question selection toolbar buttons appears below.

 Click the **Question Bank** toolbar button to select a question bank.

    You can create a test using questions from one question bank or from multiple banks. Choose a bank, select the questions you want, and then choose another bank to select more questions.

 Click the **Select Randomly** toolbar button when you want the program to randomly select questions for you.

 Use the **Select from a List** command to choose questions if you know which ones you want to select. Identify the questions you want by reviewing a question bank printout.

 Click the **Select while Viewing** button to display a window that shows all of the questions in the current question bank. Click the check boxes to select the questions you want.

 You can use the **Select by Criteria** option to choose questions based on question type, difficulty, and objective (if available).

 Click the **Select All** button to choose all of the questions in the current question bank.

Step 6

Save the test.

Step 7

Print the test.

    You can use the options in the **Test** menu to customize the appearance of a test, edit test instructions, and choose to leave space for students to write their answers. When you print a test, you may choose how many variations of the test you want, whether you want all the versions to be the same, and whether you want to scramble the questions and the multiple choice options. If you choose to scramble the questions, *ExamView* will print a custom answer sheet for each variation of the test.

    If you want your students to take a test online, first create the test. Then, publish the test as an Internet test/study guide (page 15) or use the Online Test Wizard (page 10) to create a test for delivery over a LAN (local area network). The software will walk you through the steps to turn any test into an online (Internet or LAN-based) test.

    IMPORTANT: You may edit questions or create new questions as you build your test. However, those questions can be used only as part of the current test. If you plan to create several new questions that you would like to use on other tests, switch to the Question Bank Editor to add the new questions.

Question Bank Editor

The Question Bank Editor allows you to edit questions in an existing publisher-supplied question bank or to create your own new question banks. Always use the Question Bank Editor if you want to change a question permanently in an existing question bank. If you want to make a change that applies only to a particular test, create a new question or edit that question in the Test Builder.

A question bank may include up to 250 questions in a variety of formats including multiple choice, true/false, modified true/false, completion, yes/no, matching, problem, essay, short answer, case, and numeric response. You can include the following information for each question: difficulty code, reference, text objective, state objectives, topic, and notes.

Step 1
Start the *ExamView* software.

Step 2
At the Startup window as illustrated in Figure 1 on page 4, choose to *Create a new question bank* or *Open an existing question bank.*

If you are working in the Test Builder, click the **File** menu and choose *Switch to Question Bank Editor* to edit or create a new question bank.

Step 3
Click the **New** button to create a new question or click the **Edit** button to modify an existing question. Both of these buttons appear at the bottom of the Question Bank Editor window. (See Figure 3.)

You may add new questions or edit questions in a question bank by using the built-in word processor. The word processor includes many features commonly found in commercially available word processing applications. These features include the following: fonts, styles, tables, paragraph formatting, ruler controls, tabs, indents, and justification.

Step 4
Save your work. Then, exit the program or switch back to the Test Builder.

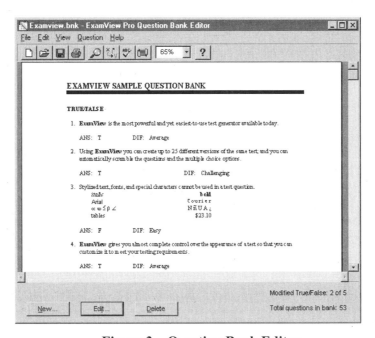

Figure 3 – Question Bank Editor

Online Testing (LAN-based vs. Internet)

The *ExamView* software allows you to create paper tests and online tests. The program provides two distinct online testing options: **LAN-based** testing and **Internet** testing. The option you choose depends on your particular testing needs. You can choose either option to administer online tests and study guides.

The **LAN-based** testing option is designed to work on a local area network server. That is, you can copy the test/study guide along with the Test Player software onto your local area network. Then students can take the test at computers connected to your server.

To take a LAN-based test, you must provide access for your students to the Test Player program included with the *ExamView* software. The Test Player is a separate program that lets your students take a test/study guide at a computer. You can store the Test Player program and the test on a local area network for easy access by your students.

The **Internet** testing option provides a computerized testing solution for delivering tests via the Internet or an Intranet. This option is great for distance learning environments or simply to make a sample test/study guide available to students at home. Students do not need any other program (unlike the LAN-based option). When your students take a test, the results are automatically sent to you via email.

You can publish an Internet test to your own website, or you can use the *ExamView* Internet test-hosting service. If you subscribe to the *ExamView* test-hosting service, you can publish a test directly to the Internet with just a few simple steps. Students will have immediate access to the tests that you publish and you can get detailed reports. For more information on the Internet test-hosting service, visit our website at www.examview.com.

SECTION 3 — ONLINE (LAN-BASED) TESTING

Online testing features are seamlessly integrated into the *ExamView* software. If you want to take advantage of these capabilities, simply create a test and then use the Online Test Wizard to set up the testing parameters. Students can then take the test at the computer using the Test Player program.

IMPORTANT: If you want to prepare a test/study guide for delivery via the Internet, use the *Publish Internet Test* option as described on page 16.

ExamView includes many features that let you customize an online (LAN-based) test. You can create a test for a specific class, or you can prepare a study guide for anyone to take. Using the Online Test Wizard, you can schedule a test or allow it to be taken anytime. As your students work on a test, *ExamView* will scramble the question order, provide feedback for incorrect responses, and display a timer if you selected any of these options.

ONLINE (LAN-BASED) TESTING OVERVIEW

Refer to the steps below for an overview of the online (LAN-based) testing process. Specific instructions for creating a test, taking a test, and viewing results are provided on the following pages.

Step 1
Talk with your network administrator to help you set up a location (folder) on your local area network where you can install the Test Player software and copy your tests/study guides.

Make sure that the administrator gives you and your students full access to the designated folders on the server. You may also want your network administrator to install the Test Player software.

Step 2
Create a test/study guide, and then use the Online Test Wizard to set up the online (LAN-based) test. Save your work and exit the *ExamView* software.

Step 3
Transfer the test/study guide file [e.g., chapter1.tst (Windows) or Chapter 1 (Macintosh)] and any accompanying multimedia files from your computer to the local area network server.

Copy the files from your hard drive to the folder set up by your network administrator. You need only copy the test file unless you linked an audio or video segment to one or more questions.

Step 4
Instruct your students to complete the test/study guide.

Students must have access to a computer connected to the local area network on which the Test Player and test/study guide are stored.

Step 5
After all students finish taking the test, copy the test/study guide file back to your hard drive. It is recommended that you copy the test to a different location from the original test file. The test file, itself, contains all of the students' results.

Note: If you set up a class roster, the test file will contain item analysis information and the results for each student. If you did not set up a roster, no results are recorded so you do not have to complete this step or the next.

Step 6
Start the *ExamView* software and open the test file to view your students' results.

CREATING AN ONLINE (LAN-BASED) TEST

Follow the steps shown below to create an online (LAN-based) test or study guide. Depending on the options you set, you can create a test or study guide. Before you begin, make sure that you installed the *ExamView* test generator and test player software. **Note**: See the next section (page 12) for instructions to set up the test player. (See page 15 for Internet testing features.)

Step 1
Start the *ExamView* software.

Step 2
Create or open a test/study guide.

Select the questions you want to include on the test. You can include any of the following types: True/False, Multiple Choice, Yes/No, Numeric Response, Completion, and Matching.

Step 3
Select the *Online Test Wizard* option from the **Online** menu.

ExamView presents step-by-step instructions to help you prepare the online test/study guide. (See Figure 4.) Read the instructions provided and complete each step. **Note**: Click the **Help** button if you need more assistance.

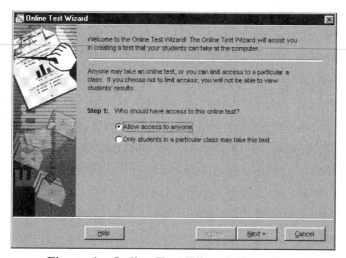

Figure 4 – Online Test Wizard (Step 1)

Step 4
Click the **Finish** button after you complete the last step using the Online Test Wizard. As you can see in Figure 5 on page 11, *ExamView* shows a summary that describes the settings for the online test.

Step 5
Save the test/study guide to a location where your students can easily access it. For example, save it in the same location where you installed the Test Player program.

It is recommended that you save the test/study guide to a location on a network server where students have read/write access. The Test Player will store all of your students' results (if you entered a class roster) in the test file itself. You can copy the test to individual computers, but this configuration takes more time to gather the results.

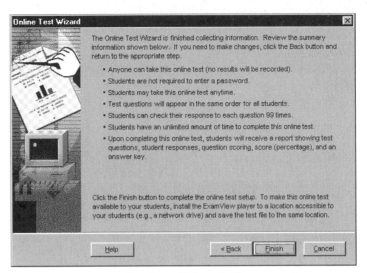

Figure 5 – Online Test Wizard (Summary)

Step 6

If you included multimedia links in any of the questions, copy those files to the same location where you saved the test/study guide.

If the multimedia files are on a CD-ROM or DVD disc, you may leave them on the disc, but provide this information to your students. To play one of these links, students will have to specify the location of the multimedia file.

NOTES:

- Use the *Test Preferences* and *Class Roster* options in the **Online** menu if you want to make any changes to the test parameters. These two options let you change any of the settings you selected using the Online Test Wizard.

- You must close the test before your students can access it with the Test Player.

- If you set up a class roster for a test/study guide, you cannot modify the test (e.g., edit a question, change the order, etc.) once any student has taken it unless you clear the results first.

- Provide your students with the Test Player setup program and a copy of the test/study guide if you want them to take it at home.

INSTALLING THE TEST PLAYER

Follow the instructions provided here to install the Test Player program for your students. You may copy the Test Player to a network (recommended), install it on individual computers, or provide it on floppy disk for your students to take home.

Even if you have a network, you can install the Test Player on individual computers. Students will still be able to access tests/study guides you store on a local area network.

ExamView Test Player Installation

Windows

Step 1
Turn on your computer.

Step 2
Insert the *ExamView* disc into your CD-ROM drive. If the software was provided on floppy disks, insert the *ExamView–Test Player* installation disk into Drive A.

Step 3
Click the **Start** button on the *Taskbar* and choose the *Run* option.

Step 4
If the *ExamView* software is provided on a CD-ROM, use the drive letter that corresponds to the CD-ROM drive on your computer (e.g., **d:\evplayer\setup** or **d:\evpro\evplayer\setup**).

If you are installing the software from a floppy disk, type **a:\setup** and press **Enter** to run the installation program.

Step 5
When prompted for a location to install the program, select a folder (e.g., **x:\programs\evplayer** for network installations or **c:\evplayer** on your local hard drive).

Step 6
For local area network (LAN) installations, complete the following steps at each workstation:

- Click the **Start** button and choose **Taskbar** from the **Settings** menu.
- Click the **Start Menu Programs** tab and click **Add.**
- Type the location and program name for the Test Player software, or use the **Browse** button to enter this information (e.g., **x:\programs\evplayer\evplayer.exe**).
- Proceed to the next screen and add a new folder (e.g., **ExamView Test Player**).
- Enter **ExamView Test Player** as the shortcut name and then click the **Finish** button.

Repeat Steps 1–5 if you plan to install the software at each computer instead of installing the program once on your network.

Macintosh

Step 1
Turn on your computer.

Step 2
Insert the *ExamView* installation disc into your CD-ROM drive. If the program is provided on floppy disks, insert the *ExamView–Test Player* installation disk into a disk drive.

Step 3
Open the installer window, if necessary.

Step 4
Double-click the installation icon to start the program.

Note: The installation program is configured to copy the test player to a new folder on your hard drive. You can, however, change this location. For example, you can select a location on your network server.

Step 5
When prompted for a location to install the program, select a folder on your local area network that is accessible to all students. If you are installing the software on a stand-alone computer, choose a location on the hard drive.

Step 6
At each workstation, enable file sharing and program linking if you installed the application on your network server.

For stand-alone computers, repeat Steps 1–5.

Installing the Test Player at Home

You can give your students the Test Player software to take home. If the *ExamView* software was sent to you on floppy disks, give your students the separate Test Player setup disk. If you received the software on CD-ROM, copy all of the setup files in the *evplayer* folder onto a floppy disk. Students should follow Steps 1-5 to install the software on their computer. When students take a test home, they should copy it into the same folder as the Test Player program.

TAKING AN ONLINE (LAN-BASED) TEST

Make sure that you have properly installed the *ExamView* Test Player software and copied the test/study guide to a location easily accessible to your students. If you linked multimedia files to any of the questions, it is recommended that you copy those files to the same folder as the test/study guide.

If you created a test with a class roster, students must correctly enter their IDs to be able to take the test/study guide. Provide this information to your students, if necessary. **Note**: If you do not want to track student scores, you should set up a test to allow anyone to take it.

Step 1
Start the *ExamView* Test Player software.

Step 2
Enter your name and ID. (See Figure 6.)

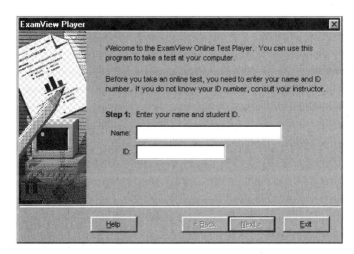

Figure 6 – Online Test/Study Guide Registration

Step 3

Select a test/study guide. (See Figure 7.)

If no tests (or study guides) appear in the list, click the **Folder** button to identify where the tests are located.

Step 4

(Optional) Enter a password, if prompted.

Step 5

Review the summary information and click **Start** when you are ready to begin.

Step 6

Answer all of the questions and click the **End** button when you finish.

Verify that you want to end the test. If you do not answer all of the questions in one session, you will *not* be able to resume the test at a later time.

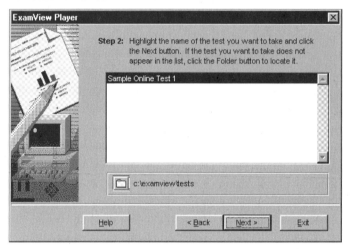

Figure 7 – Online Test/Study Guide Selection

Step 7

Review the test report.

Step 8

Click **New Test** to take another test or click **Exit** to quit the program.

VIEWING ONLINE (LAN-BASED) RESULTS

If you set up a test with a class roster (instead of allowing anyone to access a test/study guide), the *ExamView* Test Player will automatically collect the results for each student. The program saves this information in the test/study guide file itself.

Step 1

Start the *ExamView* software and open the online test/study guide that your students have already taken.

Step 2

Choose *View Test Results* from the **Online** menu.

Step 3

Review the results, item-by-item analysis, and statistics reports.

Step 4

Choose *Export Test Results* if you want to export the scores to your favorite gradebook program or spreadsheet application.

SECTION 4 — INTERNET TESTING

ExamView lets you easily create Internet tests and study guides. Build a test and then simply choose the *Publish Internet Test* option. You can choose to post tests to your own website or to publish tests directly to the *ExamView* website. (Visit us at www.examview.com to learn more about subscribing to the Internet test-hosting service.)

With the Internet test-hosting feature, you can publish a test or study guide directly to the *ExamView* website. Simply create a test and then follow the easy step-by-step instructions to publish it to the Internet. It's that simple! You can manage tests online, view reports, and download results. Students access your tests from one convenient location.

If you do not use the ExamView test-hosting service, you can manually post tests/study guides to your own website. If you create a test, your students' results are sent to you via email automatically. Or, you can create a study guide that your students can use to review various topics at their own pace.

INTERNET TESTING FAQs

Review the FAQs (frequently asked questions) below for more information on the Internet test-hosting features available to *ExamView Pro 3.0* users.

What are the advantages to using the Internet test-hosting feature? (1) Publishing an Internet test to your own website and setting up links can be quite challenging. With the Internet test-hosting feature, the process is completely automated. In minutes, you can post a test to the Internet. (2) When you post tests/study guides to your own website, only a few options are available. Using the *ExamView* test-hosting service, you have many more options available such as setting up a class roster and viewing detailed item analysis reports.

How do you register for the test-hosting service? Visit our website at www.examview.com to learn how to register. Before you can post tests/study guides, you must sign up to obtain a valid instructor ID and a password.

Is there an additional charge for the Internet test-hosting service? Yes, there is an additional yearly subscription charge to use this service. If you received the *ExamView* software from a publisher, you may be eligible for a discount or a free trial membership. (See our website for current prices and special promotions.)

Do you have to use the Internet test-hosting service? No, using the test-hosting service is not required. The *Publish Internet Test* feature includes an option to save an Internet test/study guide to a local hard drive. Then, you can manually post it to your own website.

Why aren't the same features available for tests posted to my own website? To offer the numerous Internet test-hosting features, we have developed many programs and databases that are stored on our servers. If you post to your own server or website, these programs are not available.

IMPORTANT: Your students must use a browser such as Netscape 4.0/Internet Explorer 4.0 (or a more recent version) that supports cascading style sheets (CSS1) and JavaScript. To post tests or study guides for delivery via the Internet, you must have your own access to an Internet server.

USING THE INTERNET TEST-HOSTING SERVICE

Using the *ExamView* test generator software, you can publish tests directly to the *ExamView* website if you have signed up for the test-hosting service. With a few simple steps, you can publish tests and study guides directly to the Internet. Refer to the following instructions to register for the Internet test-hosting service, create a test, publish a test to the Internet, take tests online, manage tests, and view student results.

Register for the Internet Test-Hosting Service

Step 1
Launch your web browser and go to www.examview.com.

Step 2
Go to the **Instructor Center** to register for the test-hosting service. Follow the instructions provided at the website to sign up.

Record the instructor ID and password assigned to you. You will need this information to publish a test or study guide to the *ExamView* website. When you choose to publish a test, you will be prompted to enter this information.

Step 3
Quit the browser.

Publish a Test/Study Guide to the ExamView Website

Step 1
Start the *ExamView* software.

Step 2
Create a new test or open an existing test.

Select the questions you want to include on the test. You can include any of the twelve (12) question types on a test, but only the objective questions are scored.

Step 3
Select the *Publish Internet Test* option from the **File** menu.

ExamView presents a window with various Internet testing options to help you prepare the online test. (See Figure 8.) **Note:** Click the **Help** button if you need more assistance.

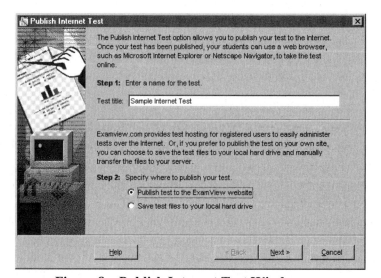

Figure 8 – Publish Internet Test Window

Step 4

Name the test.

Step 5

Select the option to publish your test to the *ExamView* website, and then click the **Next** button.

Step 6

Enter your instructor ID and password.

If you do not already have an instructor ID and password, click the **Register Now** button to launch your web browser and go to the www.examview.com website. You cannot proceed until you have a valid instructor ID and password.

Step 7

Choose whether you want to publish a test or a study guide.

Step 8

Specify when students may access the test/study guide.

Step 9

Enter the expiration date.

Step 10

Specify who should have access to this test/study guide.

Anyone may take it, or you may limit access to a particular group of students. If you specify a roster, students must enter an ID and password.

Step 11

Enter a student password, and click **Next**.

Step 12

Review the summary information. Click the **Back** button if you need to make changes. (See Figure 9.)

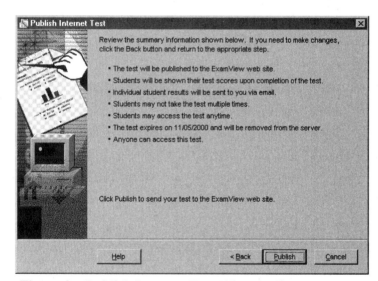

Figure 9 – Publish Internet Test Window (Summary)

Step 13

Click the **Publish** button when you are ready to post the test/study guide to the *ExamView* website.

The program automatically connects to the Internet and posts the test/study guide to the *ExamView* server. Access the instructor options on the *ExamView* website (www.examview.com) to preview a test, change selected parameters, or view results. If you need to edit or delete questions, you must change the test locally and then publish a new version. **Note:** An Internet connection is required to publish a test/study guide.

Step 14

Print a copy of the test/study guide for your records, create another test, or exit the software if you are finished.

Take a Test/Study Guide Online at www.evtestcenter.com

Once you publish a test/study guide to the *ExamView* server, anyone in the world can access it if you provide him or her with your instructor ID and the appropriate password. (**IMPORTANT:** *Do **not** give students your password, just your ID.*) Provide the instructions below to your students so that they can take the test or study guide.

Note: You must use a browser such as Netscape 4.0/Internet Explorer 4.0 (or a more recent version) that supports cascading style sheets level 1 (CSS1) and JavaScript. An active Internet connection is also required.

To take a test:

Step 1
Start your web browser.

Step 2
Go to the URL: www.evtestcenter.com.

Step 3
Enter your instructor's ID code. (See Figure 10.)

Upon entering a valid instructor code, you will see a list of tests your instructor has published.

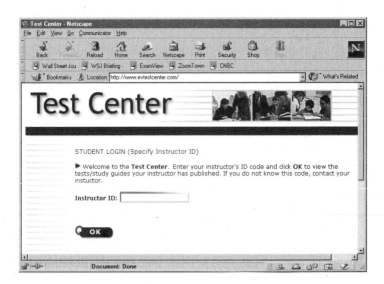

Figure 10 – Test Center Login (www.evtestcenter.com)

Step 4
Select a test.

Step 5

Enter your name (if requested), student ID, and student password.

Contact your instructor if you have not been assigned a student ID or you do not have a student password.

Step 6

Review the test and respond to all of the questions. (See the sample test in Figure 11.)

If you need help while working with a test, click the **Help** button shown at the bottom of the test. Click the browser's **Back** button to return to the test.

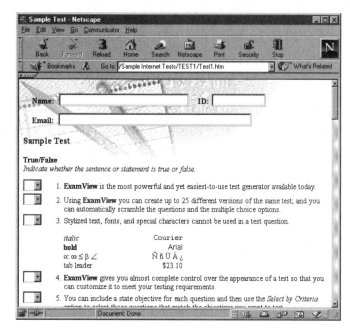

Figure 11 – Sample Internet Test

Step 7

When you complete the test, review the entire test and then click the **Grade & Submit** button located at the bottom of the test.

Your results will be emailed to your instructor. Depending on the test settings, you may be notified of your results immediately.

To complete a study guide:

Step 1

Start your web browser.

Step 2

Go to the URL: www.evtestcenter.com.

Step 3

Enter your instructor's ID.

You will see a list of study guides and tests your instructor has published.

Step 4

Select a study guide.

Step 5

Enter your name (if requested), student ID, and password.

Contact your instructor if you have not been assigned a student ID or you do not have a password.

Step 6

Review the study guide and answer all of the questions.

If you need help while working with a study guide, click the **Help** button shown at the bottom of the screen. Click the browser's **Back** button to return to the study guide.

Step 7

When you complete the study guide, review your responses and then click the **Check Your Work** button located at the bottom of the study guide.

Your work is scored and you will see whether you answered each question correctly or incorrectly. No results are sent to your instructor.

Step 8

Click the **Reset** button to erase all of your responses if you want to start over.

Review Student Results and Manage Tests

When your students complete an Internet test, their results are automatically stored on the server so that you can easily access this information. If you chose to receive results via email, you will also receive the following information for each student: (1) student name and ID, (2) raw score and percentage score for objective-based questions, and (3) responses for each question (objective and open-ended questions).

At the *ExamView* website, you may also change test-setup options, preview tests, download student results, and view your account information.

Step 1

Start your web browser.

Step 2

Go to the URL: www.examview.com and access the Instructor Center.

Step 3

Log in using your instructor ID and password to view the main menu options. (See Figure 12.)

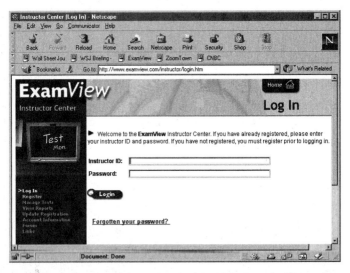

Figure 12 – *ExamView* Website (Instructor Center)

PUBLISHING TESTS TO YOUR OWN WEBSITE

If you choose not to sign up for the *ExamView* test-hosting service, you can still publish tests/study guides to your own website. You must save the test/study guide to your hard drive, upload the files to your website, and then provide access to your students. Refer to the following sections for step-by-step instructions.

Save an Internet Test/Study Guide to Your Hard Drive

Follow the steps shown below to create an Internet test/study guide and save it to your hard drive. Before you begin, make sure that you installed the *ExamView* test generator software.

Step 1
Start the *ExamView* software.

Step 2
Create a new test or open an existing test.
Select the questions you want to include on the test. You can include any of the twelve (12) question types on a test, but only the objective questions will be graded.

Step 3
Select the *Publish Internet Test* option from the **File** menu.
ExamView presents a window with various Internet testing options to help you prepare the online test. (See Figure 13.) **Note**: Click the **Help** button if you need more assistance.

Step 4
Name the test.

Step 5
Select the option to save the test files to your local hard drive, and then click the **Next** button.

Step 6
Choose whether you want to publish a test or a study guide.

Step 7
Review the summary information. Make changes, if necessary.

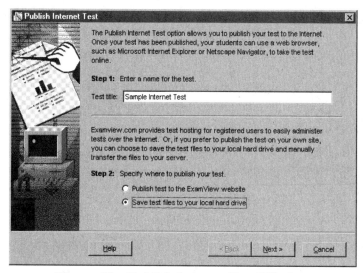

Figure 13 – Publish Internet Test Window

Step 8
Click the **Save** button to save the test/study guide files.

When you choose to save an Internet test to your local hard drive, *ExamView* creates an HTML file and an accompanying folder with all of the necessary image files. This makes it easier for you to post the files to a web server. If, for example, you enter a path such as **c:\examview\tests\chapter1** (Windows) or **HD:ExamView:Tests:Chapter1** (Macintosh), the software will create a file called **chapter1.htm** and a new folder called **chapter1_files** with all of the required picture files. (See the illustration below.)

Step 9
Post the test/study guide to a server to make it available to your students. (See the next section for instructions for posting a test to a server.)

Step 10
Once you post a test, you should verify that students can access it. You may also want to try the "Grade & Submit" feature for tests to make sure that the results are emailed to the correct address.

Note: When you create a test, *ExamView* encrypts the answer information so that a student cannot see the answers in the HTML page source. While this does help to prevent cheating, there is no foolproof method in an unsupervised environment.

Post a Test to Your Own Internet/Intranet Server

Once you save a test/study guide formatted for the Internet, you must post all of the related files to a location on a server that your students can access. You can post the files to a local area network, Intranet server, or an Internet server. You **must** have an Internet connection for students to be able to submit test results. (This is not required for a study guide.)

Note: Posting to a server can be a complex process. The specific steps will vary depending on the hardware and software configuration of your server. If you are not familiar with the required steps, contact your network administrator for assistance.

Step 1
Start an FTP program or other utility that allows you to copy files from your hard drive to an Internet/Intranet server.

Step 2
Log in to your server.

Step 3
Create a new folder on your server to hold the test/study guide files.

Step 4

Copy the **HTML** file and the accompanying folder to a location on your server that your students can access.

When you choose to save an Internet test to your hard drive, *ExamView* creates an HTML file and an accompanying folder with all of the necessary image files. This makes it easier for you to post the files to a web server.

IMPORTANT: By default, all of the file names are lowercase. Do not change the case since these files are referenced in the HTML document. You **must** copy the HTML file and the accompanying folder as is. Do not copy the HTML file into the corresponding folder. (See the illustration below.)

Step 5

Log off the server, if necessary.

Step 6

Record the URL for the test/study guide HTML document or set up a link to the test.

Take a Test or Study Guide Using the Internet

Once you post a test on a server, anyone in the world can access the test if you provide him or her with the Web (URL) address. Follow the instructions provided below to take a test or study guide.

Note: You must use a browser such as Netscape 4.0/Internet Explorer 4.0 (or a more recent version) that supports cascading style sheets level 1 (CSS1) and JavaScript. An active Internet connection is required to submit test results.

To take a test via the Internet:

Step 1

Start your web browser.

Step 2

Type the web address (URL) and test name (e.g., **www.school.edu/economics/test1.htm**), or enter an address for a page with a link to the test. (See the sample test in Figure 14.)

If the test is located on a local area network, use the open page command in the browser to open the test.

Step 3

Enter your name, student ID, and email address (optional).

Step 4

Answer all of the questions.

If you need help while working with a test, click the **Help** button shown at the bottom of the test. Click the browser's **Back** button to return to the test.

Step 5

When you complete the test, review your responses and then click the **Grade & Submit** button located at the bottom of the screen.

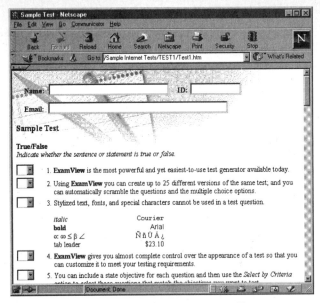

Figure 14 – Sample Internet Test

To complete a study guide via the Internet:

Step 1

Start your web browser.

Step 2

Type the web address (URL) and study guide name (e.g., **www.school.edu/history/study.htm**), or enter an address for a page with a link to the study guide.

Step 3

Enter your name.

Step 4

Answer all of the questions.

Step 5

When you complete the study guide, review the entire test and then click the **Check Your Work** button located at the bottom of the study guide.

Your work is scored and you will see whether you answered each question correctly or incorrectly. No results are sent to your instructor.

Step 6

Click the **Reset** button to erase all of your responses if you want to start over.

Receive Student Results via Email

When your students complete an Internet test, the browser sends the students' test results and all of their responses directly to you via email. The email will include the following information:

- student name and ID
- raw score and percentage score for objective-based questions
- responses for each question (objective and open-ended questions)

Note: **You will not receive any student results for Internet study guides.**

MATCHING

Match each item with the correct statement below.

a. Marco Polo
b. John Cabot
c. Ferdinand Magellan
d. Johann Gutenberg
e. Bartholomeu Dias

f. Hernando de Soto
g. Giovanni da Verrazzano
h. Prince Henry
i. Esteban
j. Francisco Pizarro

1. Conqueror of the Inca Empire.
2. Invented the first system of movable type.
3. Italian who first explored the northeast coast of North America in search of water passage to the West.
4. Ran a school for explorers in Portugal.
5. First to round the Cape of Good Hope, thus opening an eastern route to the Indies.
6. Former slave who helped search for the Seven Cities of Cibola.
7. Led the first round-the-world expedition.
8. Wrote a book telling Europeans of the riches of China.
9. Led an expedition down the Mississippi River in search of a second Inca empire.
10. His voyage laid the basis for the English claims to North America.

1. ANS: J   DIF: Easy   REF: 18   OBJ: 1.0
    TOP: Explorers, Spain

2. ANS: D   DIF: Easy   REF: 10–11   OBJ: 1.0
    TOP: European History, Gutenberg

3. ANS: G   DIF: Easy   REF: 13   OBJ: 1.0
    TOP: Explorers, Italy

4. ANS: H   DIF: Easy   REF: 12   OBJ: 1.0
    TOP: Exploration, Portugal

5. ANS: E   DIF: Easy   REF: 4   OBJ: 1.0
    TOP: Explorers, Portugal

6. ANS: I   DIF: Easy   REF: 18–20   OBJ: 1.0
    TOP: Exploration, Esteban

7. ANS: C   DIF: Easy   REF: 15–16   OBJ: 1.0
    TOP: Explorers

8. ANS: A   DIF: Easy   REF: 12   OBJ: 1.0
    TOP: Exploration

9. ANS: F   DIF: Easy   REF: 20   OBJ: 1.0
    TOP: Explorers, Spain

10. ANS: B   DIF: Easy   REF: 22   OBJ: 1.0
    TOP: Explorers, England

MULTIPLE CHOICE

1. Which of the following continents would be considered part of the New World?
   a. South America
   b. Europe
   c. Asia
   d. Africa

   ANS: A   DIF: Medium   REF: 13   OBJ: 1.1
   TOP: Geography, Exploration

2. Which area would be considered part of the Orient?
   a. Florida
   b. Mexico
   c. China
   d. Brazil

   ANS: C   DIF: Medium   REF: 11–12   OBJ: 1.1
   TOP: Geography, Exploration

3. "Enterprise of the Indies" describes
   a. Prince Henry's contribution to exploration.
   b. the Indian migration to the Americas.
   c. the five tribes of the Iroquois.
   d. Columbus' plan for exploration.

   ANS: D   DIF: Medium   REF: 4   OBJ: 1.1
   TOP: Exploration, Columbus

4. Which of the following was NOT part of the Portuguese effort to find a water route to the Orient?
   a. exploring the west coast of Africa
   b. the development of the caravel
   c. Prince Henry's school for navigation
   d. financial support from Venetian merchants

   ANS: D   DIF: Medium   REF: 12   OBJ: 1.1
   TOP: Exploration, Portugal

5. Who was the explorer who first became famous for sailing west to try to reach the Orient?
   a. Magellan
   b. Prince Henry of Portugal
   c. Columbus
   d. Isabella

   ANS: C   DIF: Medium   REF: 4–6   OBJ: 1.1
   TOP: Columbus

6. Which is NOT a Native American tribe of Central or South America?
   a. Iroquois
   b. Maya
   c. Inca
   d. Aztec

   ANS: A   DIF: Medium   REF: 7   OBJ: 1.2
   TOP: Native Americans

7. Which country focused its exploration on the American Southwest?
   a. France
   b. England
   c. Portugal
   d. Spain

   ANS: D   DIF: Medium   REF: 16–17   OBJ: 1.4
   TOP: Exploration, Spain

8. Which of the following factors contributed to the Spanish conquest of the Aztecs?
   a. The Spanish had not brought enough horses.
   b. The Incas allied with the Spanish.
   c. The Aztecs thought the Spanish might be gods.
   d. The Aztecs had less powerful guns.

   ANS: C   DIF: Medium   REF: 17   OBJ: 1.4
   TOP: Native Americans, Spain

9. Which Native American group is INCORRECTLY paired with its geographic region?
   a. Mayan — Yucatan peninsula
   b. Iroquois — Central America
   c. Incas — Andes Mountains
   d. Aztecs — present-day Mexico

   ANS: B   DIF: Medium   REF: 8–9   OBJ: 1.2
   TOP: Native Americans

10. Which of the following was NOT a strong and centralized empire of Native American people?
   a. Aztec
   b. Incas
   c. Eskimo
   d. Mayas

   ANS: C   DIF: Medium   REF: 8   OBJ: 1.2
   TOP: Native Americans

11. The first people of North America most likely came from
   a. Europe.
   b. Asia.
   c. Africa.
   d. Australia.

   ANS: B   DIF: Medium   REF: 8   OBJ: 1.2
   TOP: Native Americans

12. Which man led an expedition down the Mississippi River in search of a second Inca Empire?
   a. de Soto
   b. Esteban
   c. Cabot
   d. Ericson

   ANS: A   DIF: Medium   REF: 20   OBJ: 1.4
   TOP: Explorers, Spain

13. Which man was the first to explore the northeast coast of North America for France?
   a. de Soto
   b. Henry VII
   c. da Gama
   d. Verrazzano

   ANS: D   DIF: Medium   REF: 22   OBJ: 1.4
   TOP: Explorers, France

14. Which man was the former slave who helped search for the Seven Cities of Cibola?
    a. Cabot
    b. Esteban
    c. Pizarro
    d. Cortez

    ANS: B   DIF: Medium   REF: 18–20   OBJ: 1.4
    TOP: Exploration, Esteban

15. Which man named Florida?
    a. de Leon
    b. de Soto
    c. Gilbert
    d. Cartier

    ANS: A   DIF: Medium   REF: 18   OBJ: 1.4
    TOP: Explorers

16. Which man discovered the Grand Canyon?
    a. Cortez
    b. Esteban
    c. Coronado
    d. Balboa

    ANS: C   DIF: Medium   REF: 19   OBJ: 1.4
    TOP: Explorers, Spain

17. Which explorer is CORRECTLY paired with the people he conquered?
    a. Cortez / Aztecs
    b. Balboa / Incas
    c. Columbus / Mayans
    d. Pizarro / League of the Iroquois

    ANS: A   DIF: Medium   REF: 17   OBJ: 1.4
    TOP: Explorers, Spain

18. Pizarro conquered the
    a. Aztecs.
    b. League of the Iroquois.
    c. Mayans.
    d. Incas.

    ANS: D   DIF: Medium   REF: 17–18   OBJ: 1.4
    TOP: Explorers, Spain

19. Balboa reached the Pacific Ocean after
    a. sailing around Africa.
    b. sailing around South America.
    c. crossing the Isthmus of Panama.
    d. traveling downstream on the Mississippi River.

    ANS: C   DIF: Medium   REF: 14–15   OBJ: 1.4
    TOP: Explorers, Spain

20. All of the following helped bring about the voyages of discovery after 1450 EXCEPT
    a. the rise of nation states.
    b. the Renaissance.
    c. Portuguese navigators.
    d. Norse navigators.

    ANS: D   DIF: Medium   REF: 13   OBJ: 1.3
    TOP: Exploration

21. When the Europeans discovered the New World, the Native Americans they found
    a. lacked any form of religion.
    b. were as varied as the people of Europe.
    c. were mostly farmers.
    d. mostly lived in what today is the northeastern United States.

    ANS: B   DIF: Medium   REF: 10   OBJ: 1.4
    TOP: Exploration, Native Americans

22. Native Americans from which region were the LAST to feel the effects of European exploration?
    a. Central America   c. the Pacific Northwest
    b. the Atlantic Coast   d. the Caribbean

    ANS: C   DIF: Medium   REF: 8   OBJ: 1.2
    TOP: Exploration, Native Americans

23. Spain's first major goal in the New World was to
    a. reduce the Native American population.
    b. establish permanent colonies.
    c. convert the Indians to Christianity.
    d. seek gold.

    ANS: D   DIF: Medium   REF: 16–17   OBJ: 1.4
    TOP: Exploration

24. Columbus died
    a. in poverty and disgrace.
    b. after making only two voyages to the New World.
    c. not realizing he had discovered a new world.
    d. in poverty and disgrace AND not realizing he had discovered a new world.

    ANS: D   DIF: Medium   REF: 6   OBJ: 1.1
    TOP: Columbus

25. Which city was probably LAST to feel the impact of increased exploration and commerce?
    a. Genoa   c. Lisbon
    b. Venice   d. Munich

    ANS: D   DIF: Medium   REF: 10–12   OBJ: 1.3
    TOP: Exploration, Economics

26. Which explorer's voyage could best be compared to the voyage of a modern astronaut?
    a. Verrazzano   c. Dias
    b. Magellan   d. da Gama

    ANS: B   DIF: Medium   REF: 15–16   OBJ: 1.4
    TOP: Explorers

27. The main goal of early French and English explorers was to
    a. develop large colonies in the New World.
    b. seize Indians for slaves.
    c. find a northwest passage to India.
    d. develop large colonies in the New World AND find a northwest passage to India.

    ANS: D   DIF: Medium   REF: 22–23   OBJ: 1.5
    TOP: Explorers

28. In the late 15th century, which of the following would have had the LEAST incentive to search for a new water route to the Orient?
    a. Queen Isabella of Spain   c. a Portuguese merchant
    b. Prince Henry the Navigator   d. a Venetian merchant

    ANS: D   DIF: Medium   REF: 10–11   OBJ: 1.3
    TOP: Exploration

29. The rise of kings was a significant factor in the development of the age of exploration because it
    a. centralized power and stimulated trade.
    b. reduced the conflicting national claims over newly discovered lands.
    c. reduced conflicts between European nations.
    d. helped eliminate Papal claims to the New World.

    ANS: A   DIF: Medium   REF: 11   OBJ: 1.3
    TOP: Exploration

30. Which of the following did Europeans bring to the New World?
    a. horses   c. tobacco
    b. gold   d. dogs

    ANS: A   DIF: Medium   REF: 17   OBJ: 1.4
    TOP: Exploration

31. An unexpected result of the Treaty of Tordesillas was
    a. cultural division of South America.
    b. the loss of all Portuguese claims to the New World.
    c. a delay in Spanish exploration.
    d. the planting of French culture in Brazil.

    ANS: A   DIF: Medium   REF: 13–14   OBJ: 1.4
    TOP: Treaty of Tordesillas

32. Before the arrival of Europeans, Native Americans
    a. had developed great empires in Mexico and Central America.
    b. were all hunter-food gatherers.
    c. were skilled riders of horses.
    d. were overpopulated in the Great Plains.

    ANS: A   DIF: Medium   REF: 7   OBJ: 1.2
    TOP: Native Americans

© Prentice-Hall, Inc.

33. Which continent was unknown to Europeans before the age of exploration?
    a. Asia
    c. Europe
    b. Africa
    d. North America

    ANS: D   DIF: Medium   REF: 2   OBJ: 1.1
    TOP: Exploration, Geography

34. What do the explorers de Soto and Magellan share in common?
    a. the region of their exploration
    c. the point of origin for their expedition
    b. their method of traveling
    d. their failure to return safely home

    ANS: D   DIF: Medium   REF: 16, 21   OBJ: 1.4
    TOP: Explorers

35. Who was the Norse explorer who traveled to the New World?
    a. Gutenberg
    c. Leif Ericson
    b. Marco Polo
    d. Columbus

    ANS: C   DIF: Medium   REF: 13   OBJ: 1.4
    TOP: Explorers

36. Which of the following explorers was killed before finishing his famous voyage?
    a. Columbus
    c. Marco Polo
    b. da Gama
    d. Magellan

    ANS: D   DIF: Medium   REF: 16   OBJ: 1.4
    TOP: Explorers

37. The explorations of Cartier became the basis for what colony?
    a. New France
    c. Florida
    b. New England
    d. Mexico

    ANS: A   DIF: Medium   REF: 23   OBJ: 1.5
    TOP: Explorers

38. Which explorer is correctly paired with the nation he sailed for?
    a. Cartier — Spain
    c. Verrazzano — Portugal
    b. Columbus — Italy
    d. John Cabot — England

    ANS: D   DIF: Medium   REF: 22   OBJ: 1.5
    TOP: Explorers

39. Columbus was LEAST concerned with
    a. being a financial success.
    c. finding a new route to the Orient.
    b. bringing fame to Italy.
    d. being remembered as a success.

    ANS: B   DIF: Medium   REF: 4–6   OBJ: 1.1
    TOP: Columbus

40. On the eve of his first voyage, Columbus had the LEAST accurate information about
   a. the use of a compass.
   c. the size of the earth.
   b. how to determine latitude.
   d. how to sail a caravel.

   ANS: C   DIF: Medium   REF: 4   OBJ: 1.1
   TOP: Columbus

41. Native Americans probably migrated to North America
   a. around the time of Christ.
   c. after being driven out of Asia.
   b. while hunting for food.
   d. across the Straights of Magellan.

   ANS: B   DIF: Medium   REF: 8   OBJ: 1.2
   TOP: Native Americans

42. What was MOST likely the attitude of merchants and kings regarding exploration?
   a. They both opposed them.
   b. They both encouraged them.
   c. Kings supported and merchants opposed them.
   d. Merchants supported and kings opposed them.

   ANS: B   DIF: Medium   REF: 11   OBJ: 1.3
   TOP: Exploration, Economics

43. As a result of the Treaty of Tordesillas,
   a. Portugal was given all the lands of South America.
   b. Spain lost her claims to the New World.
   c. most people in Brazil speak Portuguese.
   d. Catholicism became the official religion of the New World.

   ANS: C   DIF: Medium   REF: 13–14   OBJ: 1.4
   TOP: Exploration, Treaty of Tordesillas

ESSAY

1. Which of the following statements is an example of evidence, according to the definition of evidence given in Chapter 1? Write your answer on a separate sheet of paper and support your answer with a paragraph explaining why you chose it.

   A. Columbus showed other sailors how to sail and where to sail so the winds would carry them to America and back.
   B. Prince Henry the Navigator set up a school for explorers in Portugal.
   C. Francisco Pizarro landed in Peru with a small force of men in 1531.
   D. The survivors of the Narvaez expedition told a hair-raising story of Indian battles, loss of boats, and the death of hundreds in their party.

   ANS:
   answer D Students' paragraphs should support their answer.

   DIF: Hard   REF: 18–20   OBJ: 1.0   TOP: Exploration

2. Choose one of the following paragraphs as the introduction of your essay. Add two paragraphs with specific examples to illustrate your topic. (Notice that each paragraph below contains two big ideas.) Develop each of the two ideas in a separate paragraph.
    A. The history of the United States begins in Europe before an America was known there. And the history of our country begins in America before the Europeans came.
    B. The reasons European explorers ventured into the dangerous unknown were as varied as their nations. At the same time, changing trends in European history gave all the nations a common basis for an age of exploration.

    ANS:
    Part A: Explorers from Europe (Spain, France, England, and the Netherlands) established settlements that became the America of today. They brought their cultures when they came to America, seeking gold and other riches, spreading the Gospel, gaining fame and glory for themselves and their countries, and seeking a Northwest Passage to India. Native cultures were already old by the time Europeans came to America. Maya, Aztec, and other culture groups numbered in the millions of people and passed their cultures on to their descendants. Part B: A rebirth of learning and curiosity about the world, the rise of nation-states with a resultant drive toward increased trade, the desire for Eastern riches, and new navigational tools gave European nations a common basis for exploration.

    DIF: Hard   REF: 6–12   OBJ: 1.0   TOP: Exploration

3. Choose one of the Native American cultures described in the chapter. Then explain to what extent you agree with the following statement: "Some of the Native American societies that existed during the time of Columbus were highly advanced." Be sure to give specific examples of major accomplishments to support your answer.

    ANS:
    Answers will vary but could include the following ideas: The Mayans - writing, temples, pyramids, calendars, and astronomy. Aztecs - architects, jewelers, warriors. Incas - government, farming, construction projects. Iroquois - confederation of tribes, fur traders.

    DIF: Hard   REF: 6–10   OBJ: 1.2   TOP: Native Americans

4. Based on your reading of the chapter, describe the MOST important changes taking place in Europe in the 1400s and 1500s and the way in which they helped bring about the voyages of discovery.

    ANS:
    Answers will vary but could include the following ideas: Movable type and a spread of literacy, rise of nation states, tales of Marco Polo, increased wealth and investment in exploration, new developments in navigation and sailing, strong support for exploration by merchants and kings.

    DIF: Hard   REF: 10–12   OBJ: 1.3
    TOP: Exploration, European History

5. Given what you have read about French and English exploration of the New World, write a paragraph comparing the major goals of each country's explorers.

   ANS:
   Answers will vary but could include the following ideas: The French and English sponsored explorers who went out in search of a northwest passage to the Orient. Both wanted to exploit the land for its wealth.

   DIF: Hard   REF: 22–23   OBJ: 1.5   TOP: Exploration, Explorers

6. To what extent is the following statement true: "Columbus died a failure but ultimately is remembered as a success."

   ANS:
   Answers will vary but could include the following ideas: Columbus failed to create a profit-making enterprise from his voyages; he died without influence or power. History has credited him with "discovering" the New World and noted his seamanship and courage.

   DIF: Hard   REF: 3–6   OBJ: 1.1   TOP: Columbus

7. To understand why Spain agreed to fund Columbus' voyages, one must understand what Spain was expecting in return. What did Spain expect Columbus' voyage to accomplish? Name at least two long-term benefits Spain hoped to reap in the years that followed the voyage.

   ANS:
   Answers will vary but could include the following ideas: The Spanish wanted to find an efficient route to the Orient and took the risk of sailing west, rather than following Portugal around the tip of Africa; Spain hoped that a new all-water route would bring her fame, power, gold, and a monopoly on trade with the Orient.

   DIF: Hard   REF: 4–6   OBJ: 1.1
   TOP: Columbus, Exploration

8. Locate the Aztec and Iroquois people and describe two distinctive aspects of each culture.

   ANS:
   Answers will vary but could include the following ideas: The Aztecs lived in central Mexico. They were a warlike people who ruled over neighboring tribes. They built sophisticated cities with temples, canals, pyramids. The Iroquois were based in northern New York. They had a sophisticated confederacy of tribes and ruled an area west to the Mississippi and south to the Carolinas.

   DIF: Hard   REF: 7–10   OBJ: 1.2   TOP: Native Americans

9. Explain how three of the following contributed to the Age of Exploration: a. rise of nation states; b. Crusades; c. Renaissance; d. printing press.

    ANS:
    Answers will vary but could include the following ideas: a. Nation states - provided money, ships, and manpower to explorers. b. Crusaders - brought attention to the riches of the east, stirred Europe out of a static feudal system. c. Renaissance - renewed interest and appreciation in classical knowledge and human endeavor. Focused energy away from church-related matters to affairs of state and commerce. d. Printing press - spread literacy and information.

    DIF: Hard   REF: 10–12   OBJ: 1.3
    TOP: Exploration, European History

10. Describe at least two similarities and two differences between the voyage of Magellan and a modern space project.

    ANS:
    Answers will vary but could include the following ideas: Both circumnavigated the earth with the benefit of new technologies. Magellan died, while space projects have both succeeded and failed. New technologies have enabled more sophisticated missions.

    DIF: Hard   REF: 15–16   OBJ: 1.4   TOP: Explorers, Exploration

11. To what extent do you agree with the statement, "Accidents, rumors, and miscalculations played an important part during the Age of Exploration"? Discuss at least three examples of how such events and miscalculations affected exploration.

    ANS:
    Answers will vary but could include the following ideas: Sea voyages intended to reach the Orient reached America. Columbus accidentally found the best westward and eastward route. Storms, Indian attacks, disasters had halted missions. Search for Northwest passage, gold, and a "fountain of youth" led to exploration of the interior.

    DIF: Hard   REF: 4–5   OBJ: 1.5   TOP: Exploration

(page intentionally left blank)

MATCHING

Match each item with the correct statement below.

a. Humphrey Gilbert
b. John Rolfe
c. John Winthrop
d. Miles Standish
e. Elizabeth I

f. Samuel de Champlain
g. Anne Hutchinson
h. Victoria
i. Walter Raleigh
j. Peter Stuyvesant

1. Dutch governor who tried to resist the English takeover of New Netherland.
2. Queen who was determined to make England a major sea power.
3. Persuaded people to buy shares of stock to help finance his Roanoke Island settlement.
4. Puritan governor who hoped to establish Massachusetts Bay as a model community.
5. He made the first unsuccessful attempt to establish a British colony in the New World.
6. Established the first permanent French settlement in the New World.
7. Married Pocahontas—helped to establish tobacco as a staple crop at Jamestown.

1. ANS: J DIF: Easy REF: 45 OBJ: 2.0
 TOP: Exploration, Dutch
2. ANS: E DIF: Easy REF: 31 OBJ: 2.0
 TOP: British Expansion
3. ANS: I DIF: Easy REF: 32–33 OBJ: 2.0
 TOP: Exploration, Financial
4. ANS: C DIF: Easy REF: 41 OBJ: 2.0
 TOP: Puritans
5. ANS: A DIF: Easy REF: 32 OBJ: 2.0
 TOP: Explorers, British
6. ANS: F DIF: Easy REF: 44 OBJ: 2.0
 TOP: French Colonies
7. ANS: B DIF: Easy REF: 37–38 OBJ: 2.0
 TOP: British Colonists

MULTIPLE CHOICE

1. What was the effect of the great wealth of the Spanish colonies?
   a. It raised the standard of living for the Indians.
   b. It caused Spain to grow powerful, then decline.
   c. It halted the spread of Christianity to the New World.
   d. It caused Spain to lose interest in an overseas empire.

   ANS: B DIF: Medium REF: 30 OBJ: 2.1
   TOP: Spanish History

2. The Spanish believed that it was their sacred duty to
    a. find gold.
    b. defeat the British.
    c. convert the Native Americans to Christianity.
    d. discover America.

    ANS: C   DIF: Medium   REF: 28   OBJ: 2.1
    TOP: Spanish History

3. The "Starving Time" is a term best used to describe the bitter winter of 1609–10 in
    a. New Amsterdam.   c. Jamestown.
    b. Roanoke.   d. Plymouth.

    ANS: C   DIF: Medium   REF: 37   OBJ: 2.2
    TOP: British Colonization

4. The Spanish called their large naval fleet of warships
    a. the Armada.   c. haciendas.
    b. the Santa Maria.   d. encomiendas.

    ANS: A   DIF: Medium   REF: 32   OBJ: 2.2
    TOP: Spanish History

5. To help raise capital for his American colony, Sir Walter Raleigh
    a. formed a joint stock company.
    b. exported tobacco to Europe.
    c. used the Native Americans as slave labor.
    d. turned to the Spanish monarchy.

    ANS: A   DIF: Medium   REF: 33   OBJ: 2.2
    TOP: British Colonization

6. Which of the following was NOT a result of the defeat of the Spanish Armada?
    a. the beginning of the decline of Spanish power
    b. the beginning of the rise of England
    c. the end of Spanish colonial holdings in the New World
    d. the growth of English trade

    ANS: C   DIF: Medium   REF: 32   OBJ: 2.2
    TOP: Spanish History

7. Who is most responsible for the unification of England?
    a. the Catholic Church   c. the Raleigh brothers
    b. the Tudor monarchs   d. the joint stock companies

    ANS: B   DIF: Medium   REF: 30   OBJ: 2.2
    TOP: British History

© Prentice-Hall, Inc.

8. Which term best defines a situation where the civil government can no longer keep order and there is temporary rule by the military?
   a. "feudalism"
   b. "mercantilism"
   c. "martial law"
   d. "representative government"

   ANS: C   DIF: Medium   REF: 38   OBJ: 2.3
   TOP: Martial Law

9. Which of the following was NOT an important event of 1619 in the Virginia colony?
   a. the beginning of martial law
   b. the end of martial law
   c. the arrival of black indentured servants
   d. the beginning of the House of Burgesses

   ANS: A   DIF: Medium   REF: 38   OBJ: 2.3
   TOP: British Colonization

10. Which of the following was an important French settlement?
    a. New Orleans
    b. New Amsterdam
    c. Philadelphia
    d. St. Augustine

    ANS: A   DIF: Medium   REF: 44   OBJ: 2.5
    TOP: French Colonization

11. Which of the following was NEVER a proprietary colony?
    a. Maryland
    b. New Jersey
    c. Pennsylvania
    d. Virginia

    ANS: D   DIF: Medium   REF: 46   OBJ: 2.6
    TOP: British Colonies

12. Which was NOT one of the goals of the founders of Georgia?
    a. to create a buffer against the French
    b. to create a buffer against the Spanish
    c. to develop a charity colony for the poor
    d. to develop a new supply of silk

    ANS: A   DIF: Medium   REF: 47–48   OBJ: 2.6
    TOP: British Colonies

13. Relatively few French settlers came to the New World because
    a. only Roman Catholics were permitted to come as settlers.
    b. the French lands were not suitable for settlement.
    c. large tracts of land were given to a small number of proprietors.
    d. only Roman Catholics were permitted to come as settlers AND large tracts of land were given to a small number of proprietors.

    ANS: A   DIF: Medium   REF: 44   OBJ: 2.5
    TOP: French Colonization

14. The English established colonies in the New World for which of the following reasons?
    a. to acquire raw materials
    b. to ease crowded conditions in England
    c. to expand markets for British goods
    d. all of the above

    ANS: D   DIF: Medium   REF: 34   OBJ: 2.2
    TOP: British Colonization

15. Which of the following statements refers to Spanish settlers in America?
    a. Experienced "The Starving Time" in 1609–1620
    b. Contributed the log cabin to America
    c. Bought Manhattan Island from Native Americans
    d. Used the encomienda system to enslave the Native Americans

    ANS: D   DIF: Medium   REF: 27   OBJ: 2.1
    TOP: Spanish Colonization

16. When the Spanish arrived in the New World, about 50 million Native Americans lived there. Eventually, in the areas the Spanish conquered, the Native American population
    a. was completely exterminated.   c. remained the same.
    b. dropped to about 4 million.   d. dramatically increased.

    ANS: B   DIF: Medium   REF: 27–28   OBJ: 2.1
    TOP: Spanish Colonization

17. As a result of Spanish conquests in the New World,
    a. Native American civilization failed to develop further.
    b. universities were established in Mexican and South American cities.
    c. Spain became the most powerful nation in Europe in the 1500s.
    d. all of the above

    ANS: D   DIF: Medium   REF: 30   OBJ: 2.1
    TOP: Spanish Colonization

18. What queen was determined to make England a major sea power?
    a. Virginia V   c. Elizabeth I
    b. Mary, Queen of Scots   d. Victoria

    ANS: C   DIF: Medium   REF: 31   OBJ: 2.2
    TOP: British Colonization

19. Which Europeans established the first permanent settlement in Quebec in 1608?
    a. the English   c. the Spanish
    b. the French   d. the Dutch

    ANS: B   DIF: Medium   REF: 44   OBJ: 2.5
    TOP: French History

20. Who married Pocahontas and helped establish the colony of Jamestown?
    a. John Rolfe   c. Henry James
    b. Miles Standish   d. Henry VIII

    ANS: A   DIF: Medium   REF: 37–38   OBJ: 2.3
    TOP: British Colonization

21. Which colony developed the first elected legislative assembly in America?
    a. Massachusetts   c. Virginia
    b. Georgia   d. Rhode Island

    ANS: C   DIF: Medium   REF: 38   OBJ: 2.3
    TOP: British Colonization

22. Both the Pilgrims and the Puritans
    a. had charters to settle in Massachusetts.
    b. practiced self-government.
    c. believed in religious toleration in the colonies.
    d. showed favoritism toward the Church of England.

    ANS: B   DIF: Medium   REF: 40–41   OBJ: 2.4
    TOP: British Colonies

23. Which of the following does NOT apply to a joint stock company?
    a. People without much money can invest in one.
    b. It is managed by a king or queen.
    c. It sells shares of stock to investors.
    d. It was used to fund the Roanoke colony.

    ANS: B   DIF: Medium   REF: 33   OBJ: 2.2
    TOP: British Colonies

24. Which of the following was driven from Massachusetts Bay Colony because of their religious beliefs?
    a. Henry Hudson   c. John Winthrop
    b. Miles Standish   d. Anne Hutchinson

    ANS: D   DIF: Medium   REF: 42   OBJ: 2.4
    TOP: American History

25. The Mayflower Compact eventually became the foundation for the state government of
    a. Pennsylvania.   c. Massachusetts.
    b. New York.   d. Rhode Island.

    ANS: C   DIF: Medium   REF: 40   OBJ: 2.4
    TOP: Massachusetts Government

26. This colony was best known as a haven for religious freedom and as the home of the first congregation of Jews in the thirteen colonies.
    a. New York   c. Virginia
    b. Rhode Island   d. Massachusetts Bay

    ANS: B   DIF: Medium   REF: 42   OBJ: 2.4
    TOP: Rhode Island History

27. Which colony is INCORRECTLY matched with the type of people that it was founded for?
    a. Georgia — charity cases
    b. Pennsylvania — Quakers
    c. Maryland — Catholics
    d. New York — Puritans

    ANS: D   DIF: Medium   REF: 44–45   OBJ: 2.3
    TOP: Dutch Colonies

28. Which of the following groups did NOT come to the New World because of its religious dissent from the Church of England?
    a. Puritans
    b. Quakers
    c. indentured servants
    d. Separatists

    ANS: C   DIF: Medium   REF: 38   OBJ: 2.4
    TOP: Immigration

29. Which of the following MOST helped bring economic success to the Jamestown colony?
    a. tobacco
    b. its location
    c. partnership with Native Americans
    d. the health of the colonists

    ANS: A   DIF: Medium   REF: 37–38   OBJ: 2.3
    TOP: British Colonies

30. Peter Stuyvesant was the governor of
    a. Virginia.
    b. Pennsylvania.
    c. New Netherland.
    d. Massachusetts Bay.

    ANS: C   DIF: Medium   REF: 45   OBJ: 2.5
    TOP: Dutch Colonies

31. Which Europeans first colonized New York?
    a. Swedes
    b. Spanish
    c. French
    d. Dutch

    ANS: D   DIF: Medium   REF: 44–45   OBJ: 2.5
    TOP: Dutch Colonies

32. Samuel de Champlain founded
    a. Georgia.
    b. Virginia.
    c. New Jersey.
    d. New France.

    ANS: D   DIF: Medium   REF: 44   OBJ: 2.5
    TOP: French Colonization

33. Maryland was founded as a haven for
    a. Jews.
    b. African Americans.
    c. Catholics.
    d. Puritans.

    ANS: C   DIF: Medium   REF: 46   OBJ: 2.6
    TOP: Proprietary Colonies

34. In what ways were the British and Spanish colonies MOST similar?
    a. religious freedom
    b. mercantile policy
    c. intermarriage with Native Americans
    d. democratic beliefs

    ANS: B   DIF: Medium   OBJ: 2.1
    TOP: British / Spanish Colonies

35. The first elected legislative assembly in America was
    a. the House of Representatives.
    b. the House of Burgesses.
    c. the London Company.
    d. the Mayflower Compact.

    ANS: B   DIF: Medium   REF: 38   OBJ: 2.5
    TOP: U.S. Government / Foundations

36. Which of the following colonies had the greatest impact on American culture?
    a. New France
    b. Massachusetts Bay
    c. New Netherlands
    d. New Sweden

    ANS: B   DIF: Medium   REF: 41   OBJ: 2.5
    TOP: Massachusetts Bay Colony

37. A religious dissenter would have been LEAST tolerated in
    a. Rhode Island.
    b. Massachusetts Bay.
    c. Pennsylvania.
    d. New Netherland.

    ANS: B   DIF: Medium   REF: 41   OBJ: 2.4
    TOP: Massachusetts Bay Colony

38. A person who signs an agreement to serve a master for a certain number of years is called a (an)
    a. "indentured servant."
    b. "slave."
    c. "pioneer."
    d. "mestizo."

    ANS: A   DIF: Medium   REF: 38   OBJ: 2.6
    TOP: Indentured Servants

39. Which of the following was NOT a significant contribution to the growth of democracy?
    a. Roanoke colony
    b. House of Burgesses
    c. Mayflower Compact
    d. Maryland Act of Toleration

    ANS: A   DIF: Medium   OBJ: 2.1   TOP: Democracy

40. The joint stock company is the forerunner of the
    a. House of Representatives.
    b. Senate.
    c. corporation.
    d. family farm.

    ANS: C   DIF: Medium   REF: 33   OBJ: 2.2
    TOP: Corporations

41. The colony of New France had the greatest cultural influence on
    a. Quebec.
    b. the Ohio Valley.
    c. Indiana.
    d. the Great Lakes.

    ANS: A   DIF: Medium   REF: 44   OBJ: 2.5
    TOP: French Colonies

42. Who was allowed to vote for legislators in the Massachusetts Bay Colony?
    a. all males
    b. all white males and females
    c. male church members
    d. male property owners

    ANS: C   DIF: Medium   REF: 43   OBJ: 2.4

ESSAY

1. Which of the following pieces of evidence is strongest, according to what you have learned in Chapter 2? Write your answer on a separate sheet of paper and support your answer with a paragraph explaining why you chose it.
    A. The Pilgrims stated that the Native Americans were hostile to them and really did not help them very much.
    B. The Pilgrims said that Squanto helped them to survive. They said he showed them how to grow food.
    C. Historian Samuel Eliot Morison said that Squanto helped the Pilgrims to survive.
    D. The Puritans in the Massachusetts Bay Colony said they did the right thing in banishing Anne Hutchinson from the colony.

    ANS:
    answer B Students' paragraphs should support their answer.

    DIF: Hard   REF: 40   OBJ: 2.0
    TOP: Pilgrims / Native Americans

2. Choose either A or B below as a topic sentence for an essay in which you draw a contrast.
    A. The patterns of colonization of the Spanish and the English in the New World widely differed.
    B. Whether an English settlement died, survived, or flourished depended on the settlers, their quality of planning, the environment, government policies, and luck. (Show how this was true by contrasting the Roanoke and Jamestown settlements; or the Massachusetts Bay Colony and the proprietary colonies, such as Pennsylvania and Georgia.)

    ANS:
    Part A: SPANISH PATTERNS—The Spanish sought to make Spaniards of the natives they conquered. They used the encomienda and hacienda systems and the policy of mercantilism. ENGLISH PATTERNS—The English believed that the Native Americans were an obstacle to be cleared out of the way of English expansion. The English also practiced mercantilism. Part B: ROANOKE—Sir Walter Raleigh's project was unprepared for the realities of life in the New World. The joint stock company that he began in Roanoke was lost. JAMESTOWN—In danger of being lost due to lack of organization, the colony eventually benefited from strict discipline. MASSACHUSETTS BAY—The Puritans were accustomed to hardship. They did well in the harsh New England climate. PROPRIETARY COLONIES—In Pennsylvania, the Quakers proved to be impractical, but the colony survived. The lack of self-government in Georgia prevented more substantial development there.

    DIF: Hard   OBJ: 2.0   TOP: Spanish Colonies / British Colonies

3. Based on your reading of the chapter, write a paragraph describing how the Spanish colonists treated the Native Americans.

    ANS:
    Answers will vary but could include the following ideas: Some Spaniards practiced genocide on native groups. The church sought to convert to Catholicism and discouraged slavery. Encomienda system developed into system of forced labor.

    DIF: Hard   REF: 27–28   OBJ: 2.1   TOP: Spanish History

4. Briefly explain why the defeat of the Spanish Armada was a significant event that would influence the course of English history.

    ANS:
    Answers will vary but could include the following ideas: It marked the rise of England and the decline of Spain. Control of the seas went to England - stimulated their exploration and colonization.

    DIF: Hard   REF: 32   OBJ: 2.2
    TOP: Spanish History / Armada

5. Assess the soundness of the English settlers' decision to build a colony at Jamestown.

    ANS:
    Answers will vary but could include the following ideas: Low, swampy ground off Chesapeake Bay, malaria, dysentery and vulnerability to Indian attacks.

    DIF: Hard   REF: 36–37   OBJ: 2.3   TOP: Jamestown Settlement

6. Describe and evaluate the Spanish contribution to the culture of the United States.

    ANS:
    Answers will vary but could include the following ideas: Language, art, music, literature, poetry, architecture, noted Hispanic-Americans.

    DIF: Hard   OBJ: 2.1   TOP: Spanish History

7. To what extent is the following statement true: "The English defeat of the Spanish Armada was one of the major turning points in history."

    ANS:
    Answers will vary but could include the following ideas: It marked a major shift in dominant European powers - began the rise of England as a major world power-a power that would soon dominate North America.

    DIF: Hard   REF: 32   OBJ: 2.2
    TOP: Spanish History / Armada

8. Identify three significant events that occurred in 1619 in the Virginia Colony, and describe why each is of lasting importance.

ANS:
Answers will vary but could include the following ideas: House of Burgesses - first elected assembly in the New World, first black indentured servants, origins of slavery, arrival of women, more permanent colony, new governor - ensured success of new colony.

DIF: Hard   REF: 38   OBJ: 2.3   TOP: Virginia Colony

9. Knowing what you do about the morals and values of the Puritans, describe three aspects of that culture that contributed to the success of the Puritans in the New World.

ANS:
Answers will vary but could include the following ideas: Hard-working, frugal, religious, highly educated, well-organized, democratic town meetings.

DIF: Hard   REF: 38–44   OBJ: 2.4   TOP: Puritans

10. Based on your reading, how do you explain the inability of the Georgia colony to meet the goals of the people who were its founders? Give at least two reasons why the founders' plans were not successful.

ANS:
Answers will vary but could include the following ideas: Silk industry failed, people not allowed self-government. Settlers rebelled and trustees gave up.

DIF: Hard   REF: 47–48   OBJ: 2.6   TOP: Georgia Colony

MATCHING

Match each item with the correct statement below.

a.	Duquesne	f.	Navigation Acts
b.	Virginia	g.	William Pitt
c.	privateers	h.	King's College
d.	Smugglers	i.	Huguenots
e.	John Peter Zenger	j.	Edward Braddock

1. Shippers who carried letters of marque and were legally licensed pirates were called _____.
2. _____ became English Prime Minister in 1757. He reorganized the British army.
3. French Protestants who came to America seeking religious freedom were called _____.
4. The trial of printer _____ helped establish freedom of the press in the colonies.
5. _____ were passed by Parliament to limit to whom the colonists could buy and sell goods.
6. Rich lowlands called "tide-waters" were abundant in the colony of _____.
7. After capturing it from the French, the British renamed Fort _____ as Fort Pitt.
8. _____ was the British general who stuck to military procedures and was massacred by Native Americans.

1. ANS: C   DIF: Easy   REF: 62–63   OBJ: 3.0
   TOP: British History - Pirates
2. ANS: G   DIF: Easy   REF: 68   OBJ: 3.0
   TOP: British History - Rulers
3. ANS: I   DIF: Easy   REF: 51   OBJ: 3.0
   TOP: Colonial Settlers
4. ANS: E   DIF: Easy   REF: 60   OBJ: 3.0
   TOP: Influential Colonial Settlers
5. ANS: F   DIF: Easy   REF: 56   OBJ: 3.0
   TOP: Colonial History - British Rule
6. ANS: B   DIF: Easy   REF: 53   OBJ: 3.0
   TOP: American Colonies
7. ANS: A   DIF: Easy   REF: 67   OBJ: 3.0
   TOP: French & Indian War
8. ANS: J   DIF: Easy   REF: 68   OBJ: 3.0
   TOP: French & Indian War

MULTIPLE CHOICE

1. Which BEST describes the geography of New England?
   a. a river system similar to Virginia's
   b. good soil and a long growing season
   c. no good ports for ocean vessels
   d. a rough and rocky coast with few gateways to the interior

   ANS: D   DIF: Medium   REF: 55   OBJ: 3.1
   TOP: New England Geography

2. Which area was NOT part of the triangular trade system?
   a. West Indies
   b. Africa
   c. London
   d. New England

   ANS: C   DIF: Medium   REF: 57   OBJ: 3.1
   TOP: Triangle Trade

3. Africa exported _____ as part of the triangular trade system.
   a. slaves
   b. rum
   c. tobacco
   d. woolen clothes

   ANS: A   DIF: Medium   REF: 57   OBJ: 3.1
   TOP: Triangle Trade

4. The plantation owners of Virginia felt a close tie to London because
   a. Virginia never produced any important leaders of the revolution.
   b. the Virginia river system brought ocean vessels into the interior.
   c. most plantations were on the Atlantic coast.
   d. all ships from London to the colonies stopped first in Virginia.

   ANS: B   DIF: Medium   REF: 53–54   OBJ: 3.1
   TOP: Virginia

5. The majority of white settlers in colonial America had come from
   a. England.
   b. France.
   c. Ireland.
   d. Germany.

   ANS: A   DIF: Medium   REF: 51   OBJ: 3.1
   TOP: Colonial Settlers

6. Colonial colleges were founded primarily to further the study of
   a. science.
   b. religion.
   c. medicine.
   d. business.

   ANS: B   DIF: Medium   REF: 59   OBJ: 3.1
   TOP: Colonial History - Education

7. Which did NOT contribute to the colonial population growth of the 1700s?
   a. high birthrate
   b. disease
   c. immigration
   d. growth of slavery

   ANS: B   DIF: Medium   REF: 51   OBJ: 3.1
   TOP: Colonial Settlers

8. The Protestants encouraged education because they believed that
   a. people should be able to read the Bible.
   b. children should not be allowed to farm.
   c. people need to read newspapers to be well informed.
   d. children in schools would ease the oversupply of labor.

   ANS: A   DIF: Medium   REF: 59   OBJ: 3.1
   TOP: Colonial History - Education

9. Which ethnic group had the SMALLEST number of settlers in colonial America?
    a. British   c. Irish
    b. Italian   d. German

    ANS: B   DIF: Medium   REF: 51   OBJ: 3.1
    TOP: Colonial Settlers

10. During the colonial period, most settlers made a living as
    a. farmers.   c. small business owners.
    b. merchants.   d. sailors.

    ANS: A   DIF: Medium   REF: 52   OBJ: 3.1
    TOP: Colonial Settlers

11. Which person is NOT matched with his or her major area of achievement?
    a. Ben Franklin—inventor/statesman   c. John Peter Zenger—scientist
    b. Paul Revere—craftsman   d. Margaret Brent—plantation owner

    ANS: C   DIF: Medium   REF: 60   OBJ: 3.1
    TOP: Influential Colonial Settlers

12. Which statement about the Albany Plan of Union is FALSE?
    a. The meeting was called in response to fears of French attacks.
    b. Colonial legislatures eagerly approved the plan.
    c. Its design was based on an Indian governmental council.
    d. It brought together 150 Native Americans and representatives from seven colonies.

    ANS: B   DIF: Medium   REF: 67–68   OBJ: 3.3
    TOP: French & Indian War

13. The French and Indian War began
    a. with the fall of Quebec
    b. with attacks by French and Indians on American border settlements.
    c. with an English victory.
    d. as a result of the Treaty of Paris.

    ANS: B   DIF: Medium   REF: 66   OBJ: 3.3
    TOP: French & Indian War

14. As a result of the French and Indian War,
    a. Spain received New Orleans.
    b. Canada became part of New France.
    c. Guadeloupe was given to England.
    d. France strengthened its holdings in the New World.

    ANS: A   DIF: Medium   REF: 70   OBJ: 3.3
    TOP: French & Indian War

15. Which of the following were often forced to immigrate to America?
    a. political radicals   c. Africans
    b. thieves   d. all of the above

    ANS: D   DIF: Medium   REF: 52   OBJ: 3.1
    TOP: Colonial Settlers

16. Which was NOT an important export of the southern colonies?
    a. rice   c. indigo
    b. fish   d. tobacco

    ANS: B   DIF: Medium   REF: 53   OBJ: 3.1
    TOP: Early Colonial Trade

17. Which of the colonies were most closely linked to England?
    a. New England   c. Middle Colonies
    b. Southern Colonies   d. Massachusetts Bay Colony

    ANS: B   DIF: Medium   REF: 53–54   OBJ: 3.1
    TOP: Southern Colonies

18. Which of the following colleges was the first to be founded?
    a. Yale   c. Harvard
    b. Dartmouth   d. William and Mary

    ANS: C   DIF: Medium   REF: 59   OBJ: 3.1
    TOP: Colonial History - Education

19. Women in the colonies were NOT expected to
    a. labor in the fields.
    b. hold political office.
    c. attend college.
    d. hold political office AND attend college.

    ANS: D   DIF: Medium   REF: 58–59   OBJ: 3.1
    TOP: Colonial History - Women

20. The English colonies faced all of the following problems EXCEPT
    a. labor shortages.
    b. high infant mortality.
    c. crowded conditions.
    d. high infant mortality AND crowded conditions.

    ANS: C   DIF: Medium   REF: 51   OBJ: 3.1
    TOP: Colonial History

21. A leading product of colonial New England was
    a. fish.   c. rice.
    b. sugar.   d. wheat.

    ANS: A   DIF: Medium   REF: 57   OBJ: 3.1
    TOP: Early Colonial Trade

22. All of the following goods were involved in the triangular trade EXCEPT
    a. rum   c. cotton
    b. slaves   d. sugar

    ANS: C   DIF: Medium   REF: 57   OBJ: 3.1
    TOP: Triangle Trade

© Prentice-Hall, Inc.

23. Which man fought a court case over the right of freedom of the press?
    a. Paul Revere
    b. Ben Franklin
    c. John Peter Zenger
    d. Myer Myers

    ANS: C   DIF: Medium   REF: 60   OBJ: 3.1
    TOP: Influential Colonial Settlers

24. Until the mid-1700s, England paid little attention to the colonies because
    a. of distracting political and military problems in England.
    b. the colonists always favored British trade laws.
    c. England intended to give the colonies their independence.
    d. England had little need for the raw materials in the colonies.

    ANS: A   DIF: Medium   REF: 61   OBJ: 3.2
    TOP: British / Colonial Relations

25. Myer Myers and Paul Revere are examples of colonial
    a. privateers.
    b. craftsmen.
    c. ministers.
    d. educators.

    ANS: B   DIF: Medium   REF: 61   OBJ: 3.2
    TOP: Influential Colonial Settlers

26. Which of the following contributed to the colonies' sense of independence?
    a. neglect by Britain for over 100 years
    b. distance between England and the colonies
    c. the non-English majority in most colonies
    d. neglect by Britain for over 100 years AND distance between England and the colonies

    ANS: D   DIF: Medium   REF: 61–64   OBJ: 3.2
    TOP: British / Colonial Relations

27. The Treaty of Paris of 1763 included all of the following provisions EXCEPT
    a. New Orleans being ceded to Spain.
    b. all French lands between the Mississippi River and the Appalachian Mountains being ceded to Britain.
    c. Guadaloupe and Martinique being ceded to Britain.
    d. the French lands west of the Mississippi River being ceded to Spain.

    ANS: C   DIF: Medium   REF: 70   OBJ: 3.3
    TOP: French & Indian War

28. The agreement which ended the French and Indian War was the
    a. Treaty of Versailles.
    b. Peace of Paris.
    c. Deerfield Massacre.
    d. Navigation Acts.

    ANS: B   DIF: Medium   REF: 70   OBJ: 3.3
    TOP: French & Indian War

29. The goal of the British Navigation Acts was to help
    a. ships avoid dangerous waters.
    b. the American colonies trade with France.
    c. the Indians develop trades.
    d. control American colonial trade.

    ANS: D   DIF: Medium   REF: 62   OBJ: 3.3
    TOP: Early Colonial Trade

30. As a result of the French and Indian War,
    a. France lost its claim to land between the Mississippi River and Appalachian Mountains.
    b. Quebec was given to France.
    c. France was forced to sell Louisiana.
    d. all French colonies were given to England.

    ANS: A   DIF: Medium   REF: 70   OBJ: 3.3
    TOP: French & Indian War

31. Which Native American group had a role in the French and Indian War?
    a. the Incas   c. the Pueblo
    b. the Aztecs   d. the Iroquois

    ANS: D   DIF: Medium   REF: 68   OBJ: 3.3
    TOP: French & Indian War

32. Why did plantation owners use slaves to grow and harvest crops?
    a. Native Americans made excellent slaves.
    b. Africa was a major cotton exporter.
    c. There was an oversupply of labor in the colonies.
    d. There was a shortage of labor in the colonies.

    ANS: D   DIF: Medium   REF: 52   OBJ: 3.1
    TOP: Colonial History - Slavery

33. Prior to 1775, most colonial settlements were located
    a. west of the Appalachian Mountains.
    b. east of the Appalachian Mountains.
    c. along the shore of the Great Lakes.
    d. in the "back country" areas from Pennsylvania south to the Carolinas.

    ANS: B   DIF: Medium   REF: 51   OBJ: 3.1
    TOP: Colonial Settlers

34. Which statement regarding indentured servants is MOST accurate?
    a. They were legally free once they had worked out the full term of their contract.
    b. They had to run away to become free.
    c. The system began because of an oversupply of labor in the colonies.
    d. They were always indentured against their will.

    ANS: A   DIF: Medium   REF: 52   OBJ: 3.1
    TOP: Colonial History - Slavery

35. Which of the following was a significant result of England's Glorious Revolution of 1688?
    a. It drove the French out of North America.
    b. It opened a new era of representative government in England.
    c. It established the supremacy of the English monarchy.
    d. It brought Oliver Cromwell to power.

    ANS: B   DIF: Medium   REF: 61   OBJ: 3.2
    TOP: British History

36. Which statement about the Navigation Acts is MOST accurate?
    a. They represented an attempt to control the trade activities of the colonies.
    b. They were always well enforced.
    c. They provided for free trade between the colonies and France.
    d. They were popular in the colonies.

    ANS: A   DIF: Medium   REF: 62   OBJ: 3.2
    TOP: Colonial Trade

37. Which is the BEST explanation for the Massachusetts Bay Colony's rebellious attitude toward England?
    a. The colony was landlocked and had little contact with England.
    b. England wanted all the rich agricultural products of the colony.
    c. The colony's merchants and seamen were affected by mercantile policies.
    d. Few of the colony's settlers had come from England.

    ANS: C   DIF: Medium   REF: 64   OBJ: 3.2
    TOP: British / Colonial Relations

SHORT ANSWER

In one or two sentences, define and distinguish between the terms given below.

1. triangular trade

    ANS:
    Triangular trade was commerce carried on by New England ships in which they took rum from New England to the west coast of Africa, where they traded it for slaves whom they took to the Caribbean and sold for sugar, which was then taken north to be made into more rum.

    DIF: Hard   REF: 57   OBJ: 3.0   TOP: Triangle Trade

2. dame schools

    ANS:
    Dame schools were schools run by women to teach reading to boys and sometimes girls.

    DIF: Hard   REF: 59   OBJ: 3.0
    TOP: Colonial History - Education

3. Old Colonial System

ANS:
The Old Colonial System refers to the years during which Great Britain neglected the colonies and failed to enforce the laws Parliament had passed restricting colonial trade.

DIF: Hard   REF: 66   OBJ: 3.0
TOP: British / Colonial Relations

4. Deerfield Massacre

ANS:
The Deerfield Massacre was a 1704 French and Indian raid on a Massachusetts settlement in which 50 settlers were killed and over 100 settlers were taken prisoner.

DIF: Hard   REF: 66–67   OBJ: 3.0   TOP: French & Indian War

ESSAY

1. What is the main point of the following argument? Write your answer on a separate sheet of paper and support your answer with a paragraph explaining why you chose it.
   Historians have advanced a number of theories about the Salem witch hysteria of 1692; all are weak. The best explanation is that the hysteria resulted primarily from the psychological makeup of Puritan society. The afflicted girls were teenagers who were suffering as a result of the strict control of their religious society-they had no real outlets for their natural high spirits. Their accusations were the result of their anger, mainly against older women. (According to trial records, most of the accused were unmarried women between the ages of 41 and 60.) Thus when the girls accused others of witchcraft, they were rebelling against the strict rules of the older generation.
   A. The older generation was too strict with the teenagers in Salem village.
   B. The witch hysteria resulted mainly from the frustration of teenage girls who were rebelling against a strict upbringing.
   C. Most of the accused were older women.
   D. The afflicted girls had no real outlet for their high spirits.

   ANS:
   answer B Students' paragraphs should support their answers.

   DIF: Hard   OBJ: 3.0   TOP: Salem Witch Trials

2. Based on your reading of the chapter, write a paragraph describing why the colonial population grew so rapidly in the 1700s.

   ANS:
   Answers will vary but could include the following ideas: High birthrate, immigration, the necessity of families on the frontier, large family size.

   DIF: Hard   REF: 51   OBJ: 3.1   TOP: Colonial Settlers

3. Use the following as a summary and conclusion to an essay. Precede it with two or three paragraphs that support this conclusion.

During the Colonial period the seeds of self-government were planted in the American people, an American economy sprang up, the colonists got used to living away from English control, and a generation of colonists got valuable military experience. The stage was set for the Revolution.

ANS:
Student answers will vary but could include these ideas: Britain's "salutary neglect" of almost 150 years combined with great distance and difficulties in communication to enable the colonies to develop their own institutions. In New England, fishing and world-wide shipping and trading formed the base of an economy. The middle Colonies' varied crops and products and the South's agriculture (mostly cotton and tobacco) were moneymakers. The colonies flouted British mercantilist laws, and colonial trade increased fivefold from 1700 to 1760. Conflicts in America between the British and French, beginning in the 1680s and extending through the French and Indian War of the 1750s, gave the colonist's military experience on land. Naval experience came with trade and privateering (smuggling).

DIF: Hard   REF: 51–70   OBJ: 3.1   TOP: Colonial Government

4. Explain how the geography of New England helped shape its economy.

ANS:
Answers will vary but could include these ideas: In New England, poor geography for farming—forced people to the sea for fishing and commerce, development of industry—ship building, preindustrial crafts.

DIF: Hard   REF: 54–58   OBJ: 3.1
TOP: New England Geography

5. How did distance and poor communication promote a spirit of independence in the American colonies?

ANS:
Answers will vary but could include the following ideas: The thirteen colonies were geographically remote from England and thus poorly administered. They were forced to develop their own governmental forms in the absence of British direction. The geographical divisions between the colonies heightened their spirit of independence.

DIF: Hard   REF: 61–66   OBJ: 3.1   TOP: Colonial Government

6. Knowing what you do about the French and Indian War, describe the two MOST important causes of the war's outbreak.

ANS:
Answers will vary but could include the following ideas: England and France were in a global struggle for colonial domination. In the New World, the English controlled the Atlantic coast while the French tried to establish an interior colony stretching in an arc from Montreal to the Mississippi Valley. A series of wars were fought between the two powers - King William's War (1689–1697), Queen Anne's War (1702–1713), and King George's War (1744–1748).

DIF: Hard   REF: 66–70   OBJ: 3.3   TOP: French & Indian War

7. Analyze the following statement: "The American colonies were socially, politically, and economically democratic." To what extent do you agree or disagree with this generalization?

ANS:
Answers will vary but could include the following ideas: In contrast to Europe, they were very democratic. Nonetheless, there were many undemocratic aspects. Socially - existence of slavery and subjugation of women. Politically - voting restrictions based on wealth and property. Economically - unequal distribution of wealth.

DIF: Hard   REF: 52–54, 58   OBJ: 3.1   TOP: Colonial Government

8. Explain how changes in English government and policy affected the colonies.

ANS:
Answers will vary but could include the following ideas: England was in the grip of change and revolution. Oliver Cromwell, "Glorious Revolution," growth of Parliamentary power, and wars with other European powers all had an impact on England's ability to rule the colonies. When England resolved its problems, it sought to reassert authority in the colonies.

DIF: Hard   REF: 61–66   OBJ: 3.2
TOP: British / Colonial Relations

9. In your opinion, how true is the following statement: "Britain's old colonial system worked best when it worked least."

ANS:
Answers will vary but could include the following ideas: During the period of salutary neglect, the lack of rigid enforcement of the Navigation Laws allowed the colonies to prosper economically - this ultimately benefited England.

DIF: Hard   OBJ: 3.3   TOP: British / Colonial Relations

10. To what extent was America involved in a "World War" from 1689 to 1763? How did this involvement shape the future of the colonies?

ANS:
Answers will vary but could include the following ideas: Wars involving England, France, and Spain occurred on land and sea around the globe. They were in effect "World Wars." These wars shaped the ways in which the European empires responded to the American colonies, with important results for the development of the colonies.

DIF: Hard   OBJ: 3.3   TOP: Colonial History

(page intentionally left blank)

MATCHING

Match each item with the correct statement below.

a. George III
b. Ben Franklin
c. William Dawes
d. Sons of Liberty
e. Pontiac's Conspiracy

f. John Adams
g. Breed's Hill
h. Tories
i. Thomas Jefferson
j. Hessians

1. Actual site of the Battle of Bunker Hill.
2. Helped Paul Revere warn colonists of oncoming British troops.
3. King of England during the American Revolution.
4. Chief author of the Declaration of Independence.
5. Mercenary soldiers hired by the British.
6. British name for Native American raids on western fortifications after the French and Indian War.
7. Defended British soldiers who were accused of murder in the Boston Massacre.
8. He along with John Adams and John Jay helped negotiate the Treaty of Paris.
9. Secret society that terrorized agents who sold British stamps.
10. Americans who opposed the American Revolution.

1. ANS: G   DIF: Easy   REF: 86   OBJ: 4.0
   TOP: American Revolution - Battles
2. ANS: C   DIF: Easy   REF: 85   OBJ: 4.0
   TOP: American Revolution - Heroes
3. ANS: A   DIF: Easy   REF: 86   OBJ: 4.0
   TOP: British History / American Revolution
4. ANS: I   DIF: Easy   REF: 88–89   OBJ: 4.0
   TOP: Declaration of Independence
5. ANS: J   DIF: Easy   REF: 90   OBJ: 4.0
   TOP: British History / American Revolution
6. ANS: E   DIF: Easy   REF: 77   OBJ: 4.0
   TOP: British / Native American History
7. ANS: F   DIF: Easy   REF: 81   OBJ: 4.0
8. ANS: B   DIF: Easy   REF: 98–99   OBJ: 4.0
   TOP: American Revolution
9. ANS: D   DIF: Easy   REF: 79   OBJ: 4.0
   TOP: American Revolution - Causes
10. ANS: H   DIF: Easy   REF: 87   OBJ: 4.0
    TOP: American Revolution

MULTIPLE CHOICE

1. A sudden, violent change or overthrow of a government is known as a (an)
   a. evolution.
   b. revolution.
   c. election.
   d. primary.

   ANS: B   DIF: Medium   REF: 88   OBJ: 4.1
   TOP: Revolution

2. In the Declaratory Act, Parliament declared that
   a. it would seek colonial assent for any new taxes.
   b. it could pass laws on any matters affecting the colonies.
   c. the colonies would have to provide their own defense.
   d. new taxes would be imposed.

   ANS: B   DIF: Medium   REF: 80   OBJ: 4.1
   TOP: American Revolution - Causes

3. A chief colonial objection to the Quebec Act was that it
   a. cut off colonial trade with Canada.
   b. canceled the western land claims of several colonies.
   c. made Quebec the capital of all the British colonies in North America.
   d. abolished colonial assemblies.

   ANS: B   DIF: Medium   REF: 83–84   OBJ: 4.1
   TOP: American Revolution - Causes

4. After the French and Indian War, the big problem facing the British was
   a. guerrilla warfare by the French-Canadians.
   b. quarrels with Spain over Florida.
   c. Indian uprisings west of the Appalachians.
   d. getting the colonies to form a united government.

   ANS: C   DIF: Medium   REF: 77   OBJ: 4.1
   TOP: British / Native American Relations

5. Which of the following was NOT a colonial response to the Stamp Act?
   a. boycotting British goods
   b. terrorizing tax collectors
   c. declaring independence
   d. forming the Sons of Liberty

   ANS: C   DIF: Medium   REF: 79   OBJ: 4.1
   TOP: American Revolution - Causes

6. Which of the following was NOT a provision of the Intolerable Acts?
   a. suspension of the Massachusetts Assembly
   b. closing of the port of Boston
   c. suspension of New England town meetings
   d. quartering of British troops in private homes

   ANS: A   DIF: Medium   REF: 83   OBJ: 4.1
   TOP: American Revolution - Causes

7. In which area did the Revolutionary War begin?
   a. the South
   b. New York
   c. Philadelphia
   d. Boston

   ANS: D   DIF: Medium   REF: 85   OBJ: 4.1
   TOP: American Revolution

8. When he spoke against the Stamp Act before the British Parliament, Ben Franklin told the British Parliament that colonials said they opposed
   a. it because it was an external tax.
   b. it because it was an internal tax.
   c. all external and internal taxes.
   d. all import duties.

   ANS: B   DIF: Medium   REF: 80   OBJ: 4.1
   TOP: American Revolution - Causes

9. In what way were the Quebec Act and issuance of the Proclamation Line of 1763 most similar?
   a. They both helped cause the French and Indian War.
   b. They were both part of the Peace of Paris.
   c. They both restricted westward migration.
   d. They were both passed despite the objection of the British government.

   ANS: C   DIF: Medium   REF: 77, 83–84   OBJ: 4.1
   TOP: American Revolution - Causes

10. Foreign soldiers hired by the British were known as
   a. Loyalists.
   b. mercenaries.
   c. rabble in arms.
   d. militia.

   ANS: B   DIF: Medium   REF: 90   OBJ: 4.2
   TOP: Mercenaries

11. American colonists who continued to support England during the American Revolution were known as
   a. guerrillas.
   b. Loyalists.
   c. refugees.
   d. patriots.

   ANS: B   DIF: Medium   REF: 98   OBJ: 4.3
   TOP: Loyalists

12. Which of the following was NOT a reason for American victory in the Revolution?
   a. Washington's leadership
   b. superior American equipment and training
   c. miscalculations by the British
   d. French aid

   ANS: B   DIF: Medium   REF: 100   OBJ: 4.3
   TOP: American Revolution / American Victory

13. The Townshend Acts did all of the following EXCEPT
    a. put internal taxes on colonial goods.
    b. put duties on several imported items.
    c. reorganize customs service in the colonies.
    d. press the New York legislature to provide supplies to British troops.

    ANS: A   DIF: Medium   REF: 80   OBJ: 4.1
    TOP: American Revolution - Causes

14. All of the following were reasons for the British defeat in the American Revolution EXCEPT
    a. misinformation about the strength of American forces.
    b. the French support of American forces.
    c. Howe's failure to capture New York City.
    d. overestimation of Loyalist support.

    ANS: C   DIF: Medium   REF: 100   OBJ: 4.3
    TOP: American Revolution / American Victory

15. During the American Revolution, African-Americans
    a. fought on both the British and the colonial sides.
    b. were promised their freedom in exchange for military service.
    c. fought in mixed units in most battles of the war.
    d. all of the above

    ANS: D   DIF: Medium   REF: 98   OBJ: 4.3
    TOP: American Revolution / African-Americans

16. Which of the following patriots defended the British soldiers accused of murder at the Boston Massacre?
    a. Thomas Jefferson   c. Patrick Henry
    b. John Adams   d. George Grenville

    ANS: B   DIF: Medium   REF: 81   OBJ: 4.1
    TOP: Famous Patriots

17. Which of the following is the best description of the location of the Proclamation Line of 1763?
    a. along the crest of the Appalachian Mountains
    b. along the crest of the Rocky Mountains
    c. at the Mississippi River
    d. at the Rio Grande River

    ANS: A   DIF: Medium   REF: 77   OBJ: 4.1
    TOP: American Revolution - Causes

18. The Quebec Act angered colonists because
    a. it extended Quebec into lands claimed by the colonies.
    b. it encouraged Native Americans' raids on the colonies.
    c. it created a government lacking a representative assembly for Quebec.
    d. it extended Quebec into lands claimed by the colonies AND it created a government lacking a representative assembly for Quebec.

    ANS: D   DIF: Medium   REF: 83   OBJ: 4.1
    TOP: American Revolution - Causes

19. Americans formed a secret society to terrorize British tax stamp agents. It was known as the
    a. Continental Congress.   c. Underground Railroad.
    b. Continental Army.   d. Sons of Liberty.

    ANS: D   DIF: Medium   REF: 79   OBJ: 4.1
    TOP: American Revolution - Causes

20. The Intolerable or Coercive Acts did all of the following EXCEPT
    a. forbid town meetings.
    b. require that the colonial militias disband.
    c. permit British troops to live in private homes.
    d. close the port of Boston.

    ANS: B   DIF: Medium   REF: 83   OBJ: 4.1
    TOP: American Revolution - Causes

21. By the terms of the Treaty of Paris,
    a. money was set aside to pay for confiscated Loyalist property.
    b. Britain ceded Florida to the United States.
    c. the British were prohibited from shipping on the Mississippi River.
    d. the Mississippi River became the western boundary of the United States.

    ANS: D   DIF: Medium   REF: 99   OBJ: 4.3
    TOP: American Revolution / American Victory

22. The Boston man who did the most to fan the flame of rebellion against the British was
    a. Thomas Hutchinson.   c. John Hancock.
    b. George Washington.   d. Samuel Adams.

    ANS: D   DIF: Medium   REF: 81   OBJ: 4.1
    TOP: American Revolution Supporters

23. The 4th of July marks the anniversary of the
    a. approval of the Declaration of Independence.
    b. beginning of the American Revolution.
    c. surrender of the British at Yorktown.
    d. discovery of America.

    ANS: A   DIF: Medium   REF: 89   OBJ: 4.2
    TOP: Declaration of Independence

24. During the first two years of the Revolutionary War, the Americans were most dependent upon
    the French for
    a. clothing.   c. gunpowder.
    b. ships.   d. food.

    ANS: C   DIF: Medium   REF: 88   OBJ: 4.2
    TOP: American Revolution

25. The Declaration of Independence did all of the following EXCEPT
    a. accuse members of Parliament of being tyrants.
    b. borrow ideas from English writers.
    c. inspire other nations to seek independence.
    d. list reasons for separation from Great Britain.

    ANS: A   DIF: Medium   REF: 88–90   OBJ: 4.2
    TOP: Declaration of Independence

26. Which of the following is the BEST summary of the movement for independence in America?
    a. The colonists planned the war immediately following the French and Indian War.
    b. The colonies gradually moved toward open rebellion as a result of British policy.
    c. The colonists were united in revolution.
    d. All the colonies equally shared the hardships of war.

    ANS: B   DIF: Medium   REF: 77–84   OBJ: 4.2
    TOP: American Revolution - Causes

27. Which factor most hindered the colonial war effort in the southern colonies?
    a. the failure of guerrilla tactics   c. the continued fear of slave revolt
    b. the lack of support from the French   d. British reluctance to fight in the south

    ANS: C   DIF: Medium   REF: 96   OBJ: 4.3
    TOP: American Revolution

28. Who wrote the most inflammatory statements in favor of revolution?
    a. Thomas Paine   c. Paul Revere
    b. George Washington   d. Joseph Galloway

    ANS: A   DIF: Medium   REF: 86–87   OBJ: 4.2
    TOP: American Revolution Supporters

29. The major goal of the Committees of Correspondence was to
    a. keep the British troops from landing at Boston.
    b. write letters to Parliament.
    c. write letters to French and Spanish allies.
    d. better coordinate revolutionary activities throughout the colonies.

    ANS: D   DIF: Medium   REF: 82   OBJ: 4.1
    TOP: American Revolution

30. Which battle is considered the "turning point" in the American Revolution?
    a. Bunker Hill   c. Saratoga
    b. Lexington and Concord   d   Yorktown

    ANS: C   DIF: Medium   REF: 95   OBJ: 4.3
    TOP: American Revolution - Battles

31. The Sugar and Stamp Acts were designed chiefly to
   a. raise funds for the defense of the colonies.
   b. prove the right of Parliament to tax the colonies.
   c. enrich the British upper class.
   d. reduce colonial consumption of sugar and paper.

   ANS: A   DIF: Medium   REF: 77–79   OBJ: 4.1
   TOP: American Revolution - Causes

32. The British plan to attack New York at Albany in 1777 was designed to
   a. take over the richest colony.   c. split the colonies in two.
   b. take over the most populous colony.   d. put an end to Iroquois rebels.

   ANS: C   DIF: Medium   REF: 94   OBJ: 4.3
   TOP: American Revolution - Battles

33. Which of the following happened last?
   a. passage of the Intolerable Acts   c. the Boston Massacre
   b. passage of the Stamp Act   d. the Boston Tea Party

   ANS: A   DIF: Medium   REF: 83   OBJ: 4.3
   TOP: American Revolution - Causes

34. Which of the following would be considered an external tax on the colonies?
   a. the Stamp Tax
   b. the extension of Quebec
   c. an import duty
   d. the quartering of troops in colonial homes

   ANS: C   DIF: Medium   REF: 80   OBJ: 4.1
   TOP: American Revolution - Causes

35. Which would be the BEST example of a mercenary?
   a. an American soldier fighting in the Vietnam War
   b. a U.N. sponsored observer in Israel
   c. a rebel in El Salvador fighting to overthrow his government
   d. an American paid to be a soldier in the South African Army

   ANS: D   DIF: Medium   REF: 90   OBJ: 4.2
   TOP: American Revolution - Soldiers

36. Which statement is the best summary of the Battle of Bunker Hill?
   a. The British won, but with unacceptable losses.
   b. The Americans held the position.
   c. The British proved the superiority of their army.
   d. Americans drove off the British, but suffered heavy losses.

   ANS: A   DIF: Medium   REF: 86   OBJ: 4.2
   TOP: American Revolution - Battles

37. Which of the following BEST explains why the first shot fired at Lexington has been called "the shot heard 'round the world"?
   a. Shortly after it was issued, it was printed in newspapers in every country.
   b. Copies were mailed out to every country.
   c. Its ideas inspired many people around the world.
   d. Everyone in the world eventually heard about it.

   ANS: C   DIF: Medium   REF: 84–85   OBJ: 4.2
   TOP: American Revolution - Battles

38. Which colonist would have been LEAST affected by the American Revolution?
   a. a frontiersman   c. a Boston rebel
   b. a New York merchant   d. a Philadelphia Loyalist

   ANS: A   DIF: Medium   OBJ: 4.3   TOP: American Revolution

39. Which of the following was BOTH an asset and a liability for the American revolutionaries?
   a. the disunity of their military
   b. the fact that many Americans owned guns
   c. the Americans' skill as marksmen
   d. the military skills of George Washington

   ANS: A   DIF: Medium   REF: 100   OBJ: 4.3
   TOP: Amcrican Revolution

ESSAY

1. In the following sentence, which word makes a value judgment? Write your answer on a separate sheet of paper and support your answer with a paragraph explaining why you chose it.
       It was a serious matter when the British Parliament started meddling in the colonies' affairs.
   A. matter
   B. British
   C. meddling
   D. colonies

   ANS:
   answer C Students' paragraphs should support their answer.

   DIF: Hard   REF: 77–84   OBJ: 4.0
   TOP: American Revolution - Causes

© Prentice-Hall, Inc.

2. Choose one of the topic sentences below. Write an essay of two or three paragraphs giving specific evidence to support the statement.
   A. The course toward the American War of Independence began when Britain's one hundred years of "salutary neglect" ended.
   B. It is easier to explain why the British lost the War of Independence than to understand how the Americans managed to win.

   ANS:
   A. British decisions, which precipitated the War for Independence, were the sending of an army to protect the colonies, and then asking the colonies to pay for that standing army; the Proclamation of 1763 in regard to settlement west of the Appalachians; and the Sugar Act of 1764, the Stamp Act of 1765, the Declaratory Act of 1767, the Intolerable Act of 1774, and the Quebec Act of the same year. B. British mistakes and lack of understanding of the colonial situation contributed to their defeat in the Revolutionary War. In addition there were the long lines of communication to and from their headquarters, which prevented the British government from keeping informed, and the fact that expected loyalist support did not materialize. Also, the use of traditional practices in war, such as row-by-row positioning and brightly colored uniforms, made fighting the Americans more difficult.

   DIF: Hard   REF: 77–100   OBJ: 4.1
   TOP: American Revolution - Causes/ American Victory-Revol. War

3. Based on your reading of the chapter, write a paragraph describing American reaction to the laws passed by Parliament between 1763 and 1774.

   ANS:
   Answers will vary but could include the following ideas: Americans felt Parliament's laws upset a system they had grown accustomed to, namely unenforced mercantile laws. Americans felt that their rights as Englishmen were violated by an overextension of Crown authority.

   DIF: Hard   REF: 77–78   OBJ: 4.1
   TOP: American Revolution - Causes

4. There are those who say, "The American Revolution could have been prevented by better managed British colonial policy." On what grounds could they justifiably arrive at this conclusion?

   ANS:
   Answers will vary but could include the following ideas: Americans were very conservative in their demands; perhaps they would have settled for a loosely enforced mercantile policy similar to pre-1763. Most Americans were quite loyal to England and may have settled for a "shared sovereignty" between colony and mother country. Poor communications and misperceptions compounded problems.

   DIF: Hard   OBJ: 4.1   TOP: American Revolution - Causes

5. What were the major accomplishments of the First Continental Congress?

ANS:
Answers will vary but could include the following ideas: It formed a Non-Importation Association and oversaw a boycott of British goods. It framed the Declaration of Rights and Grievances and brought the movement to battle at Lexington and Concord.

DIF: Hard   REF: 84   OBJ: 4.2   TOP: American Revolution

6. Describe the impact of the publication of "Common Sense" and the "Declaration of Independence" on the American Revolution.

ANS:
Answers will vary but could include the following ideas: "Common Sense" was a major work of inflammatory rhetoric. It was widely read and shaped public opinion. The Declaration of Independence provided an intellectual and moral rationale for the revolution. It set up American grievances and was an inspiration to revolutionary movements around the world.

DIF: Hard   REF: 86–87, 88–90   OBJ: 4.2
TOP: American Revolution - Literature

7. What were the various roles women played in the War for Independence?

ANS:
Answers will vary but could include the following ideas: There was no one single role that women played in the war. In general they assumed the responsibility of keeping the farms, shops, and families going. A small group went to war with their husbands; others gave medical assistance to the injured or disguised themselves and fought as soldiers.

DIF: Hard   REF: 97   OBJ: 4.2
TOP: American Revolution - Women

8. Discuss how African-Americans participated in the American Revolution. In what ways did they use the turmoil of the period to improve their status?

ANS:
African-Americans served on both sides during the war. At first, many fought for the British, who offered them freedom. When the Americans matched that promise, many African-Americans joined the colonists' cause. In both cases, African-Americans used the war to serve their freedom.

DIF: Hard   REF: 98   OBJ: 4.3
TOP: American Revolution - African-Americans

9. Describe the relative advantages and disadvantages for BOTH America and England during the American Revolution.

ANS:
Answers will vary but could include the following ideas: America—Advantages - heavily armed, excellent marksmen, able leadership, autonomous fighting units. Disadvantages - poorly financed and organized, few willing to fight for extended periods far from home, inconsistent participation in the Revolution. England—Advantages - rich, powerful nation, professional army, well-equipped and trained forces. Disadvantages - long lines for supplies and communications, inappropriate military tactics, difficulty with guerrilla warfare.

DIF: Hard   REF: 90–100   OBJ: 4.3   TOP: American Revolution

10. To what extent is the following statement true? "The American Revolution was to England what the Vietnam War was to the United States."

ANS:
Answers will vary but could include the following ideas: Both England and the United States fought anticolonial wars far from home. Their armies were well-equipped, trained, and funded, but fought against elusive guerrilla forces. Both nations had difficulty maintaining public support for war efforts. In contrast, the Vietnamese and American Colonists were dissimilar in cultural heritage and history.

DIF: Hard   REF: 77–100   OBJ: 4.3   TOP: American Revolution

(page intentionally left blank)

MATCHING

Match each item with the correct statement below.

a.	speculators	f.	Alexander Hamilton
b.	Rhode Island	g.	Bill of Rights
c.	Articles of Confederation	h.	John Locke
d.	Patrick Henry	i.	Ben Franklin
e.	New Jersey Plan	j.	Declaration of Independence

1. He along with Madison and Jay wrote the "Federalist Papers."
2. English philosopher who wrote of the "state of nature," a time when no governments existed.
3. It established a "firm league of friendship" among the states.
4. Businessmen who bought land and resold it to make a profit.
5. American patriot opposed to the Constitution.
6. Only state that did not attend the Constitutional Convention.
7. A series of amendments that guaranteed certain rights and liberties to the people.

1. ANS: F   DIF: Easy   REF: 122   OBJ: 5.0
   TOP: U.S. Constitution
2. ANS: H   DIF: Easy   REF: 103   OBJ: 5.0
   TOP: Government History
3. ANS: C   DIF: Easy   REF: 108–109   OBJ: 5.0
   TOP: Articles of Confederation
4. ANS: A   DIF: Easy   REF: 110   OBJ: 5.0
   TOP: Articles of Confederation
5. ANS: D   DIF: Easy   REF: 122   OBJ: 5.0
   TOP: U.S. Constitution
6. ANS: B   DIF: Easy   REF: 116   OBJ: 5.0
   TOP: Constitutional Convention
7. ANS: G   DIF: Easy   REF: 123   OBJ: 5.0
   TOP: U.S. Constitution

MULTIPLE CHOICE

1. The members of the Second Continental Congress were most likely to be
   a. farmers.
   b. lawyers.
   c. merchants.
   d. soldiers.

   ANS: B   DIF: Medium   REF: 107–108   OBJ: 5.2
   TOP: Constitutional Convention

2. Coins and paper bills that serve as money are known as
   a. credit.
   b. barter.
   c. trade.
   d. currency.

   ANS: D   DIF: Medium   REF: 114–115   OBJ: 5.3
   TOP: Currency

3. An ordinance is defined as a (an)
   a. government rule or law.   c. election.
   b. government official.   d. legislative body.

   ANS: A   DIF: Medium   REF: 111   OBJ: 5.3
   TOP: Government

4. Which of the following was NOT a power of the central government under the Articles of
   Confederation?
   a. to deal with foreign governments   c. to coin money
   b. to declare war   d. to lay and collect taxes

   ANS: D   DIF: Medium   REF: 109   OBJ: 5.3
   TOP: Articles of Confederation

5. The complete lack of government is known as
   a. "totalitarianism."   c. "anarchy."
   b. "dictatorship."   d. "monarchy."

   ANS: C   DIF: Medium   REF: 116   OBJ: 5.4
   TOP: Government

6. Which of the following is a term which refers to a type of government where powers are shared
   between one central government and a number of state governments?
   a. "federal"   c. "dictatorship"
   b. "unitary"   d. "constitution"

   ANS: A   DIF: Medium   REF: 116–117   OBJ: 5.4
   TOP: Government

7. The United States Congress is made up of the
   a. House of Representatives and the Senate.
   b. House of Representatives and the Supreme Court.
   c. Supreme Court and the Executive.
   d. judicial and executive branches.

   ANS: A   DIF: Medium   REF: 121   OBJ: 5.4
   TOP: American Government / Constitution

8. A change or addition to a constitution is known as a (an)
   a. law.   c. amendment.
   b. veto.   d. bill.

   ANS: C   DIF: Medium   REF: 120   OBJ: 5.4
   TOP: U.S. Constitution

9. The doctrine that divides power between the three branches of the national government is known
   as
   a. separation of power.   c. anarchy.
   b. the Bill of Rights.   d. states' rights.

   ANS: A   DIF: Medium   REF: 120   OBJ: 5.4
   TOP: American Government / Constitution

10. The President is a member of the _____ branch.
    a. judicial
    b. legislative
    c. executive
    d. congressional

    ANS: C   DIF: Medium   REF: 120   OBJ: 5.4
    TOP: American Government / Constitution

11. The part of the government that makes laws is the
    a. executive branch.
    b. legislative branch.
    c. judicial branch.
    d. Supreme Court.

    ANS: B   DIF: Medium   REF: 120–121   OBJ: 5.4
    TOP: American Government / Constitution

12. The group that favored approval of the Constitution of 1787 was the
    a. Federalists.
    b. Anti-Federalists.
    c. Tories.
    d. Loyalists.

    ANS: A   DIF: Medium   REF: 121   OBJ: 5.5
    TOP: U.S. Constitution

13. The American colonial system lasted about
    a. 50 years.
    b. 100 years.
    c. 150 years.
    d. 200 years.

    ANS: C   DIF: Medium   REF: 104   OBJ: 5.1
    TOP: American History / Government

14. The Articles of Confederation were drawn up by the
    a. Continental Congress.
    b. Constitutional Convention.
    c. British.
    d. Annapolis Convention.

    ANS: A   DIF: Medium   REF: 108   OBJ: 5.2
    TOP: Articles of Confederation

15. The government under the Articles of Confederation successfully
    a. planned the course for western settlement.
    b. ended the American Revolution.
    c. gained respect for European governments.
    d. planned the course for western settlement AND ended the American Revolution.

    ANS: D   DIF: Medium   REF: 114   OBJ: 5.3
    TOP: Articles of Confederation

16. Most of the early state constitutions did all of the following EXCEPT
    a. strengthen the powers of the governor.
    b. provide for two-house legislatures.
    c. include a declaration of independence.
    d. list basic rights reserved to the citizens.

    ANS: A   DIF: Medium   REF: 105   OBJ: 5.1
    TOP: U.S. Constitution / History

17. The Second Continental Congress was LEAST successful in which of the following areas?
    a. finances, or getting money from the states for the war
    b. finding a leader for the Continental Army
    c. establishing an alliance with France
    d. starting a postal service

    ANS: A   DIF: Medium   REF: 108   OBJ: 5.2
    TOP: Continental Congress

18. A major weakness of the government under the Articles of Confederation was that it
    a. gave the President too much power.
    b. favored the large states in the Congress.
    c. lacked power to collect taxes.
    d. all of the above

    ANS: C   DIF: Medium   REF: 108   OBJ: 5.3
    TOP: Articles of Confederation

19. The three-fifths compromise concerned the issue of
    a. the presidency.   c. a two-house legislature.
    b. slavery.   d. a federal or national union.

    ANS: B   DIF: Medium   REF: 119–120   OBJ: 5.4
    TOP: U.S. Constitution

20. The Chief Executive of the United States is the
    a. Senate.   c. President.
    b. House of Representatives.   d. Supreme Court.

    ANS: C   DIF: Medium   REF: 120   OBJ: 5.4
    TOP: American Government / Constitution

21. Which of the following is considered "the supreme law of the land"?
    a. the President   c. the Declaration of Independence
    b. the Constitution   d. the Great Compromise

    ANS: B   DIF: Medium   REF: 121   OBJ: 5.4
    TOP: American Government / Constitution

22. The Virginia Plan was designed to give more power to the
    a. more populated states.   c. Supreme Court.
    b. less populated states.   d. President.

    ANS: A   DIF: Medium   REF: 118   OBJ: 5.4
    TOP: U.S. Constitution

© Prentice-Hall, Inc.

23. The major difference between a federal union and a national union to the Founders was
    a. the status of new states in the western lands.
    b. the degree of the power given to the central government.
    c. the manner in which representatives in the legislature were chosen.
    d. the status of new states in the western lands AND the degree of power given to the central government.

    ANS: C   DIF: Medium   REF: 116–118   OBJ: 5.4
    TOP: U.S. Government / History

24. The Constitution was drafted by delegates from
    a. thirteen states.   c. twelve states.
    b. fifteen states.   d. seventeen states and one territory.

    ANS: C   DIF: Medium   REF: 116   OBJ: 5.4
    TOP: U.S. Constitution

25. Which of the following was NOT an issue at the Constitutional Convention?
    a. slavery   c. a strong or weak central government
    b. representation in Congress   d. independence from England

    ANS: D   DIF: Medium   REF: 116–121   OBJ: 5.4
    TOP: U.S. Constitution

26. The "Great Compromise" concerned the issue of
    a. the Presidency.   c. representation in Congress.
    b. slavery.   d. the Supreme Court.

    ANS: C   DIF: Medium   REF: 118   OBJ: 5.4
    TOP: American Government / U.S. Constitution

27. How did the Constitutional Convention address the question of whether to have a federal union or a national union?
    a. They chose a national union.
    b. They chose a federal union.
    c. They avoided all aspects of both.
    d. They chose a union partly national and partly federal.

    ANS: D   DIF: Medium   REF: 116–118   OBJ: 5.4
    TOP: U.S. Constitution

28. Which of the following occurred LAST?
    a. Constitutional Convention   c. Annapolis meeting
    b. Shays' Rebellion   d. publication of the Federalist papers

    ANS: D   DIF: Medium   REF: 122–123   OBJ: 5.5
    TOP: U.S. Constitution

29. Who was NOT an author of the "Federalist Papers"?
    a. Adams   c. Jay
    b. Madison   d. Hamilton

    ANS: A   DIF: Medium   REF: 122   OBJ: 5.5
    TOP: U.S. Constitution

30. When compared to the state constitutions, the United States Constitution is
    a. much more liberal.   c. more detailed.
    b. more conservative.   d. older.

    ANS: B   DIF: Medium   OBJ: 5.5   TOP: U.S. Constitution

31. The "Federalist Papers" are a classic statement of
    a. the need for a strong state government.
    b. the need for rebellion against the federal government.
    c. the need for the Federalists to recruit supporters.
    d. the need for a strong federal government.

    ANS: D   DIF: Medium   REF: 122–123   OBJ: 5.5
    TOP: U.S. Constitution

32. The "Federalist Papers" were written to help gain support for ratification of the Constitution in
    a. New York.   c. Virginia.
    b. Massachusetts.   d. New Hampshire.

    ANS: A   DIF: Medium   REF: 122   OBJ: 5.5
    TOP: U.S. Constitution

33. The activities of the Anti-Federalists could be considered MOST responsible for which part of
    the Constitution?
    a. the first 10 amendments
    b. Congress' power to tax
    c. the President's power as Commander-in-Chief
    d. the federal judges' term of office

    ANS: A   DIF: Medium   REF: 123   OBJ: 5.5
    TOP: U.S. Constitution

34. The Constitution forbids Congress from levying duties on
    a. exports.   c. manufactured goods.
    b. imports.   d. foreign travel.

    ANS: A   DIF: Medium   REF: 120   OBJ: 5.5
    TOP: U.S. Constitution

35. Which of the following is the BEST example of separation of power?
    a. The Supreme Court listens to a case.
    b. The President asks his advisor to resign.
    c. Congress debates a proposed bill.
    d. The Senate ratifies a treaty.

    ANS: D   DIF: Medium   REF: 120–121   OBJ: 5.4
    TOP: American Government / U.S. Constitution

36. A major reason for the continued success of the Constitution is
    a. its careful attention to the details of governing.
    b. its shortness and lack of details.
    c. the lack of any means by which to change it.
    d. its shortness and lack of details AND the lack of any means by which to change it.

    ANS: B   DIF: Medium   REF: 124   OBJ: 5.5
    TOP: U.S. Constitution

37. The activities of the people in the Anti-Vietnam War movement were MOST similar to the activities of
    a.   Daniel Shays.   c.   Oliver Ellsworth.
    b.   Alexander Hamilton.   d.   Edmund Randolph.

    ANS: A   DIF: Medium   REF: 114–115   OBJ: 5.3
    TOP: U.S. Government / History

38. Anti-Federalists would MOST strongly support the idea of a
    a.   U.S. Army.   c.   mandatory 18-year-old drinking age.
    b.   postal system.   d.   local public school system.

    ANS: D   DIF: Medium   REF: 121–123   OBJ: 5.4
    TOP: Anti-Federalists

39. The Anti-Federalists believed in keeping close local control of legislators. Which of the following would they MOST strongly oppose?
    a.   a one-year term of office c.   a limit on number of terms
    b.   a six-year term of office d.   recall elections

    ANS: B   DIF: Medium   REF: 121–123   OBJ: 5.4
    TOP: Anti-Federalists

40. Which of the following is a part of the legislative branch?
    a.   a clerk working for the Chief Justice   c.   the Secretary of Defense
    b.   a Senate page   d.   an ambassador

    ANS: B   DIF: Medium   REF: 120   OBJ: 5.4
    TOP: American Government

41. Federalists would be MOST supportive of
    a.   state controlled drinking laws.
    b.   the establishment of Washington, D.C.
    c.   state militia.
    d.   Shays's Rebellion.

    ANS: B   DIF: Medium   REF: 121–123   OBJ: 5.4
    TOP: Federalists

42. Based on the reading of the chapter, which state MOST consistently opposed the move for a strong central government?
    a. Delaware   c. Rhode Island
    b. New York   d. Virginia

ANS: C   DIF: Medium   REF: 116, 123   OBJ: 5.5
TOP: Rhode Island

ESSAY

1. What point of view does the following statement express toward the Articles of Confederation? Write your answer on a separate sheet of paper and support your answer with a paragraph explaining why you chose it.
    The weak Articles of Confederation had a few successes, but the successes were minor.
    A. favorable
    B. unfavorable
    C. extremely unfavorable
    D. unbiased

ANS:
answer B Students' paragraph should support their answer.

DIF: Hard   REF: 108   OBJ: 5.0
TOP: Articles of Confederation

2. In two or three paragraphs, summarize the decisions that enabled the thirteen sovereign states to become the United States of America.

ANS:
Student answers will vary but could include these ideas: The thirteen "sovereign" states that became the Union were able to do so only at the expense of compromises at the Constitutional Convention. Major compromises were the Great Compromise, regarding representation in two houses of Congress, the three-fifths compromise on slavery and taxation, the Commercial Compromise on slave importation (20 more years) and tax on exports (forbidden), and the promise of the addition of a Bill of Rights.

DIF: Hard   REF: 116–124   OBJ: 5.1
TOP: Constitutional Convention

3. Evaluate the successes and failures of the Second Continental Congress.

ANS:
Answers will vary but could include the following ideas: Successes - issued Declaration of Independence, maintained the army and fought the British, created a postal service, foreign policy developed, received recognition from France and drew up the Articles of Confederation. Failures - unable to obtain needed revenues and could not adequately finance war effort.

DIF: Hard   REF: 108   OBJ: 5.2   TOP: Continental Congress

4. What were the demands of Daniel Shays and his followers? Discuss the reaction to this movement.

ANS:
Answers will vary but could include the following ideas: Wanted help for debtors - more paper money, lower taxes, end to imprisonment and foreclosure of debtors, and a continuation of the democratic tradition of the revolution. Reaction - elite feared the unleashed power of masses, felt that democratic impulses had gotten out of hand. Major impact on the Philadelphia Convention.

DIF: Hard   REF: 114–115   OBJ: 5.3   TOP: Shays's Rebellion

5. In your opinion, why can it be said that we are still feeling the effects of the Great Compromise in our lives today?

ANS:
Answers will vary but could include the following ideas: It resolved the conflict between large and small states and developed the bicameral congress.

DIF: Hard   REF: 118   OBJ: 5.4   TOP: U.S. Constitution

6. "The Constitution is best described as a bundle of compromises." Explain the basis for this statement.

ANS:
Answers will vary but could include the following ideas: Compromises over - slavery, big/small states, northern/southern states, landed/liquid capital, strong/weak central government, federal/national union, and elite/republican element.

DIF: Hard   REF: 116–124   OBJ: 5.4   TOP: U.S. Constitution

7. Write a paragraph describing why the Anti-Federalists opposed the new Constitution.

ANS:
Answers will vary but could include the following ideas: They feared a strong central government and the erosion of the state governments. Feared the strong President, power to tax, power to regulate interstate commerce, and the exclusion of a bill of rights.

DIF: Hard   REF: 121–123   OBJ: 5.5   TOP: U.S. Constitution

8. Discuss three reasons why the Federalists supported the new Constitution.

ANS:
Answers will vary but could include the following ideas: The Federalists saw a need for a strong central government whose law was higher than the individual state laws in certain circumstances; saw it as a way to regulate the way states interacted with one another, formulate international policy, commerce, the monetary system, and to raise and maintain an army.

DIF: Hard   REF: 121–124   OBJ: 5.5   TOP: U.S. Constitution

9. To what extent do you agree with the following statement: "The debate over the ratification was ultimately a major contribution to American politics and thought."

ANS:
Answers will vary but could include the following ideas: The debate added greatly to political theory ("Federalist Papers"), resulted in the creation of the Bill of Rights, and a favorable climate for republican ideals.

DIF: Hard   REF: 121–124   OBJ: 5.5   TOP: U.S. Constitution

MATCHING

Match each item with the correct statement below.

a. Jacobin
b. 12th Amendment
c. Kentucky Resolution
d. Thomas Pickney
e. Judiciary Act of 1789

f. France
g. Thomas Jefferson
h. James Madison
i. Federalist
j. Sedition Act

1. Fought an "unofficial" war with the United States in 1798–1800.
2. As a member of the House of Representatives, he drew up the Bill of Rights.
3. George Washington's first Secretary of State.
4. Negotiated the 1795 treaty with Spain that provided for free navigation of the Mississippi River.
5. Any member of a radical group that carried out France's "reign of terror."
6. Declared that states could "nullify" acts of Congress.
7. Provided fines or jailing of persons who criticized the United States government.
8. With this law Congress set up the Supreme Court.
9. An early political party that favored a strong central government.
10. Provided that the offices of President and Vice-President appear separately on the ballots.

1. ANS: F   DIF: Easy   REF: 167   OBJ: 6.0
    TOP: French History
2. ANS: H   DIF: Easy   REF: 153   OBJ: 6.0
    TOP: U.S. Constitution
3. ANS: G   DIF: Easy   REF: 154   OBJ: 6.0
    TOP: Washington's Presidency
4. ANS: D   DIF: Easy   REF: 162   OBJ: 6.0
    TOP: U.S. Foreign Policy / Treaties
5. ANS: A   DIF: Easy   REF: 160   OBJ: 6.0
    TOP: French History
6. ANS: C   DIF: Easy   REF: 169   OBJ: 6.0
    TOP: States' Rights
7. ANS: J   DIF: Easy   REF: 169   OBJ: 6.0
    TOP: U.S. Constitution
8. ANS: E   DIF: Easy   REF: 153   OBJ: 6.0
    TOP: U.S. Judicial System
9. ANS: I   DIF: Easy   REF: 158   OBJ: 6.0
    TOP: U.S. Political Parties
10. ANS: B   DIF: Easy   REF: 167–168   OBJ: 6.0
    TOP: Sedition Act

MULTIPLE CHOICE

1. A privileged class of people of high rank is known as
    a. a democracy.   c. anarchy.
    b. an aristocracy.   d. citizens.

    ANS: B   DIF: Medium   REF: 152   OBJ: 6.1
    TOP: Social Class

2. In 1790, the majority of the population lived
    a. in New York State.
    b. along the Atlantic coast and connected waterways.
    c. in the five largest cities.
    d. in the Mississippi Valley.

    ANS: B   DIF: Medium   REF: 149   OBJ: 6.1
    TOP: 18th Century U.S. Demography

3. In 1790, settlers living west of the Appalachian Mountains were MOST dependent upon use of
    the
    a. Mississippi River.   c. National Road.
    b. Erie Canal.   d. Cumberland Gap.

    ANS: D   DIF: Medium   OBJ: 6.1   TOP: Cumberland Gap

4. The power of "advice and consent" is given by the Constitution to the
    a. President.   c. House of Representatives.
    b. Supreme Court.   d. Senate.

    ANS: D   DIF: Medium   REF: 154   OBJ: 6.2
    TOP: U.S. Constitution

5. Strict and broad construction refer to differing interpretations of
    a. the Constitution.   c. American history.
    b. foreign policy.   d. British history.

    ANS: A   DIF: Medium   REF: 157   OBJ: 6.2
    TOP: U.S. Constitution

6. A "tariff" is best defined as a
    a. Presidential veto.   c. tax on an export.
    b. tax on an import.   d. Supreme Court decision.

    ANS: B   DIF: Medium   REF: 157   OBJ: 6.2
    TOP: Taxes

7. Which of the following gave the MOST support to Hamilton's report regarding the public credit?
   a. bond speculators
   b. Virginians
   c. James Madison
   d. people who had already sold their war bonds

   ANS: A   DIF: Medium   REF: 156   OBJ: 6.2
   TOP: U.S. Banking / Finance

8. Which of the following was NOT favored by the Federalists?
   a. Hamilton's program   c. a strong central government
   b. England   d. the French Revolution

   ANS: D   DIF: Medium   REF: 161   OBJ: 6.3
   TOP: U.S. Political Parties

9. Anti-Federalists supported each of the following EXCEPT the
   a. national bank.   c. strict construction of the Constitution.
   b. French Revolution.   d. Thomas Jefferson.

   ANS: A   DIF: Medium   REF: 157   OBJ: 6.3
   TOP: U.S. Political Parties

10. Which of the following individuals had the greatest impact on the policy of the Washington administration?
    a. Alexander Hamilton   c. the Supreme Court
    b. John Adams   d. Thomas Jefferson

    ANS: A   DIF: Medium   REF: 155   OBJ: 6.3
    TOP: U.S. Banking / Finance

11. "Sedition" is best defined as
    a. shared state and federal power. c. inciting a rebellion.
    b. the right to vote.   d. immigration.

    ANS: C   DIF: Medium   REF: 167–168   OBJ: 6.4
    TOP: Sedition Act

12. The Sedition Act was a limitation on which fundamental freedom?
    a. religion   c. press
    b. right to counsel   d. assembly

    ANS: C   DIF: Medium   REF: 167–169   OBJ: 6.4
    TOP: Sedition Act

13. Which of the following had the LEAST impact on the development of political parties?
    a. events in Europe   c. the Constitution
    b. American social class structure d. Hamilton's financial program

    ANS: C   DIF: Medium   OBJ: 6.4   TOP: U.S. Political Parties

14. Unlike the English, Americans
    a. could move up the social class ladder more easily.
    b. rejected any notion of social class.
    c. gained social class mainly through their ancestry.
    d. had a rigid social class system.

    ANS: A   DIF: Medium   REF: 152   OBJ: 6.1
    TOP: American Social Class

15. The United States began taking a census in 1790
    a. because the Constitution required it.
    b. to fix the size of each state's delegation in the House of Representatives.
    c. because the Federalists felt it would help them remain in power.
    d. because the Constitution required it AND to fix the size of each state's delegation in the
       House of Representatives.

    ANS: D   DIF: Medium   REF: 153   OBJ: 6.2
    TOP: Constitution / Census

16. The site of our nation's capitol was the result of a "deal" regarding the
    a. choosing of Thomas Jefferson as the third President.
    b. assumption of state debts by the federal government.
    c. establishment of a national bank.
    d. tariff rates on imported goods.

    ANS: B   DIF: Medium   REF: 155–156   OBJ: 6.2
    TOP: Finance

17. All of the following were dealt with in the Constitution EXCEPT
    a. representation in the legislature.   c. the regulation of commerce.
    b. the slave trade.   d. the organization of political parties.

    ANS: D   DIF: Medium   REF: 158–159   OBJ: 6.4
    TOP: U.S. Constitution

18. Which city was the nation's first capitol?
    a. Washington, D.C.   c. Philadelphia
    b. New York City   d. Boston

    ANS: B   DIF: Medium   REF: 152   OBJ: 6.2
    TOP: U.S. History / Capitol

19. Which of the following was NOT a function of the National Bank?
    a. to serve as the government's financial agent
    b. to eliminate the use of paper currency
    c. to collect taxes
    d. to lend the government money

    ANS: B   DIF: Medium   REF: 157   OBJ: 6.2
    TOP: National Bank / Finance

20. A broad interpretation of the Constitution was necessary to
    a. pass the Northwest Ordinance.
    c. maintain neutrality with France.
    b. create the National Bank.
    d. develop political parties.

    ANS: B   DIF: Medium   REF: 157   OBJ: 6.2
    TOP: National Banking / Finance

21. The Judiciary Act of 1789 dealt with each of the following EXCEPT the
    a. U.S. Supreme Court.
    c. federal district courts.
    b. federal circuit courts.
    d. state courts.

    ANS: D   DIF: Medium   REF: 153   OBJ: 6.2
    TOP: U.S. Legal System - History

22. Which of the following was NOT part of the executive department in Washington's administration?
    a. the Secretary of Treasury
    c. the Secretary of Education
    b. the Secretary of State
    d. the Secretary of War

    ANS: C   DIF: Medium   REF: 153   OBJ: 6.2
    TOP: Washington's Presidency

23. Hamilton's financial plan for the United States
    a. favored the growth of an agrarian nation.
    b. favored the growth of an industrial nation.
    c. recommended that most federal funds would come from direct taxes on the states.
    d. would encourage increased imports from Europe.

    ANS: B   DIF: Medium   REF: 156   OBJ: 6.2
    TOP: National Banking / Finance

24. Which of the following statements about the development of political parties is INCORRECT?
    a. Jefferson supported the Federalists.
    b. Hamilton opposed the Republicans.
    c. Madison was a Republican.
    d. Washington disliked the formation of parties.

    ANS: A   DIF: Medium   REF: 158–159   OBJ: 6.2
    TOP: U.S. Political Parties / History

25. Which of the following made it easier for America to follow a policy of neutrality in its foreign policy?
    a. the Napoleonic Wars
    b. the presence of British and Spanish colonies on our borders
    c. the distance between Europe and America
    d. America's expansion into Indian territory

    ANS: C   DIF: Medium   REF: 159–163   OBJ: 6.4
    TOP: U.S. Foreign Policy

26. Which of the following was agreed to in Jay's Treaty?
    a. an end to the impressment of American sailors
    b. British compensation for slaves taken during the Revolution
    c. British withdrawal from frontier fur posts in American territory
    d. payment for American ships seized by England

    ANS: C   DIF: Medium   REF: 162   OBJ: 6.3
    TOP: British History / America

27. Which of the following was NOT a provision of Pinckney's Treaty?
    a. the right of deposit at New Orleans
    b. free use of the Mississippi River
    c. agreement as to the southern boundary of the United States
    d. an end to impressment of U.S. sailors

    ANS: D   DIF: Medium   REF: 162   OBJ: 6.3
    TOP: Spanish History / America

28. Which of the following was NOT an important treaty settled in 1795?
    a. Jay's Treaty   c. Treaty of Greenville
    b. Treaty of Paris   d. Pinckney's Treaty

    ANS: B   DIF: Medium   REF: 161–162   OBJ: 6.3
    TOP: American Foreign Policy / Treaty

29. Which treaty is INCORRECTLY matched with its co-signer?
    a. Treaty of Greenville—England   c. Jay's Treaty—England
    b. Treaty of Paris—England   d. Pinckney's Treaty—Spain

    ANS: A   DIF: Medium   REF: 162   OBJ: 6.3
    TOP: American Foreign Policy / Treaty

30. Washington's handling of the Whiskey Rebellion
    a. greatly angered members of the Federalist party.
    b. supported the doctrine of states' rights.
    c. proved the strength of the national government.
    d. nearly brought about his defeat for a second term.

    ANS: C   DIF: Medium   REF: 163–164   OBJ: 6.3
    TOP: Washington's Presidency

31. Which of the following was NOT a contributing factor to conflict between Native Americans and settlers on the frontier?
    a. British support for the Native Americans
    b. Spanish support for the Native Americans
    c. French support for the Native Americans
    d. American territorial expansion

    ANS: C   DIF: Medium   REF: 159   OBJ: 6.3
    TOP: Native Americans / Settlers

32. "Millions for defense, but not one cent for tribute" was a popular slogan that referred to American anger over
    a. the XYZ Affair.
    b. the impressment of American sailors.
    c. the Jay Treaty.
    d. British support of Native Americans on the Frontier.

    ANS: A   DIF: Medium   REF: 167   OBJ: 6.4
    TOP: Foreign Policy / France

33. What two patriots died on July 4, 1826?
    a. John Adams and Thomas Jefferson
    b. John Marshall and Thomas Jefferson
    c. Thomas Jefferson and George Washington
    d. John Adams and John Marshall

    ANS: A   DIF: Medium   REF: 170   OBJ: 6.4
    TOP: U.S. Presidents

34. During Washington's second term, the United States faced all of the following problems EXCEPT
    a. Indian raids on the western frontier.
    b. Spanish interference with United States shipping on the Mississippi River.
    c. having to win agreement of Hamilton's plan to repay war debts.
    d. bitterness and quarreling between political factions.

    ANS: C   DIF: Medium   REF: 159   OBJ: 6.3
    TOP: Washington's Presidency

35. Jefferson was elected Vice-President in 1796 because he
    a. was chosen for the post by John Adams.
    b. received the second highest number of electoral votes.
    c. was chosen for the post by the House of Representatives.
    d. had served as Washington's Vice-President.

    ANS: B   DIF: Medium   REF: 164   OBJ: 6.3
    TOP: U.S. Elections

36. Compare Americans living in 1790 with Americans living today. Which of the following conclusions is LEAST valid?
    a. Today a smaller percentage of the population is involved in food production.
    b. A greater percentage of Americans now live in cities.
    c. Today there is a smaller gap between the richest and the poorest Americans than there was in 1790.
    d. Americans in 1790 were more dependent on water transportation.

    ANS: C   DIF: Medium   REF: 151–152   OBJ: 6.1
    TOP: Social / Economic Classes

37. Which of the following factors was MOST responsible for the high level of social mobility in America in 1790?
    a. free access to education
    b. great number of aristocratic titles in America
    c. diversity of occupations
    d. availability of land

    ANS: D   DIF: Medium   REF: 152   OBJ: 6.1
    TOP: 18th Century U.S. Demography

38. Which of the following had the LEAST impact on the development of political parties?
    a. the French Revolution   c. Hamilton's financial program
    b. the Constitution   d. the social structure in early America

    ANS: B   DIF: Medium   REF: 158–159   OBJ: 6.2
    TOP: U.S. Political Parties

39. Which of the following men would have been MOST likely to agree with the goals of the Whiskey Rebellion?
    a. Alexander Hamilton   c. John Adams
    b. Daniel Shays   d. James Madison

    ANS: B   DIF: Medium   REF: 162–163   OBJ: 6.3
    TOP: Washington's Presidency

40. Which contemporary issue is MOST similar to the issue involved in the Whiskey Rebellion?
    a. lowering the drinking age
    b. getting tougher on drunk drivers
    c. favoring lower taxes
    d. criticizing government treatment of Indians

    ANS: C   DIF: Medium   REF: 162–163   OBJ: 6.3
    TOP: Washington's Presidency

41. The doctrine developed in the Kentucky Resolution became a central issue in
    a. the election of 1796.   c. the Louisiana Purchase.
    b. the Civil War.   d. Manifest Destiny.

    ANS: B   DIF: Medium   REF: 169   OBJ: 6.4
    TOP: States Rights

ESSAY

1. Read the argument and answer the question that follows. Write your answer on a separate sheet of paper and support your answer with a paragraph explaining why you chose it.

   Three things led the United States to declare war on England, rather than France, in 1812. First, the United States wanted to take Canada. Second, we wanted to stop the British from supplying weapons to the Native Americans on the Western frontier. Third, the British, not the French, mercilessly seized American ships and cut off our trade.

   Suppose you found a speech that Henry Clay once made before Congress, which stated that the United States should declare war on England in order to take Canada. How would this affect the argument above?
   A. This discovery would weaken the argument.
   B. This discovery would support the argument.
   C. This discovery would completely refute the argument.
   D. This discovery would be irrelevant to the argument.

   ANS:
   answer B
   Students' paragraphs should support this answer.

   DIF: Hard   REF: 159–164, 166–168   OBJ: 6.0
   TOP: U.S. Foreign Policy

2. During the first ten years of the American government, policy-makers had a profound influence on the future course of the nation's history. Write one paragraph each on the lasting contributions of George Washington as first President and Alexander Hamilton as first Secretary of the Treasury. Add a conclusion that restates the main point.

   ANS:
   Contributions of George Washington—Student answers will vary but could include these ideas: Washington set patterns for much of a United States President's activity. Staid and somewhat aloof, he lent an air of dignity to the office. He formed and used a "cabinet" of advisers, took charge of both foreign (recognition of revolutionary France) and domestic (the Whiskey Rebellion) affairs, and his "Farewell Address" warned against alliances. Contributions of Alexander Hamilton—Student answers will vary but could include these ideas: Hamilton restored the nation's credit by seeing that its debts were paid. He worked out a compromise for the site of the national capital and created a National Bank. His efforts built a national economy, strengthened the national government as opposed to state governments, and aided in the formation of the first political parties.

   DIF: Hard   REF: 152–165   OBJ: 6.0
   TOP: Washington's Presidency / National Banking

3. Identify and describe what you consider to be the single most important difference between European and American aristocrats.

   ANS:
   Answers will vary but could include the following ideas: In Europe social class was more rigid with less social mobility; the Constitution abolished titles of nobility.

   DIF: Hard   REF: 151–152   OBJ: 6.1
   TOP: European / American Social Class

4. Identify and discuss at least two major criticisms of Hamilton's plan to assume the debt.

   ANS:
   Answers will vary but could include the following ideas: It allowed speculators to bilk the ill-informed out of their bonds. It created a large national debt, and it forced all states to support the debt-ridden states.

   DIF: Hard   REF: 155–156   OBJ: 6.2   TOP: National Banking

5. Summarize the critical differences between the Federalists and the Republicans.

   ANS:
   Answers will vary but could include the following ideas: The Federalists, led by Hamilton, were a party of elite businessmen and aristocrats. They supported manufacturing and a strong government to control the rising tide of Republicanism. The Republicans, led by Jefferson, were Anti-Federalists who supported a decentralized agrarian system.

   DIF: Hard   REF: 158–159   OBJ: 6.2   TOP: U.S. Political Parties

6. Why has the "Whiskey Rebellion" come to represent an important step in defining the division of power between the states and the national government?

   ANS:
   Answers will vary but could include the following ideas: It represented a popular reaction to a Federal law. Its suppression by a massive federally sponsored army established the power of the central government.

   DIF: Hard   REF: 162–164   OBJ: 6.3   TOP: States Rights

7. Describe to what degree the following three goals of American foreign policy were in conflict: (a) neutrality, (b) trade, and (c) territorial expansion.

   ANS:
   Answers will vary but could include the following ideas: It was difficult to remain neutral as we expanded westward and faced British, Spanish, and Native American response. It was difficult to trade while major wars and revolutions were waged in Europe.

   DIF: Hard   REF: 159–162   OBJ: 6.3   TOP: U.S. Foreign Policy

8. Compare and contrast the Whiskey Rebellion and Shays' Rebellion.

ANS:
Answers will vary but could include the following ideas: They were both populist movements directed at the abuses of the state. The specific issues differed but both arose from the dissatisfied masses. The response to Shays' Rebellion was led by Massachusetts business interests, while the Whiskey Rebellion was put down by a massive federal army.

DIF: Hard   REF: 162–164   OBJ: 6.3   TOP: States Rights

9. To what extent were the Alien and Sedition Acts a violation of the democratic principles of the revolution?

ANS:
Answers will vary but could include the following ideas: They restricted immigration which had previously been an open door; they violated the 1st Amendment rights of speech and press; they were designed to attack the growing power of the Republicans.

DIF: Hard   REF: 167–169   OBJ: 6.4   TOP: Sedition Act

(page intentionally left blank)

MATCHING

Match each item with the correct statement below.

a. Meriwether Lewis
b. Aaron Burr
c. Napoleon
d. Pierre Charles L'Enfant
e. John Marshall

f. Albert Gallatin
g. Chesapeake
h. Pierre Dominique Toussant L'Overture
i. Marbury vs Madison
j. Embargo Act

1. French leader who sold Louisiana to the United States.
2. United States ship fired upon by the British in 1807.
3. Blamed Alexander Hamilton for his defeat as governor of New York; killed Hamilton in a duel.
4. Haitian leader who prevented a French takeover of his island.
5. Prohibited American ships from sailing for any foreign port.
6. Supreme Court decision that established the practice of judical review.
7. Architect who designed Washington, D.C.
8. Chief Justice who established the Supreme Court as the final authority in interpreting the Constitution.
9. Jefferson's Treasury Secretary; introduced the budget specifying sums for each item of national expense.
10. Jefferson's personal secretary who led an expedition into the Louisiana Territory.

1. ANS: C   DIF: Easy   REF: 185   OBJ: 7.0
   TOP: Louisiana Purchase
2. ANS: G   DIF: Easy   REF: 194   OBJ: 7.0
   TOP: Embargo Act of 1807
3. ANS: B   DIF: Easy   REF: 188   OBJ: 7.0
   TOP: Treason
4. ANS: H   DIF: Easy   REF: 184   OBJ: 7.0
   TOP: French History / Haiti
5. ANS: J   DIF: Easy   REF: 195   OBJ: 7.0
   TOP: Embargo Act of 1807
6. ANS: I   DIF: Easy   REF: 191–192   OBJ: 7.0
   TOP: Judicial System
7. ANS: D   DIF: Easy   REF: 177   OBJ: 7.0
   TOP: U.S. Capitol
8. ANS: E   DIF: Easy   REF: 191–192   OBJ: 7.0
   TOP: Judicial Review
9. ANS: F   DIF: Easy   REF: 181   OBJ: 7.0
   TOP: Jefferson's Presidency
10. ANS: A   DIF: Easy   REF: 186   OBJ: 7.0
    TOP: Lewis & Clark Expedition

MULTIPLE CHOICE

1. The Latin motto of the United States "e pluribus unum" in English means
   a. "In God we trust."
   b. "Life, liberty and happiness."
   c. "My country, right or wrong."
   d. "One, made from many."

   ANS: D   DIF: Medium   REF: 175   OBJ: 7.1
   TOP: U.S. Mottos

2. Federalists were mistrustful of
   a. Alexander Hamilton.
   b. aristocrats.
   c. city dwellers.
   d. England.

   ANS: C   DIF: Medium   REF: 180–181   OBJ: 7.1
   TOP: Political Parties

3. Thomas Jefferson was a man of many professions, including all of the following EXCEPT
   a. minister.
   b. architect.
   c. inventor.
   d. philosopher.

   ANS: A   DIF: Medium   REF: 179–180   OBJ: 7.1
   TOP: Thomas Jefferson

4. Jefferson hoped that the United States would
   a. become a nation of big cities.
   b. industrialize.
   c. remain a nation of farmers.
   d. become a major military power.

   ANS: C   DIF: Medium   REF: 181   OBJ: 7.1
   TOP: Jefferson's Presidency

5. "Legal precedent" is best defined as
   a. a legal example to be followed.
   b. the official vote of the Electoral College.
   c. the popular vote for the President.
   d. the right to a lawyer.

   ANS: A   DIF: Medium   OBJ: 7.2   TOP: Judicial System

6. Which of the following was NOT one of Jefferson's basic political beliefs?
   a. strict interpretation of the Constitution
   b. the development of a strong central government
   c. encouragement of agriculture
   d. limits on spending public money

   ANS: B   DIF: Medium   REF: 180–181   OBJ: 7.2
   TOP: Thomas Jefferson

7. The chief significance of the Louisiana Purchase was that it
    a. cost so little.
    b. assured American control of the Mississippi River.
    c. made war with France unnecessary.
    d. strengthened the Federalist party.

    ANS: B   DIF: Medium   REF: 185–186   OBJ: 7.2
    TOP: Louisiana Purchase

8. The term "midnight judges" was coined to describe judges who
    a. were of poor qualifications.   c. were appointed at the last minute.
    b. were near the end of their terms.   d. served until a very old age.

    ANS: C   DIF: Medium   REF: 190   OBJ: 7.3
    TOP: Judicial System

9. Judicial review gives the Supreme Court the power to
    a. declare Congressional laws unconstitutional.
    b. veto Congressional laws.
    c. impeach the President.
    d. ratify treaties.

    ANS: A   DIF: Medium   REF: 191–192   OBJ: 7.3
    TOP: Judicial System

10. A government order prohibiting trade with a foreign country is known as
    a. an embargo.   c. war.
    b. a tariff.   d. free trade.

    ANS: A   DIF: Medium   REF: 195   OBJ: 7.4
    TOP: Embargo Act of 1807

11. The best definition for "naturalization" is
    a. to favor only native-born citizens.
    b. to grant full citizenship to a foreigner.
    c. to strictly interpret the Constitution.
    d. the belief in the natural rights of man.

    ANS: B   DIF: Medium   REF: 181   OBJ: 7.1
    TOP: Naturalization / Immigration

12. Jefferson believed that the major role of the federal government was to
    a. manage relations with other countries.
    b. settle disputes that arose between states.
    c. build up a strong army and navy for defense.
    d. redistribute the nation's wealth.

    ANS: A   DIF: Medium   REF: 180   OBJ: 7.1
    TOP: Jefferson's Presidency

13. European nations and the United States paid the Barbary States for
    a. protection from pirates.
    b. halting the shipments of slaves from Africa.
    c. guiding their ships through the Mediterranean.
    d. repairing ships.

    ANS: A   DIF: Medium   REF: 182   OBJ: 7.1
    TOP: Barbary Pirates

14. Which of the following statements accurately describes the changes made by the Jefferson Administration?
    a. The Bank of America was abolished.
    b. The tariff was repealed.
    c. The excise tax on whiskey was repealed.
    d. The amount of money spent on the military was increased.

    ANS: C   DIF: Medium   OBJ: 7.1   TOP: Jefferson's Presidency

15. How did Jefferson handle the problem of the Barbary pirates?
    a. He continued to pay bribes.
    b. He totally ignored the problem.
    c. He appealed to the British to protect the United States.
    d. He sent navy warships to attack them.

    ANS: D   DIF: Medium   REF: 182   OBJ: 7.1
    TOP: Barbary Pirates

16. The New England Federalists opposed the Louisiana Purchase because they
    a. feared restrictions on shipping.
    b. did not want to risk war with England.
    c. thought it would increase the political power of the West.
    d. were concerned about the Indian raids on the frontier.

    ANS: C   DIF: Medium   REF: 188   OBJ: 7.2
    TOP: Louisiana Purchase

17. The Louisiana Purchase
    a. doubled the size of the United States.
    b. forced Jefferson to reverse his interpretation of the Constitution.
    c. was strongly supported by the Federalist party.
    d. doubled the size of the United States AND forced Jefferson to reverse his interpretation of the Constitution.

    ANS: D   DIF: Medium   REF: 185–186   OBJ: 7.2
    TOP: Louisiana Purchase

18. Lewis and Clark reached the Rockies by following the
    a. Oregon Trail.   c. Missouri River.
    b. Colorado River.   d. Platt River.

    ANS: C   DIF: Medium   REF: 187   OBJ: 7.2
    TOP: Lewis & Clark Expedition

19. The Great Divide was so named because it
    a. led to the Civil War.
    b. separated the east- and west-flowing rivers.
    c. separated America from Canada.
    d. marked the division between North and South America.

    ANS: B   DIF: Medium   REF: 187   OBJ: 7.2
    TOP: Lewis & Clark Expedition

20. What provision did the U.S. Constitution make for the purchase of land from foreign countries?
    a. It was specifically prohibited.
    b. It was allowed with the consent of the Senate.
    c. It was allowed with the consent of the states.
    d. The issue was not dealt with by the Constitution.

    ANS: D   DIF: Medium   REF: 185–186   OBJ: 7.2
    TOP: U.S. Constitution

21. Alexander Hamilton died as the result of
    a. disease.   c. a duel.
    b. old age.   d. an assassination.

    ANS: C   DIF: Medium   REF: 188   OBJ: 7.2
    TOP: National Banking / Finance

22. On which issue did Jefferson contradict his policy of "strict construction" of the Constitution?
    a. the National Bank   c. the "midnight judges"
    b. the Embargo Act of 1807   d. the Louisiana Purchase

    ANS: D   DIF: Medium   REF: 185–186   OBJ: 7.2
    TOP: Louisiana Purchase

23. For an individual to be convicted of treason, there must be
    a. two witnesses testifying that the person levied war against the United States.
    b. a trial before the Supreme Court.
    c. a confession by the accused person.
    d. impeachment proceedings.

    ANS: A   DIF: Medium   REF: 189   OBJ: 7.2
    TOP: Treason

24. Burr was acquitted on the charge of treason because
    a. Jefferson took his side.
    b. he won the sympathy of the jury.
    c. the judge declared a mistrial.
    d. the prosecution couldn't produce two witnesses to a treasonable act.

    ANS: D   DIF: Medium   REF: 189   OBJ: 7.2
    TOP: Treason

25. Jefferson and the Republicans feared the power of the judges on the Supreme Court because
    a. they could be removed from office only by the impeachment process.
    b. they were blocking Jefferson's appointment.
    c. most of them were Federalists.
    d. they could be removed from office only by the impeachment process AND most of them were Federalists.

    ANS: D   DIF: Medium   REF: 189–190   OBJ: 7.3
    TOP: Jefferson's Presidency / Supreme Court

26. Jefferson accomplished all of the following during his first term as President EXCEPT
    a. doubling foreign trade.
    b. reducing the national debt.
    c. doubling the nation's size.
    d. stopping British impressment of American sailors.

    ANS: D   DIF: Medium   REF: 192, 194   OBJ: 7.4
    TOP: Jefferson's Presidency

27. Which of the following had the most positive effect on American commerce?
    a. the British Orders in Council
    b. Napoleon's victory at Austerlitz
    c. the Chesapeake Affair
    d. the passage of the Nonintercourse Act

    ANS: D   DIF: Medium   REF: 196   OBJ: 7.4
    TOP: U.S. Trade

28. The primary result of the Embargo Act was that
    a. the Republican party was destroyed.
    b. the British stopped impressing American sailors.
    c. British and French merchants were hurt by the loss of American trade.
    d. American commerce suffered.

    ANS: D   DIF: Medium   REF: 195–196   OBJ: 7.4
    TOP: Embargo Act of 1807

29. Which group was LEAST affected by the embargo of 1807?
    a. western settlers   c. southern cotton growers
    b. New England merchants   d. New York dock workers

    ANS: A   DIF: Medium   REF: 195–196   OBJ: 7.4
    TOP: Embargo Act of 1807

30. When Jefferson spoke of the "Revolution of 1800," he was describing an event that could be best compared to the
    a. French Revolution.
    b. Industrial Revolution.
    c. presidential election of 1800.
    d. election of Washington to a second term.

    ANS: C   DIF: Medium   REF: 180   OBJ: 7.1
    TOP: Jefferson's Presidency

31. Which modern issue would Thomas Jefferson MOST likely support?
    a. support for small farmers
    b. increase in the military budget
    c. censorship of newspapers
    d. encouragement of industrial development

    ANS: A   DIF: Medium   REF: 181   OBJ: 7.1
    TOP: Thomas Jefferson

32. Thomas Jefferson frequently took actions that were inconsistent with his stated policies. Which of the following pairs of actions/policies is NOT inconsistent?
    a. his purchase of Louisiana/his policy of strict construction
    b. his purchase of Louisiana/his policy of curbing government spending
    c. his relations with the National Bank/his policy on the National Bank
    d. his actions regarding the Sedition Law/his policy regarding the Sedition Law

    ANS: D   DIF: Medium   OBJ: 7.1   TOP: Jefferson's Presidency

33. The case of "Marbury v. Madison" is a good example of which basic principle of U.S. government?
    a. freedom of speech   c. separation of church and state
    b. checks and balance's   d. protection of states' rights

    ANS: B   DIF: Medium   REF: 191–192   OBJ: 7.3
    TOP: Judicial Review

34. Which of the following is the best reason for "Marbury v. Madison" being considered a landmark case?
    a. Every Supreme Court case is considered a landmark.
    b. It established the Supreme Court's power of judicial review.
    c. It established the Supreme Court's jurisdiction over the states.
    d. It was the first case the Supreme Court ever heard.

    ANS: B   DIF: Medium   REF: 191–192   OBJ: 7.3
    TOP: Judicial Review

35. The Embargo Act of 1807 was an American response to a situation that was MOST similar to the situation faced by America when it
    a. attempted to stay neutral during the early years of World War I.
    b. reacted to the Japanese attack on Pearl Harbor.
    c. jailed Vietnam War protestors.
    d. instituted the federal income tax.

    ANS: A   DIF: Medium   REF: 195–196   OBJ: 7.4
    TOP: Embargo Act of 1807

SHORT ANSWER

In one or two sentences, define and distinguish between the terms given below.

1. impressed sailors

   ANS:
   Impressed sailors were sailors that the British kidnapped to serve in their navy. Some were British deserters, while others were naturalized and native Americans.

   DIF: Hard   REF: 194   OBJ: 7.0   TOP: British History / Naval

2. judicial review

   ANS:
   Judicial review refers to the right of the Supreme Court to decide upon the constitutionality of laws.

   DIF: Hard   REF: 191   OBJ: 7.0   TOP: Judicial Review

3. midnight judges

   ANS:
   Midnight judges were the last-minute appointments made by John Adams to ensure Federalist control of the courts.

   DIF: Hard   REF: 190   OBJ: 7.0   TOP: Jefferson's Presidency

ESSAY

1. In the following statement, what point of view is presented about the Embargo Act? Write your answer on a separate sheet of paper and support your answer with a paragraph explaining why you chose it.
       The Embargo Act failed to scare Britain and France into a change of policy, and it hurt the United States.
   A. favorable
   B. unfavorable
   C. extremely unfavorable
   D. none of the above

   ANS:
   answer B Students' paragraphs should support their answer.

   DIF: Hard   REF: 194–196   OBJ: 7.0   TOP: Embargo Act of 1807

2. Jefferson's difficult decisions as President upset many New England Federalists. Write an essay giving at least two specific examples to support this claim.

ANS:
Student answers will vary but could include the following ideas: The Louisiana Purchase of 1802 was seen as a threat to the Federalist Party. The party feared that settlers in the new lands would support Jeffersonian Republicans, and that new western states would pass laws unfavorable to the commercial and banking interests of the Federalist East. Jefferson's refusal to allow the "midnight appointments" of his predecessor, John Adams, combined with the repeal of the 1801 Judicary Act to reduce Federalist power in government by eliminating many Federalists in key positions. The Embargo Act was hurtful especially to the ecomomic interests of the industrial northeast, and thus was quite unpopular among Federalists.

DIF: Hard   OBJ: 7.1   TOP: Jefferson's Presidency

3. Who were the "Virginia Dynasty"? Discuss the social environment that cultivated the members of the Dynasty.

ANS:
Answers will vary but could include the following: Washington, Jefferson, Madison, and Monroe were the Virginia Dynasty. Virginia was an aristocratic state. It had no urban centers with poor or immigrant masses. The social and economic climate of Virginia created an elite corps of country gentlemen who were well-suited for the presidency.

DIF: Hard   REF: 176   OBJ: 7.1   TOP: Social Classes

4. Based on what you have learned in the chapter, discuss the inconsistencies between Jefferson in theory and Jefferson in practice.

ANS:
Answers will vary but could include the following ideas: Jefferson failed to alter many of the Federalist programs that he had previously attacked, such as the National Bank and the tariff. His purchase of Louisiana contradicted his previously stated position on the Constitution. He was willing and able to take necessary or inevitable action in spite of political differences.

DIF: Hard   REF: 185–186   OBJ: 7.1   TOP: Thomas Jefferson

5. Why was control of the Mississippi River and New Orleans so vital to the development of the American West?

ANS:
Answers will vary but could include the following ideas: Western settlers depended on the river and the right of deposit at New Orleans to bring their products to eastern and world markets.

DIF: Hard   REF: 182   OBJ: 7.2   TOP: U.S. Trade

6. Explain the Constitutional controversy that developed over the Louisiana Purchase.

ANS:
Answers will vary but could include the following ideas: The Constitution does not contain a provision for the purchase of land from a foreign country. Thus, a broad interpretation of the Constitution was required. This reversed Jefferson's prior stand on interpretation.

DIF: Hard   REF: 185–186   OBJ: 7.2   TOP: U.S. Constitution

7. The case of "Marbury v. Madison" had a lasting impact on the American legal system. Explain what its significance was.

ANS:
Answers will vary but could include the following ideas: This decision established the doctrine of judicial review and has become the cornerstone of federal judicial power.

DIF: Hard   REF: 191–192   OBJ: 7.3   TOP: Judicial Review

8. Why was control of the federal judiciary essential to the Federalist party?

ANS:
Answers will vary but could include the following ideas: The aristocratic Federalist party was facing a losing battle with the rising democratic sentiment in America. States dropped voting requirements and broadened the electorate. New western states added more voters. These additional voters were generally Republican, thus diminishing Federalist control in Congress and the White House. The judiciary was the last Federalist refuge.

DIF: Hard   OBJ: 7.3   TOP: Judicial Review

9. Describe the events during the Jefferson administration that helped to develop the power and independence of the judiciary branch.

ANS:
Answers will vary but could include the following ideas: The failure to impeach Justice Samuel Chase ensured that judges would be free from arbitrary attack through the process of impeachment. The landmark decision of "Marbury v. Madison" established the power of judicial review, which elevated the judicial system to its significant role today.

DIF: Hard   REF: 190–192   OBJ: 7.3   TOP: Judicial Review

10. For five months in 1973-74, the Arab oil-producing states put a total embargo on petroleum to the United States and other states friendly to Israel. Compare and contrast this embargo with the Embargo of 1807, and evaluate the effectiveness of an embargo as a tool of foreign policy.

ANS:
Answers will vary but could include the following ideas: The Embargo of 1807 lasted 15 months and was a total embargo of goods manufactured in the United States, rather than just a prohibition of the shipment of oil. The Embargo of 1807 had a great impact on United States production and employment but put little pressure on the English and French. The Arab oil embargo initially had a great impact on other nations, many of whom had to turn to rationing. The Arab states, to some extent, forced many nations to reconsider their policy with respect to the Middle East.

DIF: Hard   REF: 195–196   OBJ: 7.4   TOP: Embargo Act of 1807

(page intentionally left blank)

MATCHING

Match each item with the correct statement below.

a.   Eli Whitney
b.   Henry Clay
c.   Dolley Madison
d.   Francis Scott Key
e.   James Monroe

f.   Noah Webster
g.   John Marshall
h.   Andrew Jackson
i.   William Henry Harrison
j.   John Quincy Adams

1.   Last of the "Virginia dynasty," his presidency is often characterized as the "Era of Good Feelings."
2.   As Chief Justice he made many decisions that strengthened the federal government.
3.   He was known as the "hero of New Orleans."
4.   His dictionary did much to promote an "American Language."
5.   He served as Speaker of House as well as leader of the "War Hawks."
6.   As Monroe's Secretary of State he urged the issuing of the Monroe Doctrine
7.   He wrote the words to the "Star-Spangled Banner" following the bombardment of Fort McHenry.
8.   He led the successful attack on the Indian Village near the Tippecanoe River in 1811.
9.   His invention of the cotton gin increased the need for slave labor in the South.
10. She fled the White House shortly before the British burned it.

1.   ANS: E   DIF: Easy   REF: 211   OBJ: 8.0
     TOP: Monroe's Presidency
2.   ANS: G   DIF: Easy   REF: 213–214   OBJ: 8.0
     TOP: Supreme Court
3.   ANS: H   DIF: Easy   REF: 207   OBJ: 8.0
     TOP: War of 1812
4.   ANS: F   DIF: Easy   REF: 220   OBJ: 8.0
     TOP: Education
5.   ANS: B   DIF: Easy   REF: 200   OBJ: 8.0
     TOP: War Hawks
6.   ANS: J   DIF: Easy   REF: 217   OBJ: 8.0
     TOP: Monroe Doctrine
7.   ANS: D   DIF: Easy   REF: 205   OBJ: 8.0
     TOP: War of 1812
8.   ANS: I   DIF: Easy   REF: 201   OBJ: 8.0
     TOP: U.S. / Native American Relations
9.   ANS: A   DIF: Easy   REF: 214–215   OBJ: 8.0
     TOP: Inventions
10. ANS: C   DIF: Easy   REF: 205   OBJ: 8.0
     TOP: War of 1812

MULTIPLE CHOICE

1. Which was a result of the British blockade during the War of 1812?
   a.   New England's support of the war   c.   an increase in exports
   b.   Federalist support for the war   d.   the convention at Hartford

   ANS: D   DIF: Medium   REF: 208–209   OBJ: 8.1
   TOP: War of 1812

2. The treaty that ended the War of 1812
   a.   recognized America as the victor.
   b.   recognized Great Britain as the winner.
   c.   was the basis for ongoing problems between America and Great Britain.
   d.   provided for a return to the conditions before the war.

   ANS: D   DIF: Medium   REF: 207   OBJ: 8.1
   TOP: War of 1812

3. "Nationalism" is best defined as
   a.   attacking another nation.
   b.   identifying with and feeling pride in a country.
   c.   the teachings of Karl Marx.
   d.   the attempt to create an empire.

   ANS: B   DIF: Medium   REF: 198   OBJ: 8.1
   TOP: U.S. Nationalism

4. The War Hawks directed their aggression toward each of the following EXCEPT the
   a.   British in Canada.   c.   French in Louisiana.
   b.   Spanish in Florida.   d.   Indians.

   ANS: C   DIF: Medium   REF: 200–201   OBJ: 8.1
   TOP: War Hawks

5. Which of the following was NOT a goal of the Tecumseh Confederation?
   a.   to unite the Indian tribes
   b.   to attack the British in Canada
   c.   to prevent further sale of Indian lands
   d.   to fight settlers

   ANS: B   DIF: Medium   REF: 201   OBJ: 8.1
   TOP: Native Americans

6. "Specie" is a term referring to
   a.   coins.   c.   travel.
   b.   people.   d.   immigrants.

   ANS: A   DIF: Medium   REF: 210   OBJ: 8.2
   TOP: Economics

7. Which of the following INCORRECTLY identifies one aspect of the economic sectionalism following the War of 1812?
   a. The West was a land of small farms.
   b. The South depended on large plantations.
   c. New England depended on agriculture.
   d. The Middle Atlantic states were reliant on commerce.

   ANS: C   DIF: Medium   REF: 212   OBJ: 8.2
   TOP: U.S. Demography - 19th Century

8. Which of the following statements concerning the Missouri Compromise is NOT valid?
   a. The Missouri Compromise permanently settled the issue of slavery in new states.
   b. The Missouri Compromise was unlike the compromises made at the Constitutional Convention.
   c. The Missouri Compromise maintained the North-South balance of power in the Senate.
   d. Thomas Jefferson was critical of the Missouri Compromise.

   ANS: A   DIF: Medium   REF: 216   OBJ: 8.3
   TOP: Missouri Compromise

9. The question of allowing slavery in new states was related to each of the following factors EXCEPT
   a. the morality of slavery.   c. control of the Senate.
   b. the future of the tariff.   d. the Monroe Doctrine.

   ANS: D   DIF: Medium   REF: 217   OBJ: 8.4
   TOP: Slavery

10. The success of the Monroe Doctrine was most dependent on
    a. the popularity of President Monroe.   c. the active support of Great Britain.
    b. the active support of Spain.   d. American popular opinion.

    ANS: C   DIF: Medium   REF: 217   OBJ: 8.4
    TOP: Monroe's Foreign Policy

11. President Madison cited all of the following as reasons for the U.S. declaration of war on Great Britain in 1812, EXCEPT
    a. impressment of sailors.   c. blockades on American shipping.
    b. boundary disputes.   d. incitement of Native Americans.

    ANS: B   DIF: Medium   REF: 202   OBJ: 8.1
    TOP: War of 1812 - Causes

12. Who succeeded James Madison as President of the United States?
    a. James Monroe   c. John C. Calhoun
    b. Dewitt Clinton   d. Thomas Jefferson

    ANS: A   DIF: Medium   REF: 211   OBJ: 8.1
    TOP: Presidential Elections

13. What was one of James Madison's major accomplishments at the Constitutional Convention?
    a. He was the Chairman.
    b. He kept detailed records of what was said.
    c. He authored the Declaration of Independence.
    d. He wrote the preamble to the Constitution.

    ANS: B   DIF: Medium   REF: 199   OBJ: 8.1
    TOP: Constitutional Convention

14. Which of the following groups most strongly opposed American involvement in the War of 1812?
    a. Southern planters   c. Western frontier people
    b. New England merchants   d. American Indians

    ANS: B   DIF: Medium   REF: 207–208   OBJ: 8.1
    TOP: War of 1812

15. Which man attempted to unite the Native Americans of the old Northwest?
    a. Hiawatha   c. Tecumseh
    b. Squanto   d. Iroquois

    ANS: C   DIF: Medium   REF: 201   OBJ: 8.1
    TOP: Native Americans

16. Which of the following was NOT an expression of patriotism made popular during the War of 1812?
    a. "We have met the enemy, and they are ours."
    b. "The Star-Spangled Banner."
    c. "Don't give up the ship."
    d. "The British are coming!"

    ANS: D   DIF: Medium   REF: 204, 205   OBJ: 8.2
    TOP: War of 1812

17. Both Monroe and Madison
    a. were members of the Federalist party.   c. vetoed the Bonus Bill.
    b. were from Virginia.   d. died in office.

    ANS: B   DIF: Medium   REF: 211   OBJ: 8.2
    TOP: U.S. Presidents

18. Which of the following was NOT a major decision of Marshall's Supreme Court?
    a. the legality of slavery
    b. the court's power of judical review
    c. no state had the power to tax the national government
    d. no state could interfere with contracts

    ANS: A   DIF: Medium   REF: 213–214   OBJ: 8.2
    TOP: Supreme Court

19. Which of the following Supreme Court decisions affirmed the Congressional power of regulating interstate commerce?
    a. "Marbury v. Madison"
    c. "McCulloch v. Maryland"
    b. the Dartmouth College Case
    d. "Gibbons v. Ogden"

    ANS: D   DIF: Medium   REF: 214   OBJ: 8.2
    TOP: Supreme Court

20. How did the United States acquire Florida?
    a. the result of a war
    c. purchased from England
    b. purchased from Spain
    d. part of the Louisiana Purchase

    ANS: B   DIF: Medium   REF: 213   OBJ: 8.2
    TOP: U.S. Expansion / Florida

21. Which President's term is associated with the "Era of Good Feelings"?
    a. Adams
    c. Madison
    b. Jefferson
    d. Monroe

    ANS: D   DIF: Medium   REF: 211   OBJ: 8.2
    TOP: Monroe's Presidency

22. The Era of Good Feelings referred to the period
    a. of peace with England.
    c. of the Missouri Compromise.
    b. without political parties.
    d. of peace with the Native Americans.

    ANS: B   DIF: Medium   REF: 211   OBJ: 8.2
    TOP: Monroe's Presidency

23. Which section of the country most opposed the Tariff of 1816?
    a. South
    c. West
    b. Northeast
    d. New England

    ANS: A   DIF: Medium   REF: 210   OBJ: 8.2
    TOP: U.S. / Foreign Trade

24. All of the following included a call for improved transportation in the United States EXCEPT
    a. Clay's American System.
    c. Madison's annual message of 1815.
    b. the Hartford Convention.
    d. Calhoun's Bonus Bill.

    ANS: B   DIF: Medium   REF: 209, 210, 211
    OBJ: 8.3   TOP: U.S. Transportation

25. The Missouri Compromise involved the issue of
    a. war with the Indians.
    c. the border with Spain.
    b. the tariff.
    d. slavery.

    ANS: D   DIF: Medium   REF: 214   OBJ: 8.3
    TOP: Slavery

26. The chartering of the second Bank of the United States was a result of all of the following EXCEPT
    a. a lack of national currency.
    b. a soaring national debt.
    c. the federal government's difficulty in borrowing money.
    d. Madison's admiration of Hamilton's Bank of the United States.

    ANS: D   DIF: Medium   REF: 210   OBJ: 8.0
    TOP: Economics / Banking

27. Which of the following was NOT a provision of the Missouri Compromise?
    a. Missouri was admitted to the Union as a slave state.
    b. Slavery was forbidden north of 36 degrees 30 minutes, except in Missouri.
    c. For each slave state admitted to the Union, in the future, a free state had to be admitted.
    d. Maine was to be admitted to the Union as a free state.

    ANS: C   DIF: Medium   REF: 216   OBJ: 8.3
    TOP: Slavery

28. Which of the following expanded the institution of slavery?
    a. moral objections to slavery   c. the invention of the cotton gin
    b. the decline in the price of tobacco   d. the outlawing of slavery in the North

    ANS: C   DIF: Medium   REF: 214–215   OBJ: 8.3
    TOP: Slavery

29. The Monroe Doctrine was issued in response to
    a. the threat of war with England.
    b. the purchase of Florida.
    c. European efforts to colonize South America.
    d. the peaceful settlement of the U.S-Canadian border.

    ANS: C   DIF: Medium   REF: 217   OBJ: 8.4
    TOP: Monroe Doctrine

30. Which of the following individuals is NOT correctly paired with his occupation?
    a. Gilbert Stuart—artist   c. John Calhoun—banker
    b. Jedidiah Morse—geographer   d. Charles Willson Peale—artist

    ANS: C   DIF: Medium   REF: 199, 218, 220
    OBJ: 8.5

31. The attitude toward the War of 1812 that was held by New Englanders at the Hartford Convention would be MOST similar to that of the
    a. supporters of the Spanish-American War.
    b. Americans who were outraged by Japan's attack at Pearl Harbor.
    c. people who protested against the Vietnam War.
    d. men who enlisted to fight in World War I.

    ANS: C   DIF: Medium   REF: 208–209   OBJ: 8.1
    TOP: War of 1812

32. When General Eisenhower—the hero of World War II— became President, he was following a career pattern MOST similar to that of
    a. Andrew Jackson.   c. Thomas Jefferson.
    b. Henry Clay.   d. Stephen Decatur.

    ANS: A   DIF: Medium   REF: 206–207   OBJ: 8.1
    TOP: U.S. Presidents

33. "Canada is ours for the taking." Which of the following would be MOST likely to have agreed with this statement?
    a. a New York merchant   c. a Kentucky frontier person
    b. a Boston sailor   d. a Southern plantation owner

    ANS: C   DIF: Medium   REF: 202   OBJ: 8.1
    TOP: U.S. Expansion

34. When comparing the War of 1812 to modern wars, which of the following factors is MOST different?
    a. the President's role as Commander-in-Chief
    b. the process by which Congress declares war
    c. the role of public opinion
    d. the technology of warfare

    ANS: D   DIF: Medium   OBJ: 8.1   TOP: War of 1812

35. In what way was the War of 1812 MOST unique?
    a. Public opinion on the war was divided.
    b. Washington, D.C. suffered war damage.
    c. There was a patriotic response to the war.
    d. Congress issued a formal declaration of war.

    ANS: B   DIF: Medium   REF: 205   OBJ: 8.1
    TOP: War of 1812

36. Which is NOT an example of a sectional conflict?
    a. World War I   c. the Korean War
    b. the Civil War   d. the Vietnam War

    ANS: A   DIF: Medium   REF: 198   OBJ: 8.2
    TOP: Civil Wars

37. In which of the following situations would a President be MOST likely to refer to the Monroe Doctrine?
    a. South Africans rebel against the apartheid system.
    b. War breaks out in the Middle East.
    c. The Soviet Union places nuclear missiles in Cuba.
    d. Civil war breaks out in Brazil.

    ANS: C   DIF: Medium   REF: 217   OBJ: 8.4
    TOP: Monroe Doctrine

38. Which of the following contributed the LEAST to the spirit of national unity?
   a. Webster's Dictionary
   b. the Missouri Compromise
   c. the new U.S. flag of 1818
   d. the cult of George Washington

   ANS: B   DIF: Medium   REF: 218–219   OBJ: 8.5
   TOP: Slavery

39. Which of the following is NOT a symbol of the United States?
   a. an eagle
   b. a globe
   c. the American flag
   d. "Uncle Sam"

   ANS: B   DIF: Medium   REF: 218   OBJ: 8.5
   TOP: U.S. Mottos / Symbols

40. Which of the following is the best example of sectionalism?
   a. the Confederate flag
   b. the American flag
   c. the astronauts landing on the moon
   d. the Fourth of July holiday

   ANS: A   DIF: Medium   REF: 198   OBJ: 8.5
   TOP: Sectionalism

41. Which of the following phenomena contributes LEAST to the spirit of national unity?
   a. network television shows
   b. nationally advertised products
   c. chains of fast-food restaurants
   d. use of the Confederate flag

   ANS: D   DIF: Medium   REF: 198   OBJ: 8.5
   TOP: Sectionalism

SHORT ANSWER

In one or two sentences, define and distinguish between the terms given below.

1. nationalism—sectionalism

   ANS:
   Nationalism is a strong feeling of loyalty to one's country; sectionalism, to one's section or region.

   DIF: Hard   REF: 198   OBJ: 8.0
   TOP: Nationalism / Sectionalism

2. national bank—state bank

   ANS:
   The national bank was established by the federal government and provided one national currency. The state banks were private banks chartered by the states which issued their own paper money.

   DIF: Hard   OBJ: 8.0   TOP: Banking

3. national slogan—national symbol

ANS:
National slogans are words or phrases that inspire patriotism ("Don't give up the ship!") while national symbols are objects that represent ideals of a nation (the bald eagle or the flag).

DIF: Hard   REF: 218   OBJ: 8.0   TOP: U.S. Mottos / Symbols

ESSAY

1. Which of the following is an example of cause-and-effect reasoning? Write your answer on a separate sheet of paper and support your answer with a paragraph explaining why you chose it.
   A. Eli Whitney was a recent Yale College graduate who had gone south to be a tutor to the children of a plantation family.
   B. Farsighted leaders realized that the Missouri Compromise was nothing more than a truce.
   C. The Monroe Doctrine was a defiant warning to European powers.
   D. Whitney's cotton gin suddenly made the production of short-staple cotton highly profitable.

   ANS:
   answer D Students' paragraphs should support their answer.

   DIF: Hard   REF: 214–216   OBJ: 8.0   TOP: Slavery / Cotton Gin

2. The presidencies of Madison and Monroe were marked by the growth of both nationalism and sectionalism. Write a paragraph on each of these developments, giving at least two examples of each as supporting evidence.

   ANS:
   Nationalism—The rise of the War Hawks in Congress and the War of 1812, which filled many Americans with a feeling of national pride; President Madison's Annual Message of 1815, in which a national spirit is evident in the call for national defense, roads and canals, a protective tariff, a national bank, and federal assumption of some state debts; the accession of Florida and agreements with Britain regarding our northern border; John Marshall's decisions, especially those that broadened the powers of the federal government; and the issuance of the Monroe Doctrine in 1823. Sectionalism—The West's opposition to the Bank; the South's opposition to the Tariff; the fact that the North had money for internal improvements while the South had none; the divisions of economies—in the East and North, commerce and industry, whereas in the South, plantation agriculture, and in the West, small farms. Differing economic interests produced conflicting ideas.

   DIF: Hard   OBJ: 8.1   TOP: Nationalism / Sectionalism

3. In what ways can the War of 1812 be characterized as a war to maintain U.S. neutrality? In what ways was it a war for territorial expansion?

    ANS:
    Answers will vary but could include the following ideas: The United States wanted to maintain its neutrality during the Napoleonic Wars. However, its ability to remain neutral was denied when the British impressed U.S. sailors, harassed shipping, formed a blockade, and instigated problems with the Native Americans. On the other hand, the War Hawks saw the War of 1812 as an opportunity to annex Canada and Florida while the Napoleonic Wars kept the Spanish and English occupied elsewhere.

    DIF: Hard   OBJ: 8.1   TOP: War of 1812

4. Henry Clay designed his American System so that it addressed the needs of the nation as a whole, as well as a major need of each of its sections. Summarize the major features of Clay's plan.

    ANS:
    Answers will vary but could include the following ideas: There was a protective tariff for the Northeast and internal improvements for the West and South. For the entire nation Clay proposed a National Bank that would provide currency and capital.

    DIF: Hard   REF: 209–210   OBJ: 8.2   TOP: American System

5. Compare and contrast the attitudes of the North, the South, and the West concerning protective tariffs, internal improvements, and the National Bank.

    ANS:
    Answers will vary but could include the following ideas: Tariff—The North supported tariffs in order to protect its industries. The South opposed tariffs because it lacked industry and had to import most of its finished goods. The West was neutral. Internal Improvements—The North opposed internal improvements as being too costly. It had the wealth to fund its own improvements. The South and the West supported improvements in order to improve their ability to bring their goods to market. Both the South and the West lacked the capital to fund their own projects. National Bank—The North opposed the plan. The South had a mixed response. The West opposed the National Bank because its state banks were able to provide cheap money.

    DIF: Hard   OBJ: 8.2   TOP: Nationalism / Sectionalism

6. Given what you know about the United States before the Civil War, give an analysis of the reasons that westward expansion of slavery became a political issue.

    ANS:
    Answers will vary but could include the following ideas: It threatened to upset the balance of northern (industrial) and southern (agricultural) representation in the Senate. Each side feared that additional senators would have an impact on issues such as the tariffs, internal improvements, the National Bank, and slavery.

    DIF: Hard   OBJ: 8.3   TOP: Slavery

7. To what extent could Eli Whitney be considered indirectly responsible for the growth of the slave society in the South?

ANS:
Answers will vary but could include the following ideas: Whitney's invention of the cotton gin (engine) made cotton processing more cost effective. This created an increased necessity for slaves and helped institutionalize the practice in the South as well as spread slavery to the West.

DIF: Hard   OBJ: 8.3   TOP: Slavery / Cotton Gin

8. Analyze the degree to which it can be said that the Missouri Compromise was a successful resolution of the slavery question in the West.

ANS:
Answers will vary but could include the following ideas: It did not resolve the question, rather it postponed a settlement. Neither North nor South got what it wanted. Instead, they agreed on a temporary settlement that allowed the slavery debate to continue.

DIF: Hard   REF: 214–216   OBJ: 8.3   TOP: Slavery

9. In your opinion, to what degree was the Monroe Doctrine an expression of America's isolationist impulse?

ANS:
Answers will vary but could include the following ideas: The Monroe Doctrine served to keep the powers of Europe out of the Western Hemisphere, thus ensuring the neutrality of the region. In contrast, it also served to create a U.S. "sphere of interest" open to U.S. expansion and domination.

DIF: Hard   REF: 217   OBJ: 8.4   TOP: Monroe Doctrine

10. To what extent did the growing spirit of American nationalism overcome the sectional divisions in America? Support your point of view with specifics.

ANS:
Answers will vary but could include the following ideas: In the years following the War of 1812, America experienced a surge of patriotic slogans and symbols. Heroes of the Revolution were eulogized, and George Washington's legacy as the "Father of the Nation" began. Nonetheless, fundamental economic, political, and social divisions between North, South, and West endured. By mid-century they would overcome the forces for unity and give rise to the Civil War.

DIF: Hard   REF: 218–220   OBJ: 8.5
TOP: Nationalism / Sectionalism

(page intentionally left blank)

MATCHING

Match each item with the correct statement below.

a. John C. Calhoun
b. spoils system
c. Abominations
d. Martin Van Buren
e. Cherokee

f. Roger Taney
g. convention
h. Whigs
i. John Quincy Adams
j. Nat Turner

1. Vice-President _____ argued that a state could nullify a law that it considered to be unconstitutional.
2. In response to Jackson's bank policies the National Republicans renamed themselves the _____.
3. An accomplishment of _____ as President was setting the work day at ten hours on federal projects.
4. A slave rebellion in 1831, led by _____, brought death to 60 whites and to over 100 blacks.
5. Because of high rates on so many classes of goods, the 1828 tariff law became known as the Tariff of _____.
6. The House chose _____ for President in 1824 even though he had fewer electoral votes than Jackson.
7. The _____ system replaced the caucus system for nominating candidates in the early 1800s.
8. The practice by Jackson and others of rewarding political supporters with jobs was called the _____.
9. In 1838 the _____ Indians were forced west of the Mississippi in what they called the "trail of tears."
10. As Jackson's Treasury Secretary, _____ deposited federal funds in "pet banks" around the country.

1. ANS: A   DIF: Easy   REF: 232   OBJ: 9.0
    TOP: Nullification
2. ANS: H   DIF: Easy   REF: 241–242   OBJ: 9.0
    TOP: Political Parties
3. ANS: D   DIF: Easy   REF: 243   OBJ: 9.0
    TOP: Van Buren's Presidency
4. ANS: J   DIF: Easy   REF: 236   OBJ: 9.0
    TOP: Slavery
5. ANS: C   DIF: Easy   REF: 225   OBJ: 9.0
    TOP: U.S. Tariffs
6. ANS: I   DIF: Easy   REF: 223   OBJ: 9.0
    TOP: Presidential Elections
7. ANS: G   DIF: Easy   REF: 223   OBJ: 9.0
    TOP: Presidential Elections
8. ANS: B   DIF: Easy   REF: 230   OBJ: 9.0
    TOP: Jackson's Presidency
9. ANS: E   DIF: Easy   REF: 236   OBJ: 9.0
    TOP: Native Americans
10. ANS: F   DIF: Easy   REF: 241   OBJ: 9.0
    TOP: Jackson's Presidency

MULTIPLE CHOICE

1. Because of the 12th Amendment, the selection of President in 1824 was ultimately made by the
   a. House of Representatives.
   b. Senate.
   c. Supreme Court.
   d. popular vote.

   ANS: A   DIF: Medium   REF: 223   OBJ: 9.1
   TOP: Constitution

2. Which is NOT a valid statement about the election of 1828?
   a. Jackson was elected President.
   b. Adams was criticized for his "Corrupt Bargain."
   c. Adams received fewer votes than he had in 1824.
   d. Jackson carried the states west of the Appalachians and south of the Potomac.

   ANS: C   DIF: Medium   REF: 225   OBJ: 9.1
   TOP: Presidential Elections

3. A closed meeting of party members held to reach a decision in a matter of concern is known as a
   a. "convention."
   b. "primary."
   c. "caucus."
   d. "quorum."

   ANS: C   DIF: Medium   REF: 223   OBJ: 9.1
   TOP: Presidential Elections

4. Which of the following would have been considered part of the frontier in the age of Jackson?
   a. the Mississippi River
   b. the Hudson River
   c. Virginia
   d. Massachusetts

   ANS: A   DIF: Medium   OBJ: 9.2   TOP: American Frontier

5. In the early 1800s, what system replaced the caucus for nominating candidates for office?
   a. primary elections
   b. conventions
   c. Congress
   d. public opinion polls

   ANS: B   DIF: Medium   REF: 228   OBJ: 9.2
   TOP: Presidential Elections

6. A form of government in which the people rule either directly or through elected representatives is known as a (an)
   a. "aristocracy."
   b. "oligarchy."
   c. "monarchy."
   d. "democracy."

   ANS: D   DIF: Medium   OBJ: 9.2   TOP: Democracy

7. The practice by Jackson and others of rewarding political supporters with jobs was
   a. ruled unconstitutional.
   b. known as "pork-barreling."
   c. called the "spoils system."
   d. known as the "convention."

   ANS: C   DIF: Medium   REF: 230   OBJ: 9.2
   TOP: Jackson's Presidency

8. Which of the following did NOT increase voter turnout in the early 1800s?
   a. political conventions
   b. Jackson popularity
   c. printed ballots
   d. granting women the right to vote

   ANS: D   DIF: Medium   REF: 226–227   OBJ: 9.2
   TOP: Presidential Elections

9. American _____ were often called "People's Palaces" in the early 1800s.
   a. homes
   b. hotels
   c. department stores
   d. plantations

   ANS: B   DIF: Medium   REF: 229   OBJ: 9.2
   TOP: Presidential Elections

10. Which of the following does NOT accurately describe Andrew Jackson?
    a. lawyer
    b. son of an immigrant
    c. Tennessee Congressman
    d. college educated

    ANS: D   DIF: Medium   REF: 229   OBJ: 9.2
    TOP: Andrew Jackson

11. Which state was LEAST in support of high tariffs?
    a. Rhode Island
    b. New York
    c. South Carolina
    d. Pennsylvania

    ANS: C   DIF: Medium   REF: 231–232   OBJ: 9.3
    TOP: U.S. Tariffs

12. Jackson was LEAST popular with
    a. westerners.
    b. frontiers people.
    c. Federalists.
    d. urban working people.

    ANS: C   DIF: Medium   REF: 223   OBJ: 9.3
    TOP: Andrew Jackson

13. A declaration by an individual state that an act of Congress is not allowable is called
    a. "impeachment."
    b. "federalism."
    c. "treason."
    d. "nullification."

    ANS: D   DIF: Medium   REF: 232   OBJ: 9.3
    TOP: Nullification

14. In what way were Jackson and Tyler MOST different?
    a. their careers in the military
    b. their activities with Native Americans
    c. their roots in the West
    d. their political parties

    ANS: D   DIF: Medium   REF: 229, 230, 243
    OBJ: 9.4   TOP: Andrew Jackson

15. Why did the South object to high tariffs?
    a. They imported most of their finished goods.
    b. It raised the price of the cotton they exported.
    c. It increased the price of slaves.
    d. They already manufactured what they needed.

    ANS: A   DIF: Medium   REF: 231–232   OBJ: 9.4
    TOP: U.S. Tariffs

16. Which of the following was NOT a presidential candidate in 1824?
    a. Andrew Jackson   c. Martin Van Buren
    b. Henry Clay   d. John Quincy Adams

    ANS: C   DIF: Medium   REF: 223   OBJ: 9.1
    TOP: Presidential Elections

17. Which of the following changed the LEAST between the election of Washington and Jackson?
    a. property qualification   c. use of the electoral college
    b. number of states   d. activities of political parties

    ANS: C   DIF: Medium   REF: 223   OBJ: 9.1
    TOP: Presidential Elections

18. Whose Presidency was tainted by the charge of the "Corrupt Bargain"?
    a. Andrew Jackson   c. John Quincy Adams
    b. William Henry Harrison   d. Martin Van Buren

    ANS: C   DIF: Medium   REF: 223–224   OBJ: 9.1
    TOP: John Quincy Adams's Presidency

19. Which was the LAST of the original 13 states to abolish the property qualification for voting?
    a. New York   c. Massachusetts
    b. Rhode Island   d. Virginia

    ANS: D   DIF: Medium   REF: 227   OBJ: 9.2
    TOP: Voting Process

20. All of the following increased the number of voters EXCEPT
    a. written ballots.
    b. the increasing informality of candidates.
    c. the lifting of racial restrictions on voting.
    d. the lifting of property restrictions on voting.

    ANS: C   DIF: Medium   REF: 226–228   OBJ: 9.2
    TOP: Voting Process

21. Which of the following is NOT a valid comparison between the election of 1824 and that of 1828?
    a. There were fewer candidates in 1828.
    b. More males voted in 1824.
    c. Written ballots increased voter turnout.
    d. Jackson was more popular in 1828.

    ANS: D   DIF: Medium   REF: 227   OBJ: 9.2
    TOP: Presidential Elections

22. The Peggy Eaton affair was significant because it resulted in
    a. President Jackson's reliance on a group of friends for advice.
    b. the resignation of most of the Cabinet.
    c. Jackson's support of Martin Van Buren as his successor.
    d. all of the above

    ANS: D   DIF: Medium   REF: 231   OBJ: 9.3
    TOP: Jackson's Presidency

23. Which of the following issues did Jackson and Calhoun disagree upon?
    a. the Eaton affair   c. nullification
    b. Jackson's 1818 Florida campaign   d. all of the above

    ANS: D   DIF: Medium   REF: 231–234   OBJ: 9.3
    TOP: Jackson's Presidency

24. In 1832 South Carolina rescinded nullification after
    a. Jackson sent troops to South Carolina.
    b. Congress revised the tariff, reducing rates.
    c. Congress abandoned the protective tariff.
    d. the government repealed its right to tax.

    ANS: B   DIF: Medium   REF: 238   OBJ: 9.3
    TOP: Nullification

25. The courageous leader of the Seminoles was
    a. Chief Black Hawk.   c. Chief Osceola.
    b. Sequoya.   d. Sacajawea.

    ANS: C   DIF: Medium   REF: 234   OBJ: 9.3
    TOP: Native Americans

26. The forced removal of the Cherokee to Oklahoma was known as
    a. "Long March."   c. "Last Stand."
    b. "trail of tears."   d. "Walk to Freedom."

    ANS: B   DIF: Medium   REF: 236   OBJ: 9.3
    TOP: Native Americans

27. Jackson disliked the National Bank because
    a. he believed it was unconstitutional.
    b. it contributed to the national debt.
    c. he believed it favored the wealthy interests.
    d. he believed it was unconstitutional AND he believed it favored the wealthy interests.

    ANS: D   DIF: Medium   REF: 238–240   OBJ: 9.4
    TOP: National Bank

28. Which of the following was NOT a concern of the South?
    a. slave revolts   c. the impact of the cotton gin
    b. the impact of the tariff   d. the resolution of the Indian question

    ANS: D   DIF: Medium   REF: 231–232   OBJ: 9.4
    TOP: Southern Concerns in Early 1800s

29. Van Buren's presidency was unpopular because
    a. he was associated with Jackson.   c. of war with England.
    b. of a financial panic.   d. of his stand on slavery.

    ANS: B   DIF: Medium   REF: 242–243   OBJ: 9.4
    TOP: Van Buren's Presidency

30. Which of the following was the MOST distorted depiction of a presidential candidate?
    a. Harrison's log cabin origins
    b. Jackson, the Indian fighter
    c. Adams's selection of Clay as Secretary of State
    d. Clay's support of the American System

    ANS: A   DIF: Medium   REF: 243–244   OBJ: 9.4
    TOP: Presidential Elections

31. Who forced the rechartering of the National Bank in 1832 to further his political career?
    a. Andrew Jackson   c. Henry Clay
    b. Nicholas Biddle   d. Martin Van Buren

    ANS: C   DIF: Medium   REF: 238–239   OBJ: 9.4
    TOP: National Bank

32. Jackson's administration supported all of the following EXCEPT
    a. rechartering of the National Bank.
    b. moving the Indians west of the Mississippi River.
    c. the spoils system.
    d. opposition to the doctrine of nullification.

    ANS: A   DIF: Medium   REF: 230, 234–238
    OBJ: 9.4   TOP: Jackson's Presidency

33. Which of the following is the MOST recent example of the widening of suffrage?
    a. dropping the property qualification
    b. allowing 18-year-olds to vote
    c. granting the vote to former slaves
    d. granting the vote to women

    ANS: B   DIF: Medium   REF: 226–227   OBJ: 9.2
    TOP: Voting

34. During World War II, Japanese-Americans were rounded up by the U.S. government and forced to relocate to camps. This action was similar to Jackson's treatment of the _____ tribe.
    a. Seminole   c. Sioux
    b. Cherokee   d. Fox

    ANS: B   DIF: Medium   REF: 236   OBJ: 9.3
    TOP: Jackson's Presidency / Native Americans

35. South Carolina's reaction to the tariff and Jackson's response eventually led to the
    a. Civil War.   c. direct election of U.S. Senators.
    b. Spanish-American War.   d. Progressive Movement.

    ANS: A   DIF: Medium   REF: 234, 237–238
    OBJ: 9.3   TOP: Nullification

36. Three of the following supported nullification. Identify the one that did NOT.
    a. Virginia and Kentucky Resolution   c. Webster-Hayne debate
    b. the Hartford convention   d. the American System

    ANS: D   DIF: Medium   REF: 208, 232–234
    OBJ: 9.3   TOP: Nullification

37. Three of the following men ran for the presidency after achieving public recognition in the military. Identify one man who did NOT.
    a. George Washington   c. Andrew Jackson
    b. Thomas Jefferson   d. William Henry Harrison

    ANS: B   DIF: Medium   REF: 223, 243   OBJ: 9.4
    TOP: Presidential Elections

38. Which of the following issues was consistently supported by the North, South, and West?
    a. the tariff
    b. the National Bank
    c. the expansion of slavery
    d. the elimination of property qualifications for voting

    ANS: D   DIF: Medium   REF: 227   OBJ: 9.4
    TOP: Voting

SHORT ANSWER

In one or two sentences, define and distinguish between the terms given below.

1. nullify

   ANS:
   To nullify is to cancel or make of no value.

   DIF: Hard   REF: 232   OBJ: 9.0   TOP: Nullification

2. protective tariff

   ANS:
   A protective tariff is a high tax on imports that compete with domestic products. It is aimed at discouraging the purchase of imports and encouraging the growth of domestic industries.

   DIF: Hard   OBJ: 9.0   TOP: Import Tariffs

3. "Kitchen Cabinet"

   ANS:
   The "Kitchen Cabinet" refers to close presidential advisers who are not members of the Cabinet.

   DIF: Hard   REF: 231   OBJ: 9.0   TOP: Presidential Advisors

4. secession

   ANS:
   Secession is the process by which a state withdraws from the union.

   DIF: Hard   REF: 237   OBJ: 9.0   TOP: Secession

ESSAY

1. Which of the following is an effect of the others? Write your answer on a separate sheet of paper and support your answer with a paragraph explaining why you chose it.
   A. Depression in 1839
   B. Specie Circular
   C. The Bank of England reduced the flow of specie out of that country.
   D. Farmers suffered a bad crop.

   ANS:
   answer A Students' paragraphs should support their answer.

   DIF: Hard   REF: 241–243   OBJ: 9.0   TOP: Depression of 1839

2. Summarize Andrew Jackson's presidency, noting his attitudes toward the dignity of his office, political patronage, nullification, Indian policy, the national bank, and paper money. Make a generalization about Jackson's presidency based on what you have written.

ANS:
Students' answers will vary but could include these ideas: Jackson was an activist president. He believed that the "common man" had a right to hold office in the federal government (in practice, this came to be known as the "spoils system"). He believed that nullification was illegal; no state had the power to refuse to obey a federal law. He believed that the Indian must be made to give way to the white man. He disliked and distrusted banks and paper money. In summary, Jackson showed that the President of the United States had the power to do more than merely execute Congress' wishes.

DIF:　Hard　　　　REF:　226–242　　OBJ:　9.0　　　　　TOP:　Jackson's Presidency

3. Describe the "Corrupt Bargain" and its effect on the election of 1824.

ANS:
Answers will vary but could include the following ideas: The election of 1824 produced no electoral majority. The House chose between the leading three candidates—Jackson, Adams, and Crawford. Clay, a losing candidate, threw his support to Adams, who was chosen President. When Clay was selected as Secretary of State, Jackson was able to characterize it as a "Corrupt Bargain." Haunted by this charge, Adams was defeated by Jackson in 1828.

DIF:　Hard　　　　REF:　223–225　　OBJ:　9.1　　　　　TOP:　Presidential Elections

4. Analyze the effect that an expanded suffrage had on the election process.

ANS:
Answers will vary but could include the following ideas: As states dropped property requirements for voting, the electorate expanded. The new voters were more easily attracted by "image" and the concept of the "people's candidate" (i.e., Jackson).

DIF:　Hard　　　　REF:　226–227　　OBJ:　9.2　　　　　TOP:　The Election Process

5. Given what you have read in the chapter, select a political development and explain its effect on political campaigns.

ANS:
Answers will vary but could include the following ideas: Printed ballots helped increase voter turnout but also simplified the corruption of the voting process. The development of political conventions increased party participation and helped bring the masses more directly into the system.

DIF:　Hard　　　　REF:　226–230　　OBJ:　9.2　　　　　TOP:　The Election Process

6. Describe the "spoils system" and the reasons that Jackson is identified with it.

ANS:
Answers will vary but could include the following ideas: The "spoils system" is the practice of rewarding political supporters with jobs in government. Jackson felt that the average person was well qualified to hold a government position and openly boasted of his use of patronage.

DIF: Hard   REF: 230   OBJ: 9.2   TOP: Jackson's Presidency

7. Describe Jackson's treatment of the Native Americans.

ANS:
Answers will vary but could include the following ideas: Jackson had made a name for himself fighting Native Americans. As President, he forced the removal of the Cherokee from Georgia, despite the objection of the Supreme Court. On the forced march to Oklahoma ("Trail of Tears"), many Native Americans suffered and died.

DIF: Hard   REF: 234–236   OBJ: 9.3
TOP: Jackson's Presidency / Native Americans

8. Compare and contrast Jacksonian democracy with Jeffersonian democracy.

ANS:
Answers will vary but could include the following ideas: Jackson believed that common people were qualified to manage their governmental affairs. Jefferson believed that the well-educated could govern in the name of all people. Jackson moved beyond Jefferson's view of an agricultural society to include a rising industrial society.

DIF: Hard   OBJ: 9.3

9. How did the theory of nullification continue to foreshadow the coming of the Civil War?

ANS:
Answers will vary but could include the following ideas: The South continued to oppose the imposition of high tariffs on imports and utilized Jefferson's theory of nullification (the Kentucky and Virginia Resolutions). South Carolina's nullification of tariff laws and Jackson's response foreshadowed the Civil War by nearly three decades.

DIF: Hard   REF: 231–234   OBJ: 9.3   TOP: Nullification

10. The "Specie Circular" set in motion a chain of events that had an enormous impact on the American economy. Explain what happened.

ANS:
Answers will vary but could include the following ideas: When President Jackson issued the "Specie Circular," it meant that the Treasury could receive only gold and silver for payment on public land. The result was an abrupt constriction of spending and hence, growth. That, plus a British financial crisis and a poor year for the farmer, caused a severe depression.

DIF: Hard   REF: 241–243   OBJ: 9.4
TOP: Jackson's Presidency / Economics

MATCHING

Match each item with the correct statement below.

a. peculiar institution
b. Francis Cabot Lowell
c. Eli Whitney
d. chattel
e. "middle passage"

f. corporation
g. Alexis de Tocqueville
h. limited liability
i. DeWitt Clinton
j. Samuel Slater

1. The South's term for slavery.
2. French traveler who wrote his observations of America in the early 1800s.
3. Refers to slaves' status as property to be bought and sold.
4. Idea that a stockholder is not responsible for a corporation's debt.
5. A kind of "joint stock company" chartered by the state.
6. Brought plans to America for the first textile factory.
7. Developed the system of interchangeable parts.
8. Voyage that brought slaves from Africa to America.
9. New York governor responsible for building the Erie Canal.
10. He put all processing for making cloth under one roof.

1. ANS: A   DIF: Easy   REF: 273   OBJ: 10.0
   TOP: Slavery
2. ANS: G   DIF: Easy   REF: 249   OBJ: 10.0
   TOP: French Writers
3. ANS: D   DIF: Easy   REF: 275   OBJ: 10.0
   TOP: Slavery
4. ANS: H   DIF: Easy   REF: 261   OBJ: 10.0
   TOP: The Corporation
5. ANS: F   DIF: Easy   REF: 261   OBJ: 10.0
   TOP: The Corporation
6. ANS: J   DIF: Easy   REF: 259–260   OBJ: 10.0
   TOP: Industrialization
7. ANS: C   DIF: Easy   REF: 263–264   OBJ: 10.0
   TOP: Interchangeable Parts
8. ANS: E   DIF: Easy   REF: 272   OBJ: 10.0
   TOP: Slavery
9. ANS: I   DIF: Easy   REF: 251   OBJ: 10.0
   TOP: Erie Canal
10. ANS: B   DIF: Easy   REF: 261   OBJ: 10.0
    TOP: Industrialization

MULTIPLE CHOICE

1. Which statement about the early postal service is FALSE?
   a. Most postal service connected towns on the Atlantic coast.
   b. Early mail carriers were not paid by the government.
   c. George Washington issued the first government stamp.
   d. Up until the 1840s, the system was haphazard and inefficient.

   ANS: C   DIF: Medium   REF: 257–259   OBJ: 10.1
   TOP: Postal Service

2. The era that introduced power-driven machinery is known as the
   a. Agricultural Revolution.   c. Electronic Revolution.
   b. Industrial Revolution.   d. Twentieth Century.

   ANS: B   DIF: Medium   REF: 259–261   OBJ: 10.2
   TOP: Industrialization

3. Joint stock companies helped to finance the first English settlers in America. By the 1800s they had evolved into _____, a state chartered form of doing business.
   a. factories   c. corporations
   b. sweat shops   d. unions

   ANS: C   DIF: Medium   REF: 261   OBJ: 10.2
   TOP: The Corporation

4. Which statement about the national economy in 1850 is FALSE?
   a. The Northeast specialized in finished goods.
   b. The Middle States specialized in tobacco and rice.
   c. The South specialized in cotton and sugar.
   d. The West specialized in wheat and corn.

   ANS: B   DIF: Medium   OBJ: 10.2
   TOP: National Economy / 1850

5. "Wage slavery" referred to the
   a. southern black slaves.   c. New England working class.
   b. northern black slaves.   d. free white Southerners.

   ANS: C   DIF: Medium   REF: 263   OBJ: 10.2
   TOP: Industrialization

6. The two major immigrant groups that came to America before the Civil War were
   a. German and Italian.   c. German and Greek.
   b. Irish and Italian.   d. German and Irish.

   ANS: D   DIF: Medium   REF: 268–269   OBJ: 10.3
   TOP: Immigration

7. Which of the following was NOT a reason for immigration to the United States in the years before the Civil War?
   a. famine in foreign countries
   b. revolutions in foreign countries
   c. need for labor in America
   d. the presence of slaves in America

   ANS: D   DIF: Medium   REF: 266–269   OBJ: 10.3
   TOP: Immigration

8. In the first half of the 1800s, America was the world's leading importer of
   a. railroads.
   b. people.
   c. canal boats.
   d. telegraphs.

   ANS: B   DIF: Medium   REF: 268–269   OBJ: 10.3
   TOP: Immigration

9. Which of the following was NOT "an instant city"?
   a. Chicago, Illinois
   b. Detroit, Michigan
   c. Cincinnati, Ohio
   d. New York, New York

   ANS: D   DIF: Medium   REF: 269   OBJ: 10.4
   TOP: U.S. Cities

10. The North was involved in the South's production of each of the following EXCEPT
    a. cotton textiles.
    b. sugar.
    c. tools.
    d. vegetables.

    ANS: D   DIF: Medium   OBJ: 10.5   TOP: National Economy

11. The term "peculiar institution" referred to
    a. factories.
    b. Congress.
    c. immigrants.
    d. slavery.

    ANS: D   DIF: Medium   REF: 273   OBJ: 10.5
    TOP: Slavery

12. The "middle passage" is a term used to describe
    a. transatlantic shipment of slaves.
    b. the Erie Canal.
    c. travel west of the National Road.
    d. the safest sections to ride in on early trains.

    ANS: A   DIF: Medium   REF: 272   OBJ: 10.5
    TOP: Slavery

13. The first road to be funded and built by the United States government was the
    a. Boston Post Road.
    b. Mohawk Road.
    c. National Road.
    d. American Road.

    ANS: C   DIF: Medium   REF: 251   OBJ: 10.1
    TOP: Transportation

14. The Erie Canal was built to link
    a. Lake Erie to Albany and New York City.
    b. Pittsburgh to Philadelphia.
    c. Cumberland to Washington, D.C.
    d. Lake Michigan to the Mississippi River.

    ANS: A   DIF: Medium   REF: 251   OBJ: 10.1
    TOP: Erie Canal

15. Robert Fulton became famous for
    a. developing movable type.   c. making the steamboat a success.
    b. inventing the railroad.   d. developing the Erie Canal.

    ANS: C   DIF: Medium   REF: 253   OBJ: 10.1
    TOP: Transportation

16. Which of the following statements about the development of the railroad in America is MOST valid?
    a. America invented the railroad.
    b. In the 1850s New England led the nation in miles of track.
    c. In the 1850s railroads were much safer than steamboats.
    d. In the 1840s and 1850s European railroads were generally safer than American railroads.

    ANS: D   DIF: Medium   REF: 254   OBJ: 10.1
    TOP: Transportation / Railroad

17. A transatlantic telegraph line was developed by
    a. Samuel Morse.   c. DeWitt Clinton.
    b. Robert Fulton.   d. Cyrus Field.

    ANS: D   DIF: Medium   REF: 259   OBJ: 10.1
    TOP: Communication

18. Which of the following was developed last in the United States?
    a. steamboats   c. canals
    b. telegraph   d. turnpikes

    ANS: B   DIF: Medium   REF: 251–259   OBJ: 10.1
    TOP: Communication

19. The legal principle that states that shareholders in a corporation cannot be held fully responsible for the company's debts is known as
    a. limited liability.   c. mediation.
    b. popular sovereignty.   d. per capita GNP.

    ANS: A   DIF: Medium   REF: 261   OBJ: 10.2
    TOP: The Corporation

20. Which development was MOST directly responsible for the accumulation of investment capital?
    a. slavery
    b. corporations
    c. immigration
    d. westward expansion

    ANS: B   DIF: Medium   REF: 261   OBJ: 10.2
    TOP: The Corporation

21. The Industrial Revolution helped bring about
    a. the Transportation Revolution.
    b. regional specialization in goods.
    c. reduced isolation of farmers.
    d. all of the above

    ANS: D   DIF: Medium   REF: 261   OBJ: 10.2
    TOP: Industrial Revolution

22. How did the United States FIRST develop its textile industry?
    a. The United States invented textile machinery.
    b. The United States purchased rights to the machinery.
    c. Plans for the machinery were "smuggled" out of a foreign country.
    d. The United States purchased machines made in another country.

    ANS: C   DIF: Medium   REF: 259–260   OBJ: 10.2
    TOP: Industrialization

23. Which of the following was NOT a result of industrialization?
    a. migration of people
    b. expansion of the apprentice system
    c. decline of home production
    d. decline of the self-sufficient farm

    ANS: B   DIF: Medium   REF: 260–261   OBJ: 10.2
    TOP: Industrialization

24. The work force at Waltham and Lowell was at first comprised mostly of
    a. young unmarried women.
    b. former slaves.
    c. entire families.
    d. 9- to 12-year-old children.

    ANS: A   DIF: Medium   REF: 262   OBJ: 10.2
    TOP: Industrialization

25. As a result of industrialization, Americans became
    a. less productive.
    b. more dependent upon one another.
    c. more isolated from each other.
    d. more equal in wealth and social status.

    ANS: B   DIF: Medium   REF: 261   OBJ: 10.2
    TOP: Industrialization

26. Who was responsible for consolidating all of the processes for textile manufacturing in one factory?
    a. Francis Cabot Lowell
    b. Eli Whitney
    c. Samuel F. B. Morse
    d. Robert Fulton

    ANS: A   DIF: Medium   REF: 261   OBJ: 10.2
    TOP: Industrialization

27. English visitors to America's early textile mills were impressed by American use of
    a. large coal furnaces.   c. hand-powered machines.
    b. efficient steam engines.   d. water-powered machines.

    ANS: D   DIF: Medium   REF: 262   OBJ: 10.2
    TOP: Industrialization

28. The process of interchangeable parts was first put to test in the manufacture of
    a. textiles.   c. steamboats.
    b. guns.   d. locomotives.

    ANS: B   DIF: Medium   REF: 264   OBJ: 10.2
    TOP: Interchangeable Parts

29. The development of mass production resulted in all of the following EXCEPT
    a. cheaper products.   c. a greater variety of products.
    b. a demand mainly for skilled workers.   d. increased world trade.

    ANS: B   DIF: Medium   REF: 264–265   OBJ: 10.2
    TOP: Mass Production

30. Most of the immigrants who came to America between 1800 and 1860 came from
    a. Italy and Great Britain.   c. Germany and Holland.
    b. Great Britain and Ireland.   d. Germany and Ireland.

    ANS: D   DIF: Medium   REF: 269   OBJ: 10.3
    TOP: Immigration

31. Increased immigration from Ireland was triggered by
    a. a revolution.   c. the need for farmers.
    b. a famine.   d. the slave system.

    ANS: B   DIF: Medium   REF: 266   OBJ: 10.3
    TOP: Immigration

32. The institution of slavery
    a. discouraged immigrants from settling in the South.
    b. spurred the growth of industry in the South.
    c. was supported only by white Southerners who owned slaves.
    d. ended right after the importing of slaves was abolished in 1807.

    ANS: A   DIF: Medium   REF: 275   OBJ: 10.5
    TOP: Slavery

33. Which of the following materials could be assembled by a speedy method, developed in the 1830s, for building homes?
    a. heavy timber   c. mortise and tenon
    b. balloon frame   d. sod

    ANS: B   DIF: Medium   REF: 271   OBJ: 10.4
    TOP: Housing

34. Which statement about slavery is FALSE?
    a. Almost all slaves lived on plantations.
    b. Almost all slaves lived on small farms.
    c. About half of all slaves lived in groups of less than twenty.
    d. About half of all slaves lived on plantations of more than 1,000 slaves.

    ANS: D   DIF: Medium   REF: 274   OBJ: 10.5
    TOP: Slavery

35. Which of the following contributed LEAST to unifying the nation?
    a. railroads   c. canals
    b. telegraph   d. the transatlantic cable

    ANS: D   DIF: Medium   REF: 259   OBJ: 10.1
    TOP: Transportation / Communication

36. What 18th-century symbol of progress is now viewed as an example of one of society's problems?
    a. canals   c. telegraphs
    b. smokestacks   d. postal improvements

    ANS: B   DIF: Medium   OBJ: 10.1   TOP: Pollution

37. Which 18th-century technology is MOST in use today?
    a. canals   c. railroads
    b. steamboats   d. telegraph

    ANS: C   DIF: Medium   OBJ: 10.1   TOP: Transportation

38. A German immigrant coming to America in 1848 could BEST be compared to which of the following contemporary immigrants?
    a. a refugee from the civil war in El Salvador
    b. a doctor coming from India
    c. a hungry peasant from Mexico
    d. an artist from England

    ANS: A   DIF: Medium   REF: 268   OBJ: 10.2
    TOP: Immigration

39. Which of the following was the CAUSE of the other three?
    a. immigration to the United States   c. the Industrial Revolution
    b. building of railroads   d. development of a working class

    ANS: C   DIF: Medium   REF: 259–269   OBJ: 10.3
    TOP: U.S. Growth and Development

40. Which of the following is NOT a valid generalization about Americans?
    a. They tend to move frequently.
    b. They support tradition and are against change.
    c. They are a nation of immigrants.
    d. They have been divided between blacks and whites.

    ANS: B   DIF: Medium   REF: 261   OBJ: 10.3
    TOP: American People

ESSAY

1. Which of the following is the strongest example of cause-and-effect reasoning? Write your answer on a separate sheet of paper and support your answer with a paragraph explaining why you chose it.
   A. Slavery tied up capital (money) that could have gone into the purchase of machines. As a result the South did not industrialize.
   B. All craftsmen and farmers in the South received lower wages for their labor because of the competition of slaves. As a result, the South did not industrialize, but remained agricultural.
   C. Slavery tied up capital (money) that could have been invested in machinery. Since machinery is a key factor in industriaizing, the South did not industrialize, but remained agricultural.

   ANS:
   answer C Students' paragraphs should support their answer.

   DIF: Hard   REF: 275   OBJ: 10.0
   TOP: Slavery / Southern Development

2. Choose one of the items below.
   A. Organize the following topics into an essay that summarizes how the United States flourished between 1800–1860: transportation and communication, factory system and mass production, immigration and westward migration
   B. Between 1800 and 1860 the North and South emerged as distinct sections of the nation with specific interests and needs. In an essay supply information which explains why and how this happened.

   ANS:
   A. Students' answers will vary but could include these ideas: Transportation advanced with the development of turnpikes, canals, and railroads. Communications advanced with national mail systems and the development of the steamboat and telegraph. The Lowell labor system and Eli Whitney's idea of interchangeable parts advanced mass production. Immigrants became the labor force needed by the rapidly expanding nation. Westward migration accelerated in the early 1800s and cities sprang up even where there were no people as yet. New, easy-to-build balloon frame housing encouraged families to move west.
   B. Students' answers will vary but could include these ideas: Most of the railroads and canals were concentrated in the North and West; the factory system and the use of mass production were centered in the North; most immigration was to Northern cities.

   DIF: Hard   REF: 251–276   OBJ: 10.0
   TOP: Transportation Developments / North South Develop. in 1800s

3. The Erie Canal played a critical role in making New York the "Empire State." What was that role?

ANS:
Answers will vary but could include the following ideas: In the early 19th century, the Erie Canal was the major link between the East Coast and the interior. Beginning at Lake Erie and the Great Lakes basin, it traveled eastward and, with the Hudson, ended at New York City. It stimulated growth at both ends of the line—Buffalo and New York City—and was a stimulus to the development of the cities along the route.

DIF: Hard   REF: 251–252   OBJ: 10.1   TOP: Erie Canal

4. Describe the developments in transportation made during the early 19th century, noting how each was an improvement in technology.

ANS:
Answers will vary but could include the following ideas: Turnpikes enabled travel through the countryside but were rough, slow, and inefficient for heavy loads. Canals were costly to build and limited by terrain. When constructed, they dramatically reduced the cost of shipping heavy loads. Steamboats were a rapid and elegant form of river transportation but plagued by explosions. Railroads could swiftly carry heavy loads over a variety of terrains, but were, in the early years, quite unsafe.

DIF: Hard   REF: 251–257   OBJ: 10.1
TOP: Transportation Developments

5. How did Eli Whitney's development of interchangeable parts revolutionize production? Explain your answer.

ANS:
Answers will vary but could include the following ideas: Whitney standardized the production of interchangeable parts in order to mass produce rifles. Relatively unskilled workers could produce manufactured goods in less time at less cost.

DIF: Hard   REF: 263–265   OBJ: 10.2   TOP: Interchangeable Parts

6. Why was the development of the corporation central to the development of the industrial society?

ANS:
Answers will vary but could include the following ideas: The development of the corporation enabled business to accumulate large amounts of capital to finance the major ventures of the industrial era. The limitation of liability allowed corporations to develop at a rapid pace, insulated from the limits of community control and personal liability.

DIF: Hard   REF: 261   OBJ: 10.2   TOP: The Corporation

7. Discuss the factors that led millions of Irish and Germans to immigrate to the United States in the years before the Civil War.

ANS:
Answers will vary but could include the following ideas: America was in need of labor and had abundant, cheap land. America's opportunities were well known in Europe and actively advertised. Hunger in Ireland and political upheavals in the German states contributed to the European exodus.

DIF: Hard   REF: 266–269   OBJ: 10.3   TOP: Immigration

8. Based on what you have read in the chapter, summarize the unique way that cities in the West grew.

ANS:
Answers will vary but could include the following ideas: American cities in the West were built at an astonishing rate. They were actively promoted, and it was not unusual to see promoters building hotels and establishing newspapers in advance of the population. The American West was a land of boom towns.

DIF: Hard   REF: 269–271   OBJ: 10.4
TOP: U.S. Western Expansion

9. Describe the variety of conditions encountered by slaves. What feature or features were common to all?

ANS:
Answers will vary but could include the following ideas: Treatment varied but central to the system of slavery was control of the labor force. Some slaves were treated with decency, but, for the majority, slavery was a dehumanizing and humiliating experience.

DIF: Hard   REF: 272–276   OBJ: 10.5   TOP: Slavery

10. In what way did slavery infect American culture with the "disease of racism"?

ANS:
Answers will vary but could include the following ideas: To maintain a slave culture, it was necessary to create myths about "the inferiority" of African-Americans and "the justness" of their exploitation. Two hundred fifty years of legal slavery and oppression contributed greatly to the prejudicial treatment of African-Americans.

DIF: Hard   REF: 271–276   OBJ: 10.5   TOP: Slavery / Racism

MATCHING

Match each item with the correct statement below.

a. Manifest Destiny
b. Dorothea Dix
c. Sam Houston
d. Henry David Thoreau
e. Ralph Waldo Emerson

f. William Lloyd Garrison
g. Elizabeth Cady Stanton
h. Sojourner Truth
i. gag rule
j. James K. Polk

1. Transcendentalist leader who believed that man was born to be a reformer.
2. Former slave who became an advocate of women's rights.
3. Wrote on the duty of civil disobedience in defense of his protest of the Mexican War by refusing to pay his taxes.
4. Editor of abolitionist newspaper, The Liberator.
5. She started the crusade for more humane treatment of the mentally ill.
6. Under this, the House of Representatives refused to discuss any petition against slavery.
7. "Dark horse" candidate for President in 1844.
8. Idea that it was God's will that the United States gain possession of the entire continent.
9. She and Lucretia Mott organized a Women's Right's convention at Seneca Falls, New York, in 1848.
10. Led Texas army to independence and became the first President of Texas.

1. ANS: E   DIF: Easy   REF: 279   OBJ: 11.0
   TOP: Transcendentalism
2. ANS: H   DIF: Easy   REF: 284–285   OBJ: 11.0
   TOP: Women's Rights
3. ANS: D   DIF: Easy   REF: 279   OBJ: 11.0
   TOP: Mexican War
4. ANS: F   DIF: Easy   REF: 287   OBJ: 11.0
   TOP: Abolition Movement
5. ANS: B   DIF: Easy   REF: 282   OBJ: 11.0
   TOP: Reformers
6. ANS: I   DIF: Easy   REF: 295   OBJ: 11.0
   TOP: Slavery
7. ANS: J   DIF: Easy   REF: 297   OBJ: 11.0
   TOP: Presidential Elections
8. ANS: A   DIF: Easy   REF: 298   OBJ: 11.0
   TOP: U.S. Expansion
9. ANS: G   DIF: Easy   REF: 284   OBJ: 11.0
   TOP: Women's Rights
10. ANS: C   DIF: Easy   REF: 295   OBJ: 11.0
    TOP: Texas History

MULTIPLE CHOICE

1. In the early 1800s, higher education included
    a. women's colleges.
    b. large universities.
    c. technical institutions.
    d. coed colleges.

    ANS: C   DIF: Medium   REF: 281   OBJ: 11.1
    TOP: Higher Education

2. The Industrial Revolution limited women's work in which area?
    a. factories
    b. schools
    c. home manufacture
    d. reform movements

    ANS: C   DIF: Medium   REF: 283   OBJ: 11.1
    TOP: Industrialization

3. The term "temperance" refers to the campaign
    a. for women's rights.
    b. to end slavery.
    c. to prohibit the use of liquor.
    d. for religious revival.

    ANS: C   DIF: Medium   REF: 279   OBJ: 11.1
    TOP: Temperance

4. The abolition movement campaigned for
    a. an end to slavery.
    b. women's rights.
    c. abolishing the evils of alcohol.
    d. territorial expansion.

    ANS: A   DIF: Medium   REF: 286   OBJ: 11.2
    TOP: Abolition Movement

5. Which of the following was NOT a southern reaction to the anti-slavery movement?
    a. voting to end slavery
    b. banning anti-slavery literature
    c. discussing the issue of slavery in the Virginia legislature
    d. limiting the discussion of slavery in Congress

    ANS: A   DIF: Medium   REF: 286   OBJ: 11.2
    TOP: Slavery / Abolition Movement

6. What best describes Mexico's reaction to early American settlers in Texas?
    a. The Mexicans fought to keep Americans out.
    b. The Mexicans opposed Americans nonviolently.
    c. The Mexicans were indifferent to American settlers.
    d. The Mexicans encouraged American settlements.

    ANS: D   DIF: Medium   REF: 288   OBJ: 11.3
    TOP: U.S. / Mexican Relations

7. Which factor did NOT encourage American settlement of the Mexican province of Texas?
   a. the price of the land
   b. the attitude of Stephen Austin
   c. the ease of travel to Texas
   d. Mexican support for slavery

   ANS: D   DIF: Medium   REF: 288–289, 294
   OBJ: 11.3   TOP: U.S. / Mexican Relations

8. When Mexico gained its independence from Spain,
   a. Americans were no longer allowed into Mexican territory.
   b. Mexico went to war over Texas.
   c. Mexico gave up the Mexican cession.
   d. Americans were encouraged to trade and settle in Mexico.

   ANS: D   DIF: Medium   REF: 289   OBJ: 11.3
   TOP: U.S. / Mexican Relations

9. The wagon trains moving west could be compared to towns for each of the following reasons EXCEPT that they
   a. required cooperative action.
   b. performed community functions.
   c. could provide defense from Indian attacks.
   d. were made up of people from the same towns.

   ANS: D   DIF: Medium   REF: 291–293   OBJ: 11.3
   TOP: U.S. Western Expansion

10. The Mormons' migration was UNIQUE in that they
    a. traveled westward.
    b. traveled west to escape persecution.
    c. traveled in wagon trains.
    d. were very cooperative.

    ANS: B   DIF: Medium   REF: 293   OBJ: 11.3
    TOP: Mormon Migration

11. Which of the following did NOT contribute to war with Mexico in 1846?
    a. the annexation of Texas
    b. the Oregon border dispute
    c. the disputed Texas boundary
    d. the U.S. troops sent to the Rio Grande River

    ANS: B   DIF: Medium   REF: 299–300   OBJ: 11.5
    TOP: Mexican War

12. Which of the following territories became part of the United States in order to provide a railroad route through the southern Rockies?
    a. Texas
    b. Gadsden Purchase
    c. Mexican cession
    d. Oregon country

    ANS: B   DIF: Medium   REF: 301   OBJ: 11.5
    TOP: U.S. Expansion

13. The religious group that preached that the world would end in 1843 was known as the
    a. Millerites.   c. Rappites.
    b. Shakers.   d. Transcendentalists.

    ANS: A   DIF: Medium   REF: 279   OBJ: 11.1
    TOP: Religion

14. The Transcendentalists believed that
    a. the world would end.
    b. important truths of life linked all people together.
    c. the government should dictate all human behavior.
    d. slavery was inevitable.

    ANS: B   DIF: Medium   REF: 279   OBJ: 11.1
    TOP: Transcendentalism

15. Prior to 1850, Americans worked to bring about reform in all of the following areas EXCEPT
    a. women's rights.   c. education.
    b. treatment of the mentally ill.   d. child labor.

    ANS: D   DIF: Medium   REF: 282–285   OBJ: 11.1
    TOP: American Reform

16. The modern public school movement can trace its origins back to
    a. the Constitutional Convention.   c. the Puritans.
    b. early German immigrants.   d. the Federalists.

    ANS: C   DIF: Medium   REF: 281   OBJ: 11.1
    TOP: Education

17. Who was best known for campaigning for better treatment of the mentally ill and retarded?
    a. Horace Mann   c. Margaret Fuller
    b. Abigail Adams   d. Dorothea Dix

    ANS: D   DIF: Medium   REF: 282   OBJ: 11.1
    TOP: American Reform

18. The convention held at Seneca Falls, New York, in 1848 focused on the topic of
    a. temperance.   c. slavery.
    b. women's rights.   d. educational reform.

    ANS: B   DIF: Medium   REF: 284   OBJ: 11.1
    TOP: Women's Rights

19. She was a former slave who became an advocate of women's rights.
    a. Susan B. Anthony   c. Sojourner Truth
    b. Elizabeth Cady Stanton   d. Lucretia Mott

    ANS: C   DIF: Medium   REF: 284–285   OBJ: 11.1
    TOP: Women's Rights

20. The American Colonization Society promoted
    a. Manifest Destiny.
    b. violence against abolitionists.
    c. the "back-to-Africa" movement.
    d. the Mexican War.

    ANS: C   DIF: Medium   REF: 286   OBJ: 11.2
    TOP: Abolition Movement

21. Which man died a martyr for the abolitionist movement?
    a. James G. Birney
    b. William Lloyd Garrison
    c. Frederick Douglass
    d. Elijah Parish Lovejoy

    ANS: D   DIF: Medium   REF: 287–288   OBJ: 11.2
    TOP: Abolition Movement

22. Which of the following is an INACCURATE statement about California in the 1830s?
    a. The first Americans reached there by boat.
    b. It had about 4,000 Mexican settlers.
    c. It was popularized in the book "Two Years Before the Mast."
    d. The gold rush of 1830 touched off a land rush there.

    ANS: D   DIF: Medium   REF: 291   OBJ: 11.3
    TOP: California History

23. Which of the following was NOT part of the original Mexican land grant to American settlers?
    a. Americans received free land from Mexico.
    b. Americans paid 12 and 1/2 cents per acre to an American land agent.
    c. Americans were expected to become Roman Catholics.
    d. Americans were expected to become Mexican citizens.

    ANS: D   DIF: Medium   REF: 288   OBJ: 11.3
    TOP: Mexican History

24. All of the following characterize the United States between 1820 and 1850 EXCEPT
    a. reform movements.
    b. territorial expansion.
    c. a war with Great Britain over Oregon.
    d. settlement in the West.

    ANS: C   DIF: Medium   REF: 279–302   OBJ: 11.4
    TOP: U.S. - 1820–1850

25. Which of the following was NOT a reason for the Texas movement for independence?
    a. The Americans in Texas were denied the right to trial by jury.
    b. The Americans in Texas lacked adequate representation in the Mexican government.
    c. Americans lacked an adequate Bill of Rights.
    d. The Americans objected to the Mexican practice of slavery.

    ANS: D   DIF: Medium   REF: 294   OBJ: 11.4
    TOP: Texas History

26. The leader of the Texan army in its fight for independence from Mexico was
    a. Stephen Austin.
    b. General Santa Anna.
    c. Sam Houston.
    d. Jim Bowie.

    ANS: C   DIF: Medium   REF: 295   OBJ: 11.4
    TOP: Mexican War

27. Which country NEVER controlled Texas?
    a. Spain
    b. England
    c. the United States
    d. Mexico

    ANS: B   DIF: Medium   REF: 294–295   OBJ: 11.5
    TOP: Texas

28. After its war for independence, Texas was denied admission into the United States because its admission was opposed by
    a. slave owners.
    b. southern states.
    c. western states.
    d. northern states.

    ANS: D   DIF: Medium   REF: 295–296   OBJ: 11.4
    TOP: Texas

29. The United States gained western territory between 1820 and 1860 through all of the following methods EXCEPT a (an)
    a. purchase from Mexico.
    b. annexation from Mexico.
    c. treaties with Britain.
    d. purchase from the Native Americans.

    ANS: D   DIF: Medium   OBJ: 11.4   TOP: U.S. Expansion

30. Northerners tended to oppose annexation of western territory because they
    a. feared the extension of new slave states.
    b. feared the extension of anti-slave states.
    c. were concerned about the rights of the Native Americans.
    d. feared the extension of prohibition.

    ANS: A   DIF: Medium   REF: 295–296   OBJ: 11.4
    TOP: Slavery

31. The slogan "Fifty-four forty or fight!" refers to a boundary dispute with
    a. Spain.
    b. Great Britain.
    c. France.
    d. Mexico.

    ANS: B   DIF: Medium   REF: 298   OBJ: 11.5
    TOP: U.S. / British Relations

32. The nonviolent protest of Martin Luther King is MOST directly linked to the beliefs of
    a. Stephen Austin.
    b. James K. Polk.
    c. Henry David Thoreau.
    d. the back-to-Africa movement.

    ANS: C   DIF: Medium   REF: 279   OBJ: 11.1
    TOP: Reformers

33. In 1987 the most recent development in the temperance movement was
    a. the 18-year-old vote.   c. direct election of U.S. Senators.
    b. raising the drinking age.   d. the income tax.

    ANS: B   DIF: Medium   REF: 287   OBJ: 11.1
    TOP: Temperance

34. The best example of a modern form of civil disobedience is
    a. a nonviolent protest.   c. robbing a store.
    b. a riot.   d. escaping from prison.

    ANS: A   DIF: Medium   REF: 279   OBJ: 11.1
    TOP: Civil Disobedience

35. Which demand of the 18th-century women's movement has been COMPLETELY met?
    a. educational opportunity   c. the right to vote
    b. career opportunity   d. equality with men

    ANS: C   DIF: Medium   REF: 283–285   OBJ: 11.1
    TOP: Women's Rights

36. Much of the Spanish-speaking population in the United States lives in a section of the country
    that
    a. outlaws the Spanish language.   c. was purchased from France.
    b. was once part of Mexico.   d. was known as the Oregon country.

    ANS: B   DIF: Medium   OBJ: 11.5   TOP: Mexican War

SHORT ANSWER

In one or two sentences, define and distinguish between the terms given below.

1. Transcendentalism

    ANS:
    Transcendentalism is the belief that life's most important truths are beyond human
    understanding, that man is good, and the world will become perfect with no need for
    government.

    DIF: Hard   REF: 279   OBJ: 11.0   TOP: Transcendentalism

2. dark horse

    ANS:
    A dark horse is a political candidate who is not known nationally but is nominated as a good
    compromise.

    DIF: Hard   REF: 297   OBJ: 11.0   TOP: Presidential Elections

ESSAY

1. What is the main point of the following argument? Write your answer on a separate sheet of paper and support your answer with a paragraph explaining why you chose it.

   The national differences over slavery might not have come to a head so soon if the nation had not been growing and moving so fast. But Americans were pushing into Texas, into New Mexico, into California, and into Oregon. The transplanted Americans out there naturally wanted their new homes to become part of the United States. Americans in the East also dreamed of a Grand Empire for Liberty.

   A. The growth of the United States helped the differences over slavery to come to a head.
   B. Americans were pushing into Texas, New Mexico, California, and Oregon.
   C. Americans in the West wanted their new homes to become a part of the United States.
   D. Americans in the East and West dreamed of an Empire.

   ANS:
   answer A Students' paragraphs should support their answer.

   DIF: Hard   OBJ: 11.0   TOP: Slavery

2. Choose one of the topics below.
   A. In a paragraph, characterize a point of view that all of the following people shared. In a second paragraph, identify their specific areas of interest or achievement.

Ralph Waldo Emerson	Dorothea Dix
Henry David Thoreau	Susan B. Anthony
Horace Mann	Theodore Dwight Weld

   B. During the Presidency of James K. Polk, the theory of "Manifest destiny" supported demands for the expansion of the continental United States to its present boundaries. But this vast new land, acquired by purchases, treaties, and conquests, only served to divide the nation further. In two or three paragraphs, provide the information needed to explain this.

   ANS:
   Part A. In America there was a chance for a more perfect society. Ralph Waldo Emerson believed human beings were born to make civilization better. Henry David Thoreau protested policies he thought were wrong. Horace Mann crusaded for education reform in Massachusetts and worked for better training and pay for teachers, new schools, and school libraries. Dorothea Dix crusaded for humane treatment of the mentally ill. Susan B. Anthony began the women's rights movement. Theodore Dwight Weld was an early abolitionist.

   Part B. John L. Sullivan's statement that it was America's "manifest destiny to overspread and to possess the whole continent which Providence has given us" capsulized the shared feeling that the whole continent should be ours. However, in the highly charged atmosphere prior to the Civil War, the addition of any state or territory was considered in terms of its impact upon the balance in Congress regarding slavery.

   DIF: Hard   REF: 279–302   OBJ: 11.0
   TOP: 19th Century U.S. Reformers / U.S. Expansion

3. How were women's rights restricted in the early 19th century? What gains were made between 1828 and 1860?

ANS:
Answers will vary but could include the following ideas: Women could not vote and in some states had no legal rights apart from their husbands'. Between 1828 and 1860, some states liberalized divorce laws and gave women control over their own property and a share of the guardianship of their children.

DIF: Hard   REF: 282–285   OBJ: 11.1   TOP: Women's Rights

4. In your opinion, has the women's rights movement achieved its goals? Explain your answer.

ANS:
Answers will vary but could include the following ideas: Many goals have clearly been achieved—property rights, the vote, legal autonomy. Some goals have been partially met—career and educational opportunities, economic independence. Some goals have not been met—an end to sexual harassment and to all discrimination, for example.

DIF: Hard   OBJ: 11.1   TOP: Women's Rights

5. Choose two of the following people and identify their specific areas of interest or their achievements: (a) Ralph Waldo Emerson, (b) Henry David Thoreau, (c) Horace Mann, (d) Dorothea Dix, (e) Susan B. Anthony, and (f) Theodore Dwight Weld.

ANS:
Answers will vary but could include the following ideas: a. Emerson—A spokesman and major proponent of Transcendentalism. b. Thoreau—He refused to pay his taxes because of his opposition to the Mexican War. He spent the night in jail because of his act of civil disobedience, and wrote "Essay on the Duty of Civil Disobedience." c. Mann—A crusader for educational reform in Massachusetts, he worked for better training and pay for teachers, new schools, and larger school libraries. d. Dix—A crusader for better treatment for the mentally ill. e. Anthony—She campaigned for women's rights. f. Weld—An abolitionist crusader, he wrote "Slavery As It Is: Testimony of a Thousand Witnesses."

DIF: Hard   REF: 279, 281, 282, 285, 286, 287   OBJ: 11.1
TOP: 19th Century U.S. Reformers

6. What efforts did northern abolitionists make to stir up public opinion against slavery? Explain your answer.

ANS:
Answers will vary but could include the following ideas: They published accounts of the cruel and brutal aspects of slavery and tied the abolitionist cause to Christian teachings.

DIF: Hard   REF: 286–288   OBJ: 11.2   TOP: Slavery

7. Given what you have read in the chapter, explain the degree to which the abolitionist movement heightened the division between North and South. Explain your answer.

ANS:
Answers will vary but could include the following ideas: Northern abolitionists stirred up public feelings about slavery by publishing accounts of the most horrible and cruel aspects of it. In reaction, the South limited dissent and more ardently defended slavery.

DIF: Hard   REF: 286–288   OBJ: 11.2   TOP: Slavery

8. Choose two of the following people and identify their activities and contributions to the settlement of the West: (a) Stephen Austin, (b) John Jacob Astor, (c) Francis Parkman, (d) Charles Bent, (e) John Sutter, and (f) Brigham Young.

ANS:
Answers will vary but could include the following ideas: a. Austin—He obtained a land grant from the Mexican government to settle Texas in 1821. He founded Austin, Texas, and attracted 8,000 settlers. b. Astor—He became wealthy in the fur trade and was the first to create a permanent American settlement in Oregon. c. Parkman—He was a New Englander who vividly described his journey on the Oregon Trail. d. Bent—He was an American trader who settled in New Mexico and attracted other settlers to the area. e. Sutter—He was a Swiss who settled in Sacramento, California, which became a thriving community in America. f. Young—He led the Mormons on their journey to Utah.

DIF: Hard   REF: 288, 289, 290, 291, 293   OBJ: 11.3
TOP: Western Expansion

9. Identify the candidates, issues, and outcomes of the election of 1844.

ANS:
Answers will vary but could include the following ideas: The Whigs nominated Henry Clay, who initially took no stand on the annexation of Texas. Democrats passed over Van Buren, who had come out against the annexation of Texas. The Democrats nominated James K. Polk, who campaigned on the platform of annexation of Texas and Oregon (pleasing both Northern and Southern states). Clay switched positions on Texas and drove many followers to James G. Birney, an abolitionist candidate. Polk's victory was considered a mandate for expansion.

DIF: Hard   REF: 297, 298   OBJ: 11.4   TOP: Presidential Elections

10. What do you consider to be the most fundamental cause of the Mexican War? Explain your answer.

ANS:
Answers will vary but could include the following ideas: The American belief in Manifest Destiny pushed President Polk and many Americans to instigate a war with Mexico in the hopes of acquiring much of its territory.

DIF: Hard   REF: 299–302   OBJ: 11.5   TOP: Mexican War

MATCHING

Match each item with the correct statement below.

a. Wilmot Proviso
b. John Brown
c. Underground Railroad
d. Sutter's Fort
e. popular sovereignty

f. Dred Scott
g. Republican
h. Ostend Manifesto
i. Henry Clay

1. Senator who authored and proposed the Compromise of 1850.
2. Document advising the United States to seize Cuba from Spain if it could not be purchased.
3. Policy permitting settlers of each new territory to vote whether to allow slavery in that territory.
4. Site of the first gold strike in California.
5. Political party formed in 1854 to resist the extension of slavery.
6. Series of routes and stopovers that led runaway slaves north to freedom.
7. Led an abolitionist raid on the federal arsenal at Harpers Ferry, Virginia.
8. Proposal that slavery not be permitted in any territory acquired from Mexico.
9. In 1857, the Supreme Court ruled that as a slave, he could not be a citizen or bring suit in Missouri.

1. ANS: I   DIF: Easy   REF: 308   OBJ: 12.0
   TOP: Slavery
2. ANS: H   DIF: Easy   REF: 312   OBJ: 12.0
   TOP: Pierce's Foreign Policy
3. ANS: E   DIF: Easy   REF: 313   OBJ: 12.0
   TOP: Slavery / States Rights
4. ANS: D   DIF: Easy   REF: 305   OBJ: 12.0
   TOP: California Gold Rush
5. ANS: G   DIF: Easy   REF: 314   OBJ: 12.0
   TOP: Political Parties
6. ANS: C   DIF: Easy   REF: 310   OBJ: 12.0
   TOP: Underground Railroad
7. ANS: B   DIF: Easy   REF: 320–321   OBJ: 12.0
   TOP: Abolitionist Movement
8. ANS: A   DIF: Easy   REF: 306   OBJ: 12.0
   TOP: Slavery
9. ANS: F   DIF: Easy   REF: 318   OBJ: 12.0
   TOP: Supreme Court

MULTIPLE CHOICE

1. Which of the following was NOT a response in the North to the Fugitive Slave Act?
   a. passage of Personal Liberty laws
   b. nullification conventions
   c. support of the Underground Railroad
   d. mass protest meetings

   ANS: B   DIF: Medium   REF: 310   OBJ: 12.1
   TOP: Slavery

2. Which of the following was a widely popular antislavery novel of the 1850s?
   a. "Black Like Me"   c. "Uncle Tom's Cabin"
   b. "I Have a Dream"   d. "Slavery as It Is"

   ANS: C   DIF: Medium   REF: 311–312   OBJ: 12.1
   TOP: Slavery

3. The policy permitting settlers of each new territory to vote on whether to allow slavery in that territory was known as
   a. "freedom of speech."   c. "Manifest Destiny."
   b. "popular sovereignty."   d. "settler's rights."

   ANS: B   DIF: Medium   REF: 313   OBJ: 12.1
   TOP: Slavery / States Rights

4. Which political party was formed to oppose the extension of slavery into the territories?
   a. Republican   c. Know-Nothing
   b. Democrat   d. Whig

   ANS: A   DIF: Medium   REF: 314   OBJ: 12.2
   TOP: Political Parties

5. Which political party was formed to oppose the growing political power of immigrants?
   a. Republican   c. Know-Nothing
   b. Democrat   d. Whig

   ANS: C   DIF: Medium   REF: 315   OBJ: 12.2
   TOP: Political Parties

6. Which of the following was NOT an event of May, 1856 that further inflamed the slavery issue?
   a. the election of Lincoln
   b. the John Brown raid on Pottawatomie Creek
   c. the burning of Lawrence, Kansas
   d. the attack on Charles Sumner

   ANS: A   DIF: Medium   REF: 316   OBJ: 12.2
   TOP: Slavery

7. The dispute over slavery in the United States did NOT result in
   a. bloodshed in Kansas.   c. violence in the United States Senate.
   b. the creation of new political parties. d. the growth of the Whig party.

   ANS: D   DIF: Medium   REF: 310   OBJ: 12.2
   TOP: Slavery

8. Douglas broke with Buchanan over the latter's attempt to
   a. admit Kansas as a free state.
   b. withdraw official patronage from Illinois.
   c. disregard the Lecompton Constitution.
   d. deprive Kansas of popular sovereignty.

   ANS: D   DIF: Medium   REF: 319   OBJ: 12.3
   TOP: Slavery / States Rights

9. The position of Stephen Douglas on the issue of slavery in the territories was that
   a. the Missouri Compromise should not be changed.
   b. the voters of a territory should decide the issue.
   c. the number of slaves in any territory should be limited.
   d. slavery should be abolished west of the Mississippi.

   ANS: B   DIF: Medium   REF: 319   OBJ: 12.3
   TOP: Slavery / States Rights

10. The slavery issue getting most attention in Congress from 1820 to 1860 was
   a. stopping the importation of slaves.
   b. emancipation of slaves.
   c. humane treatment of slaves.
   d. extension of slavery into the western territories.

   ANS: D   DIF: Medium   REF: 305–312   OBJ: 12.3
   TOP: Slavery

11. Which of the following was NOT a point made in the Dred Scott decision?
   a. The Missouri Compromise was void.
   b. Slaves were not citizens.
   c. Congress could not restrict slavery in the territories.
   d. A slave taken into a free state became free.

   ANS: D   DIF: Medium   REF: 318   OBJ: 12.3
   TOP: Supreme Court

12. Which Supreme Court judge is most closely associated with the Dred Scott decision?
   a. John Marshall   c. John Jay
   b. Roger Taney   d. Warren Burger

   ANS: B   DIF: Medium   REF: 318   OBJ: 12.3
   TOP: Supreme Court

13. Which of the following was NOT a reaction to John Brown's raid?
   a. southern fear of a slave rebellion   c. the martyrdom of Brown by abolitionists
   b. the execution of John Brown   d. the outbreak of a slave rebellion

   ANS: D   DIF: Medium   REF: 320–321   OBJ: 12.3
   TOP: Abolitionist Movement

14. In their 1860 national convention, the Democrats split over the issue of
   a. support for slavery in the territories.   c. land grants to railroads in the West.
   b. the protective tariff.   d. emancipation.

   ANS: A   DIF: Medium   REF: 322   OBJ: 12.4
   TOP: Presidential Elections

15. In 1860 which of the following was NOT one of Lincoln's views on slavery?
    a.   It was morally wrong.
    b.   It must not be extended.
    c.   It should be abolished at once.
    d.   There should be no interference where slavery was already established.

    ANS: C   DIF: Medium   REF: 320, 323   OBJ: 12.4
    TOP: Slavery / Lincoln

16. Both Zachary Taylor and Winfield Scott were
    a.   Democratic candidates for President.   c.   military leaders in the Mexican War.
    b.   strongly opposed to slavery.   d.   former members of Congress.

    ANS: C   DIF: Medium   REF: 307, 310   OBJ: 12.1
    TOP: Mexican War

17. The "gold rush" to California pointed out the need for
    a.   better communications with Europe.   c.   more slaves in California.
    b.   a canal in Panama.   d.   more national newspapers.

    ANS: B   DIF: Medium   REF: 305   OBJ: 12.1
    TOP: California Gold Rush

18. Which of the following probably had the greatest effect on popular opinions about slavery?
    a.   the Wilmot Proviso
    b.   the publication of "Uncle Tom's Cabin"
    c.   the efforts of Harriet Tubman
    d.   the Lincoln-Douglas debate

    ANS: B   DIF: Medium   REF: 311–312   OBJ: 12.1
    TOP: Slavery

19. All of the following contributed to the passage of the Compromise of 1850 EXCEPT the
    a.   support of northern merchants.
    b.   success of the Missouri Compromise.
    c.   death of President Taylor.
    d.   political maneuvering of Stephen Douglas.

    ANS: B   DIF: Medium   OBJ: 12.1   TOP: Slavery

20. What is the source of the following quote? ". . . neither slavery nor involuntary servitude shall
    ever exist in any part of the territory acquired from Mexico."
    a.   Wilmot Proviso   c.   Kansas-Nebraska Act
    b.   Compromise of 1850   d.   Ostend Manifesto

    ANS: A   DIF: Medium   REF: 306   OBJ: 12.1
    TOP: Slavery

21. Who became best known for leading slaves to freedom?
    a.   Stephen Douglas   c.   Harriet Tubman
    b.   Abraham Lincoln   d.   Harriet Beecher Stowe

    ANS: C   DIF: Medium   REF: 310   OBJ: 12.1
    TOP: Abolitionist Movement

22. The Compromise of 1850 provided for all of the following except
    a. a strong Fugitive Slave Act.
    b. admission of California as a slave state.
    c. abolition of slave trade in the District of Columbia.
    d. popular sovereignty in the area acquired from Mexico, except for California.

    ANS: B   DIF: Medium   REF: 308   OBJ: 12.1
    TOP: Slavery

23. The proposal that slavery not be permitted in any territory acquired from Mexico
    a. easily passed the House and the Senate.
    b. was most strongly supported by the Senate.
    c. was equally supported by both House and Senate.
    d. was never approved by the Senate.

    ANS: D   DIF: Medium   REF: 306   OBJ: 12.1
    TOP: Slavery

24. With respect to slavery, the Kansas-Nebraska Act
    a. repealed the slavery restriction of the Missouri Compromise.
    b. provided for slavery in Kansas.
    c. abandoned the principle of popular sovereignty.
    d. was vigorously resisted by those who supported slavery.

    ANS: A   DIF: Medium   REF: 313   OBJ: 12.2
    TOP: Slavery

25. The document that advised the United States to seize Cuba from Spain if it could not be
    purchased was known as
    a. the Compromise of 1850.   c. the Ostend Manifesto.
    b. Remember the Maine.   d. the Wilmot Proviso.

    ANS: C   DIF: Medium   REF: 312   OBJ: 12.2
    TOP: Pierce's Foreign Policy

26. Which person led an abolitionist raid on the federal arsenal at Harpers Ferry, Virginia?
    a. Harriet Tubman   c. Stephen Douglas
    b. John Brown   d. General Zachary Taylor

    ANS: B   DIF: Medium   REF: 320–321   OBJ: 12.2
    TOP: Abolitionist Movement

27. The Supreme Court ruling in "Dred Scott v. Sanford"
    a. supported the idea that slaves were property.
    b. meant that Congress could not abolish slavery in the western territories.
    c. met with cheers in the South.
    d. all of the above

    ANS: D   DIF: Medium   REF: 318   OBJ: 12.3
    TOP: Supreme Court / Slavery

28. During the 1850s, in which territory was the most blood spilled over the issue of slavery?
    a. Kansas   c. Iowa
    b. Nebraska   d. Utah

    ANS: A   DIF: Medium   REF: 315–316   OBJ: 12.3
    TOP: Kansas History / Slavery

29. Which of the following stated that a slave was NOT a citizen and could not bring suit in Missouri courts?
    a. the Missouri Compromise   c. the Emancipation Proclamation
    b. the Compromise of 1850   d. "Dred Scott v. Sanford"

    ANS: D   DIF: Medium   REF: 317–318   OBJ: 12.3
    TOP: Supreme Court / Slavery

30. In the Lincoln-Douglas debates, Abraham Lincoln
    a. supported the idea of popular sovereignty.
    b. gained support that helped him defeat Douglas for the Senate in 1858.
    c. insisted that the territories be kept free from slavery.
    d. demanded the abolition of slavery in the United States.

    ANS: C   DIF: Medium   REF: 320   OBJ: 12.3
    TOP: Slavery / Lincoln

31. Which is the correct chronological order of presidential administrations?
    a. Fillmore, Taylor, Buchanan, Pierce, Lincoln
    b. Buchanan, Pierce, Fillmore, Taylor, Lincoln
    c. Taylor, Fillmore, Pierce, Buchanan, Lincoln
    d. Pierce, Fillmore, Buchanan, Lincoln, Taylor

    ANS: C   DIF: Medium   REF: 307–323   OBJ: 12.4
    TOP: Presidential Elections

32. The first battle of the Civil War was fought at
    a. Gettysburg.   c. Bleeding, Kansas.
    b. Fort Sumter.   d. Washington, D.C.

    ANS: B   DIF: Medium   REF: 326   OBJ: 12.4
    TOP: Civil War Battles

33. What was the last attempt at compromise before the outbreak of the Civil War?
    a. the Missouri Compromise
    b. the Compromise of 1850
    c. the Kansas-Nebraska Act
    d. the proposed Crittenden Amendments to the Constitution

    ANS: D   DIF: Medium   REF: 324–325   OBJ: 12.4
    TOP: Civil War

34. Which of the following contributed LEAST to the causes of the Civil War?
    a. slavery   c. the Mexican cession
    b. the industrialization of the North d. immigration to the United States

    ANS: D   DIF: Medium   OBJ: 12.4   TOP: Civil War

© Prentice-Hall, Inc.

35. Which of the following men could be considered the "father" of the Republican party?
    a. George Washington   c. Henry Clay
    b. Stephen Douglas   d. Abraham Lincoln

    ANS: D   DIF: Medium   REF: 322–323   OBJ: 12.4
    TOP: Political Parties

36. In the election, which candidate received a proportion of the electoral votes that was much lower than his proportion of the popular vote?
    a. Lincoln   c. Breckinridge
    b. Douglas   d. Bell

    ANS: B   DIF: Medium   REF: 323   OBJ: 12.4
    TOP: Presidential Elections

37. Which of the following did NOT have a positive effect on the settlement of the West?
    a. the gold rush   c. the results of the Mexican War
    b. relations with the Native Americans   d. immigration to the United States

    ANS: B   DIF: Medium   REF: 305–307   OBJ: 12.1
    TOP: U.S. Expansion West

38. Which event occurred FIRST?
    a. the Compromise of 1850   c. the gold rush
    b. the Mexican cession   d. the Kansas-Nebraska Act

    ANS: B   DIF: Medium   OBJ: 12.1   TOP: Mexican History

39. Which of the following has been the MOST popular American expression of progress and the opportunity for success?
    a. living on a farm   c. moving west
    b. getting older   d. living in a small town

    ANS: C   DIF: Medium   OBJ: 12.1   TOP: Western Expansion

40. The current practice of secretly smuggling political refugees from foreign countries into the United States would be MOST like the activities of
    a. Harriet Beecher Stowe.   c. John Brown.
    b. Harriet Tubman.   d. the Know-Nothing party.

    ANS: B   DIF: Medium   REF: 310   OBJ: 12.1
    TOP: Underground Railroad

41. The fact that the Wilmot Proviso passed in the House of Representatives but failed in the Senate is best explained by the fact that the
    a. South had more power in the Senate.
    b. North had a lower population than the South.
    c. South had more power in the House.
    d. Senate was controlled by Republicans.

    ANS: A   DIF: Medium   REF: 305–307   OBJ: 12.1
    TOP: Slavery

SHORT ANSWER

In one or two sentences, define and distinguish between the terms given below.

1. martyr

    ANS:
    A martyr is a person who is willing to sacrifice his or her life for a cause.

    DIF: Hard   OBJ: 12.0

2. fugitive

    ANS:
    A fugitive is a person who flees or tries to run away.

    DIF: Hard   REF: 310   OBJ: 12.0

3. prejudice

    ANS:
    Prejudice is an irrational preference for or against some group or their supposed attributes.

    DIF: Hard   OBJ: 12.0   TOP: Discrimination

ESSAY

1. What is the cause-and-effect fallacy in the following argument? Write your answer on a separate sheet of paper and support your answer with a paragraph explaining why you chose it.
        Economic differences were the main cause of the Civil War. Problems only began after the North and South started becoming economically different.
    A. single cause
    B. preceding event as cause (post hoc)
    C. both A and B
    D   no fallacy

    ANS:
    answer B Students' paragraphs should support their answer.

    DIF: Hard   OBJ: 12.0   TOP: Civil War

© Prentice-Hall, Inc.

2. In an essay, describe how an abolitionist in the mid-1800s would most likely have reacted to four of the following events, and explain why. Wilmot Proviso, Compromise of 1850, Fugitive Slave Act, publication of Uncle Tom's Cabin, Ostend Manifesto, Kansas-Nebraska Act, Dred Scott decision, Lecompton Constitution, John Brown's raid on Harpers Ferry

    ANS:
    Students' answers will vary but could include these ideas: An abolitionist probably would have supported the following: The Wilmot Proviso's ban on slavery; the publication of and reaction to "Uncle Tom's Cabin"; and John Brown's raid on Harpers Ferry. These events all tried to discourage and limit slavery. An abolitionist also may have supported the Compromise of 1850 since it forbade slavery in some areas. The following would not have been supported by abolitionists: The Fugitive Slave Act because it allowed slavery to reach into the North; the Ostend Manifesto's stand to expand American slavery; the Kansas-Nebraska Act because it allowed slavery in this new territory; the Dred Scott Decision because it labeled Negroes as property; and the Lecompton Constitution because it allowed slavery in Kansas.

    DIF: Hard   REF: 308–312   OBJ: 12.0
    TOP: Abolitionist Movement

3. How did the framers of the Compromise of 1850 attempt to settle the slavery issue? Explain the most important provisions of the Compromise and the effect those provisions had on the North and the South.

    ANS:
    Answers will vary but could include the following ideas: The main provisions of the Compromise of 1850 were that California be admitted as a free state, that slave trade be stopped in Washington, D.C. (though slavery itself could be maintained there), and that a strong Fugitive Slave law be enacted. The question of slavery in the other territories acquired in the Mexican Cession would be left to the voters in those territories.

    DIF: Hard   REF: 306–309   OBJ: 12.1   TOP: Slavery

4. Compare the elections of 1848 and 1852, and discuss the impact of the slavery question on factionalization of the political parties.

    ANS:
    Answers will vary but could include the following ideas: Whigs nominated General Zachary Taylor. They remained silent on slavery and had no official platform. The Democrats nominated Lewis Cass who had little to say about slavery. The Free-Soil candidate Martin Van Buren took away enough New York votes from the Democrats to give the election to Taylor. In 1852, Democrats nominated Franklin Pierce; Whigs chose Winfield Scott. Pierce won overwhelmingly in the only popular majority between 1840 and 1864. The Whigs began to fall apart as a result.

    DIF: Hard   REF: 307, 310–313   OBJ: 12.1
    TOP: Presidential Elections

5. Based on what you have learned in the chapter, explain how the Kansas-Nebraska Act contributed to the growing split between the North and the South.

ANS:
Answers will vary but could include the following ideas: The act organized the Kansas and Nebraska territories and repealed the Missouri Compromise. This development reopened the possibility that slavery would be allowed in these new territories. The act declared that "popular sovereignty" would determine whether slavery would be permitted. This situation set the stage for the violence of "Bloody Kansas."

DIF: Hard   REF: 313–314   OBJ: 12.2   TOP: Slavery / States Rights

6. Describe the events in May 1856 that further inflamed the slavery issue.

ANS:
Answers will vary but could include the following ideas: In May 1856, Senator Charles Sumner of Massachusetts was beaten unconscious by South Carolina Representative Preston Brooks, after Sumner gave a speech attacking the South. A proslavery mob sacked and burned the antislavery town of Lawrence, Kansas. John Brown led an antislavery mob that killed five men in the proslavery settlement of Pottawatomie Creek, Kansas.

DIF: Hard   REF: 316–317   OBJ: 12.2   TOP: Slavery

7. Knowing what you do about the Dred Scott decision, explain how it widened the gap between the North and the South.

ANS:
Answers will vary but could include the following ideas: The decision pleased the South and outraged the North because in it, the Supreme Court ruled that Congress could not restrict slavery in the territories. The decision reopened questions settled by past compromises.

DIF: Hard   REF: 317–318   OBJ: 12.3   TOP: Supreme Court

8. In your opinion, should the Dred Scott decision be considered one of the major Supreme Court decisions in history? Give specifics to support your argument.

ANS:
Answers will vary but could include the following ideas: The Dred Scott decision widened the gulf between the North and South. It said that the Missouri Compromise, Northwest Ordinance of 1787, and the Kansas-Nebraska Acts were unconstitutional. It stated that slaves were property and therefore Congress could not prohibit slavery from the territories. The decision enraged northern abolitionists and moved the nation one step closer to war.

DIF: Hard   REF: 317–318   OBJ: 12.3   TOP: Supreme Court

9. How did Lincoln manage to become President when he received only 39 percent of the popular vote?

ANS:
Answers will vary but could include the following ideas: The election of 1860 had a field of four candidates. The electoral system is based on a winner-take-all system for each state. Lincoln won a plurality of popular votes in a group of states that together gave him the electoral vote needed to win.

DIF: Hard   REF: 323   OBJ: 12.4   TOP: Presidential Elections

10. Evaluate the extent to which the political parties of 1860 were able to act as a force for national unity.

ANS:
Answers will vary but could include the following ideas: The parties divided along sectional lines and came to represent sectional interests. The Democratic party divided into northern and southern factions. The Republican party emerged the winner through the distortion of the popular vote by the Electoral College. Lincoln's election proved to be a catalyst to southern secession. Thus it cannot be said that any party was able to unite the nation.

DIF: Hard   REF: 321–326   OBJ: 12.4   TOP: Sectionalism

(page intentionally left blank)

MATCHING

Match each item with the correct statement below.

a.	Stonewall Jackson	f.	Winfield Scott
b.	Philip Sheridan	g.	Dorothea Dix
c.	William Sherman	h.	Jefferson Davis
d.	Clara Barton	i.	John Pope
e.	David Farragut	j.	Mathew Brady

1. He led the "March to the Sea," cutting a path through the "breadbasket" of the Confederacy.
2. She helped injured soldiers during the war and later led the American Red Cross.
3. He was the president of the Confederate States.
4. He often risked his life to photograph battles of the war.
5. Nicknamed "Old Fuss and Feathers," he planned the "anaconda," or blockade of the South.
6. The Confederate leader at the first Battle of Bull Run, he was later killed by one of his own men.
7. He heroically captured New Orleans, shutting off the southern supply line through the Gulf of Mexico.

1. ANS: C   DIF: Easy   REF: 356–357   OBJ: 13.0
   TOP: Civil War / Military Leaders
2. ANS: D   DIF: Easy   REF: 338   OBJ: 13.0
   TOP: Civil War - Women
3. ANS: H   DIF: Easy   REF: 339   OBJ: 13.0
   TOP: Civil War Leaders
4. ANS: J   DIF: Easy   REF: 337   OBJ: 13.0
   TOP: Civil War - Photography
5. ANS: F   DIF: Easy   REF: 341   OBJ: 13.0
   TOP: Civil War - Military Leaders
6. ANS: A   DIF: Easy   REF: 341   OBJ: 13.0
   TOP: Civil War - Military Leaders
7. ANS: E   DIF: Easy   REF: 344–345   OBJ: 13.0
   TOP: Civil War - Military Leaders

MULTIPLE CHOICE

1. The pioneer photographer who frequently risked his life to take battlefield pictures was
   a. Mathew Brady.   c. Irvin McDowell.
   b. John C. Fremont.   d. Thomas J. Jackson.

   ANS: A   DIF: Medium   REF: 337   OBJ: 13.1
   TOP: Civil War - Photography

2. A court order giving a judge the power to free a person who is being held illegally or without just cause is a
   a. bill of attainder.
   c. judicial review.
   b. writ of habeas corpus.
   d. pardon.

   ANS: B   DIF: Medium   REF: 339–346   OBJ: 13.1
   TOP: Laws

3. The commander of the Union Army at the outset of the Civil War who offered a plan to "envelop the insurgent states" was
   a. Winfield Scott.
   c. George B. McClellan.
   b. Irvin McDowell.
   d. Joseph E. Johnston.

   ANS: A   DIF: Medium   REF: 341   OBJ: 13.2
   TOP: Civil War - Military Leaders

4. The incident in which a Union warship stopped a British steamer and removed two Confederate diplomats became known as the
   a. Slidell affair.
   c. Seward affair.
   b. Merrimac affair.
   d. Trent affair.

   ANS: D   DIF: Medium   REF: 343   OBJ: 13.2
   TOP: Civil War

5. The Union commander of a fleet of ironclad gunboats who helped capture Fort Henry and Fort Donelson was
   a. David Glasgow Farragut.
   c. Irvin McDowell.
   b. D. C. Buell.
   d. A. H. Foote.

   ANS: D   DIF: Medium   REF: 343   OBJ: 13.2
   TOP: Civil War - Military Leaders

6. The Union commander at Gettysburg was
   a. John Pope.
   c. George Gordon Meade.
   b. George Pickett.
   d. Philip Sheridan.

   ANS: C   DIF: Medium   REF: 354   OBJ: 13.4
   TOP: Civil War - Military Leaders

7. The key to control of the Mississippi River, captured by Grant on July 4, 1863, was
   a. Port Hudson.
   c. Vicksburg.
   b. New Orleans.
   d. Fort Henry.

   ANS: C   DIF: Medium   REF: 354–355   OBJ: 13.4
   TOP: Civil War - Battles

8. The two Union generals most responsible for breaking the spirit of the civilian South were
   a. George McClellan and Philip Sheridan.
   b. William Tecumseh Sherman and Philip Sheridan.
   c. Ulysses S. Grant and Ambrose Burnside.
   d. A. H. Foote and William Tecumseh Sherman.

   ANS: B   DIF: Medium   OBJ: 13.4
   TOP: Civil War - Military Leaders

9. Grant and Lee arranged the surrender of Confederate forces at
   a. Richmond.
   b. Petersburg.
   c. Washington, D.C.
   d. Appomattox Court House.

   ANS: D   DIF: Medium   REF: 358   OBJ: 13.4
   TOP: Civil War - Victory

10. Which of the following does NOT apply to the Confederacy?
    a. produced only a few staple crops
    b. had 22,000 miles of railroads
    c. was forced to retreat at the Battle of Gettysburg
    d. site of the Andersonville prison camp

    ANS: B   DIF: Medium   REF: 333   OBJ: 13.1
    TOP: Civil War - Union

11. Which of the following does NOT apply to the Union?
    a. appealed to Britain and France for aid and recognition
    b. apologized to Britain over the Trent affair
    c. experienced rioting over its draft
    d. developed the ironclad "Monitor"

    ANS: A   DIF: Medium   OBJ: 13.1   TOP: Civil War - Union

12. The Northern war strategy for dividing up the South and preventing it from receiving outside help was called the
    a. Cobra policy.
    b. Conda policy.
    c. Exhaustion policy.
    d. Scott policy.

    ANS: B   DIF: Medium   REF: 336   OBJ: 13.1
    TOP: Civil War - Northern Strategy

13. The Southern economy at the start of the Civil War
    a. was based on a wide range of agricultural products and manufacturing activities.
    b. led Southerners to expect help from Great Britain and France.
    c. produced nearly everything Southerners needed.
    d. was in a state of depression.

    ANS: B   DIF: Medium   REF: 334   OBJ: 13.1
    TOP: Civil War - Southern Economy

14. At the beginning of the Civil War, Southerners believed all of the following EXCEPT that
    a. the North was too divided to fight effectively.
    b. "Cotton was King."
    c. they had a superior culture to that of the North.
    d. they should immediately attack Northern cities.

    ANS: D   DIF: Medium   REF: 334   OBJ: 13.1
    TOP: Civil War - Southern View

15. In order to win their independence, Southerners would have had to
    a. capture Washington, D.C.
    b. prevent subjugation by the North.
    c. invade and occupy large parts of the North.
    d. free their slaves.

    ANS: B   DIF: Medium   REF: 334   OBJ: 13.1
    TOP: Civil War

16. The rifle was superior to the smoothbore flintlock musket because it was
    a. faster to reload.   c. more reliable in wet weather.
    b. much more accurate.   d. all of the above

    ANS: D   DIF: Medium   REF: 334–335   OBJ: 13.1
    TOP: Civil War Weapons

17. The rifle changed military tactics by giving the advantage to troops
    a. attacking in solid ranks.
    b. defending in protected, well-supplied positions.
    c. on horseback.
    d. who had no training.

    ANS: B   DIF: Medium   REF: 335   OBJ: 13.1
    TOP: Civil War Weapons

18. Which of the following would NOT be evidence that the Civil War was a "people's war"?
    a. Nearly every family lost a soldier.
    b. Newspapers carried eyewitness accounts of battles.
    c. Women took over responsibilities formerly held by men.
    d. The spade became as important as the gun.

    ANS: D   DIF: Medium   REF: 337–339   OBJ: 13.1
    TOP: Civil War

19. Between the first Battle of Bull Run and the Battle of Petersburg, Union Army strategy changed from
    a. using Indian tactics to attacking with solid lines of soldiers.
    b. trying to destroy all of the South's resources to concentrating on a single decisive battlefield victory.
    c. seeking a single decisive battlefield victory to cutting off enemy supply lines.
    d. fighting an all-out war to avoid high numbers of killed and wounded soldiers.

    ANS: C   DIF: Medium   OBJ: 13.1   TOP: Civil War - Union

20. Lincoln's suspension of the "writ of habeas corpus" demonstrated that he
    a. would use almost any means to save the Union.
    b. viewed the Civil War as an opportunity to vastly increase the powers of the President.
    c. cared little about the rights of secessionists.
    d. knew nothing about the law.

    ANS: A   DIF: Medium   REF: 339–340   OBJ: 13.1
    TOP: Lincoln - Civil War

21. Lincoln saved the border states for the Union by
    a. imposing martial law in each of them.
    b. moving slowly to allow Union sentiment to develop in each of them.
    c. handling each state differently.
    d. imprisoning the secessionists in each of them.

    ANS: C   DIF: Medium   REF: 340   OBJ: 13.1
    TOP: Lincoln - Civil War

22. In 1861, when General Fremont freed the slaves of rebels in Missouri, Lincoln
    a. decided to issue the Emancipation Proclamation.
    b. overruled Fremont's decision.
    c. sought to enlist the former slaves in the Union Army.
    d. readmitted Missouri to the Union.

    ANS: B   DIF: Medium   REF: 340   OBJ: 13.1
    TOP: Lincoln - Slavery

23. Which of these was NOT one of the major areas of battle during the Civil War?
    a. Richmond and Washington
    b. the valley of the Ohio, Cumberland, and Tennessee rivers
    c. the Mississippi River Valley
    d. New England

    ANS: D   DIF: Medium   REF: 341   OBJ: 13.2
    TOP: Civil War Battle Sites

24. The West Point graduate and Mexican War veteran who was offered command of all Union
    forces when the Civil War erupted was
    a. Ulysses S. Grant.   c. William Tecumseh Sherman.
    b. Robert E. Lee.   d. "Stonewall" Jackson.

    ANS: B   DIF: Medium   OBJ: 13.2
    TOP: Civil War - Military Leaders

25. At Shiloh, Grant learned that Northern victory in the Civil War
    a. could be won with a single decisive battle.
    b. could be won with a minimum of bloodshed.
    c. required strict adherence to what he had been taught at West Point.
    d. required a war of exhaustion.

    ANS: D   DIF: Medium   REF: 344   OBJ: 13.2
    TOP: Civil War - Battles

26. Farragut's capture of New Orleans was most significant because it
    a. gave the North complete control over the Mississippi River.
    b. prevented the South from supporting its troops in the West with supplies brought in from
        the Gulf of Mexico.
    c. destroyed the Confederate navy.
    d. demonstrated the value of disregarding orders in an all-out war.

    ANS: B   DIF: Medium   REF: 344–345   OBJ: 13.2
    TOP: Civil War - Battles

27. What prevented both the North and the South from winning the Civil War in the first year?
    a. a lack of well-trained military leaders
    b. a lack of manpower
    c. a failure to recognize how the rules of war had changed
    d. a failure to recognize how decisive the role of African-American troops would be

    ANS: C   DIF: Medium   REF: 336   OBJ: 13.2
    TOP: Civil War

28. The battle on September 17, 1862, at Sharpsburg, Maryland, which proved to be the worst single day of the war for both sides, is better known as
    a. the second Battle of Bull Run.   c. Shiloh.
    b. Antietam.   d. Fredericksburg.

    ANS: B   DIF: Medium   REF: 348   OBJ: 13.2
    TOP: Civil War - Battles

29. Lincoln's main concern in fighting the Civil War was
    a. strengthening Northern industries.   c. restoring the Union.
    b. freeing the slaves.   d. retreat of the slaves.

    ANS: C   DIF: Medium   REF: 349   OBJ: 13.3
    TOP: Lincoln - Civil War

30. The abolitionists were seeking the
    a. emancipation of the slaves.   c. secession of the slaves.
    b. suppression of the slaves.   d. retreat of the slaves.

    ANS: A   DIF: Medium   OBJ: 13.3
    TOP: Abolitionist Movement

31. Slavery in the United States was ended by
    a. the Preliminary Emancipation Proclamation.
    b. the Emancipation Proclamation.
    c. an act of Congress.
    d. ratification of the Thirteenth Amendment.

    ANS: D   DIF: Medium   REF: 351   OBJ: 13.3
    TOP: Slavery / Emancipation

32. African-Americans were used in the armed forces in the Civil War
    a. chiefly by the Union.   c. mainly by both sides.
    b. mainly by the Confederacy.   d. by neither side.

    ANS: A   DIF: Medium   REF: 352   OBJ: 13.3
    TOP: Civil War - African-Americans

33. The financial needs of the United States during the Civil War led to
    a. the first income tax.
    b. a return to the gold system.
    c. the rise of new industries.
    d. borrowing large sums of money from the British.

    ANS: D   DIF: Medium   OBJ: 13.3
    TOP: Civil War - Economics

34. Lincoln's Emancipation Proclamation had all of the following effects EXCEPT
    a. increasing Southern anger toward the North.
    b. freeing the slaves in the South.
    c. increasing African-American enlistment in the Union Army.
    d. ending any chance of European nations recognizing the Confederacy.

    ANS: B   DIF: Medium   REF: 350   OBJ: 13.3
    TOP: Lincoln / Slavery - Emancipation

35. At the Battle of Gettysburg, Lee took the offensive because
    a. he had more troops.
    b. he held the high ground.
    c. he knew that he could depend on the leadership of Stonewall Jackson.
    d. the South was desperate for a victory.

    ANS: D   DIF: Medium   REF: 355   OBJ: 13.4
    TOP: Civil War - Battles

36. On July 4, 1863, the Confederacy suffered two great defeats when
    a. Pickett's charge at Gettysburg failed and Grant captured Vicksburg.
    b. Lee began his retreat from Gettysburg and Sherman burned Atlanta.
    c. Lee began his retreat from Gettysburg and Grant captured Vicksburg.
    d. Pickett's charge at Gettysburg failed and Grant captured Richmond.

    ANS: C   DIF: Medium   REF: 355   OBJ: 13.4
    TOP: Civil War - Battles

37. All of the following statements about the Civil War are true EXCEPT
    a. It was the bloodiest war in our nation's history.
    b. Nearly every family in the country lost a soldier in the war.
    c. It was the last war with navies of wooden ships.
    d. The war brought the westward movement to a virtual halt.

    ANS: D   DIF: Medium   REF: 332, 337, 346
    OBJ: 13.4   TOP: Civil War

38. What is most likely the reason that the states of the upper South waited until April 1861 to secede?
    a. They waited until they were convinced that the Confederacy enjoyed a military superiority over the North.
    b. They waited until Lincoln showed that he would use force against the seceded states.
    c. They waited until they were sure the other slaveholding states had seceded.
    d. They waited until Lincoln had broken the law.

    ANS: B   DIF: Medium   REF: 333   OBJ: 13.1
    TOP: Civil War - Secession

39. What is most likely the reason Lincoln called the action of the Southern states an "insurrection"?
    a. He wanted to minimize the seriousness of the problem to prevent panic in the North.
    b. He hoped that by using the term he could encourage a slave insurrection in the South.
    c. He viewed secession as illegal and wanted the conflict to be seen as a rebellion against rightful authority.
    d. He knew that the Constitution gave him enormous power to deal with insurrections.

    ANS: C   DIF: Medium   REF: 324   OBJ: 13.1
    TOP: Civil War - Secession

40. Why did most people in the North think that the rebellion of the South would be quickly crushed?
    a. The North's greater economic resources and population and the belief that the attacking army always had the advantage led to Northern overconfidence.
    b. Northerners knew that they had a great President in Abraham Lincoln and a military genius in Ulysses S. Grant.
    c. They knew that the North could blockade the South, but the South could not blockade the North.
    d. They thought that a slave rebellion would occur as soon as Southern whites left home to fight against the North.

    ANS: A   DIF: Medium   REF: 334   OBJ: 13.1
    TOP: Civil War - Secession

41. What MOST LIKELY caused Lincoln to wait until 1862 before taking steps to end slavery?
    a. He was unsure that the Constitution gave him the power to end slavery.
    b. He did not want to lose what support he still had in the South.
    c. He was unsure that Northern public opinion would support the abolition of slavery.
    d. He was not convinced that freeing the slaves would save the Union.

    ANS: D   DIF: Medium   REF: 349   OBJ: 13.3
    TOP: Lincoln / Slavery

42. Which of the following was NOT a problem for Lincoln during the last three months of 1862?
    a. The Democrats won House seats in the fall elections.
    b. Defeatism was widespread throughout the North.
    c. Riots against the draft took place in New York City.
    d. West Virginia seceded from Virginia.

    ANS: D   DIF: Medium   REF: 351   OBJ: 13.3
    TOP: Civil War

ESSAY

1. What point of view does the following statement present of General McClellan? Write your answer on a separate sheet of paper and support your answer with a paragraph explaining why you chose it.

    Northern operations were paralyzed by the caution and indecision of General McClellan.
    A. favorable
    B. very unfavorable
    C. unfavorable
    D. both favorable and unfavorable

    ANS:
    answer C Students' paragraphs should support their answer.

    DIF: Hard   REF: 345–346   OBJ: 13.0   TOP: Civil War

2. Compare the points of view and advantages of the North and the South in the Civil War.

    ANS:
    Students' answers will vary but could include these ideas: Initially, the North went to war to preserve the Union. It believed no state had the authority to withdraw from the Union. Later, the North would consider emancipation as a motive for the war. The South saw itself as defending its "liberty" against those who would place limits on it. Southerners believed they had the same right to withdraw from the Union as the colonies had to withdraw from the British Empire. The Southerners wanted the right of self-government. The South's advantages included experienced military leaders and the strength of fighting on home ground, but most advantages belonged to the North. The North had over twice as many people, more railroads, more production facilities, and more food resources.

    DIF: Hard   REF: 333–358   OBJ: 13.0   TOP: Civil War

3. Does a national crisis like the Civil War justify a suspension of civil liberties? Support your answer with specific examples.

    ANS:
    Answers will vary but could include the following ideas: Yes: Lincoln knew that he had to keep the border states in the Union if the Union was to stand a chance of surviving. Maryland was especially crucial because Washington, D.C., would be lost if Maryland seceded. Lincoln suspended civil liberties, temporarily, to ensure the long-term survival of American democracy and freedom. No: Lincoln set a precedent that could be abused by later presidents during wartime or in other national crises. For example, the internment of Japanese-Americans by President Roosevelt during World War II, though widely accepted as a necessary suspension of civil liberties at the time, is now seen as an unjust attack upon innocent people.

    DIF: Hard   OBJ: 13.1   TOP: Civil War - Civil Liberties

4. Compare Robert E. Lee and Ulysses S. Grant as men and as military leaders.

ANS:
Answers could include the following: Although Grant came from a modest background and Lee from a prominent family, both went to West Point and had their combat experience during the Mexican War. Lee remained with the U.S. Army until the outbreak of the Civil War. Grant resigned from the army and led an undistinguished life in the years before the Civil War as a clerk in his father's store. Neither Grant nor Lee was immediately placed in command of the main armies of the North and South. Lee took command in 1862; Grant in 1864. Lee was probably the finest military strategist of the war. Grant lacked Lee's strategic talent, but he doggedly pursued victory despite horrendous casualties. Both men could be said to have made maximum use of their resources.

DIF: Hard   OBJ: 13.2   TOP: Civil War - Military Leaders

5. Lincoln and Davis had to make many of the same kinds of decisions during the Civil War. For instance, each had to choose capable leaders. What other decisions did both men face? Evaluate the overall effectiveness of each leader.

ANS:
Answers will vary but could include the following ideas: Leaders on both sides during the Civil War were influenced by such factors as slavery, foreign involvement in the war, maintaining a stable economy, dealing with dissent, finding the best military leaders and the right military strategy, and keeping their armies well supplied. Overall, Abraham Lincoln made much better decisions and was a far more effective political leader than was Jefferson Davis.

DIF: Hard   REF: 333–358   OBJ: 13.3   TOP: Civil War Leaders

6. Discuss Abraham Lincoln's position on the emancipation of slaves at the beginning of the Civil War and again in 1863.

ANS:
Answers will vary but could include the following ideas: As much as he personally disliked slavery, Lincoln's decisions about emancipation were based on political and military considerations. His first priority was to preserve the Union. For example, Lincoln refused to emancipate the slaves in the border states because he wanted those states to stay in the Union. By 1862, however, he saw the need to make emancipation a war goal in order to maintain the support of a war-weary North. But his Emancipation Proclamation, which took effect on the first day of 1863, was very limited. It was really a military measure that freed the slaves only in those areas of the Confederacy still in rebellion.

DIF: Hard   REF: 340–341, 349–351   OBJ: 13.3
TOP: Lincoln / Slavery

7. Why is the Gettysburg Address so memorable? Discuss the setting, timing, rhetoric, and content of Lincoln's speech.

ANS:
Answers will vary but could include the following ideas: Setting: Lincoln delivered his address on the site of what was even then recognized as a crucial battle, perhaps the most crucial battle, of the Civil War. Timing: The Gettysburg Address came at a time when Northerners needed reassurance that the enormous sacrifices they were called upon to make were worthwhile. Rhetoric: Lincoln's simple but eloquent phrases displayed his extraordinary ability to put profound thoughts into language everyone could understand and remember. Content: The Gettysburg Address ranks with the Declaration of Independence in stating the significance of the American experiment in popular government. It gave meaning to the high price being paid to wage the Civil War, and it gave a moral grandeur to the important role American democracy played in the history of the world.

DIF: Hard   REF: 355   OBJ: 13.4   TOP: Civil War

8. Your textbook states: "After Gettysburg and Vicksburg the death of the Confederacy was only a matter of time." Do you agree or disagree that the outcome of the war was decided in 1863? Defend your position by citing specific events.

ANS:
Answers could include the following: Agree—After Gettysburg and Vicksburg, the Confederacy was fighting a defensive war with major disruptions in its supply lines. Northern morale was bolstered, and Lincoln had a general (Grant) who knew how to win. Disagree—The South was far from defeated in 1863. In the month that the North won at Gettysburg and Vicksburg, riots against the draft broke out in New York City. Many Northerners called for a negotiated settlement. In 1864, Grant suffered tremendous losses at Petersburg, Northern morale sank to an all- time low, and Lincoln feared he might lose his bid for reelection. Had Sherman and Sheridan not broken the back of Southern resistance in the fall of 1864, Northern public opinion might have turned against the war, allowing the Confederacy to survive.

DIF: Hard   REF: 354–355   OBJ: 13.4   TOP: Civil War

(page intentionally left blank)

MATCHING

Match each item with the correct statement below.

a. 15th Amendment
b. Credit Mobilier
c. Tenure of Office Act
d. 13th Amendment
e. Freedmen's Bureau

f. Black Codes
g. Plessy v. Ferguson
h. Radical Republicans
i. impeach
j. scalawags

1. They wished to treat the South as conquered territory.
2. This scandal involved the building of the transcontinental railroad.
3. It gave African-American males the right to vote.
4. Accuse of wrongdoing.
5. It forbade the President from dismissing federal officials without Senate approval.
6. It was established to provide meals, jobs, and schooling to former slaves.
7. Southern name for white Southerners who helped with Reconstruction.
8. This decision upheld the "separate but equal" doctrine.
9. Southern laws that limited African-American mobility and employment.
10. Prohibited slavery in the United States.

1. ANS: H   DIF: Easy   REF: 369   OBJ: 14.0
   TOP: Post Civil War
2. ANS: B   DIF: Easy   REF: 375   OBJ: 14.0
   TOP: Government Scandals
3. ANS: A   DIF: Easy   OBJ: 14.0   TOP: Constitution
4. ANS: I   DIF: Easy   REF: 370   OBJ: 14.0
   TOP: Impeachment
5. ANS: C   DIF: Easy   REF: 370   OBJ: 14.0
   TOP: U.S. Government
6. ANS: E   DIF: Easy   REF: 367–368   OBJ: 14.0
   TOP: African-American Rights
7. ANS: J   DIF: Easy   REF: 372   OBJ: 14.0
   TOP: Reconstruction
8. ANS: G   DIF: Easy   REF: 381   OBJ: 14.0
   TOP: Supreme Court
9. ANS: F   DIF: Easy   REF: 366   OBJ: 14.0
   TOP: African - American Rights
10. ANS: D   DIF: Easy   REF: 365   OBJ: 14.0
    TOP: Constitution / Slavery

MULTIPLE CHOICE

1. During the Reconstruction period, Southerners generally referred to the Civil War as
   a. the Second War for American Independence.
   b. the War between the States.
   c. the War of the Bloody Shirt.
   d. the War of Rebellion.

   ANS: B   DIF: Medium   REF: 361   OBJ: 14.1
   TOP: Reconstruction

2. The member of Congress from Pennsylvania, sometimes called "a humanitarian without humanity," who chaired the Joint Committee of Fifteen was
   a. Charles Sumner.   c. Thaddeus Stevens.
   b. William Seward.   d. Benjamin F. Wade.

   ANS: C   DIF: Medium   REF: 362   OBJ: 14.1
   TOP: African-American Rights

3. The Massachusetts senator described as "the conscience of the North" who fought for equal rights for African-Americans was
   a. Charles Sumner.   c. Thaddeus Stevens.
   b. William Seward.   d. Benjamin F. Wade.

   ANS: A   DIF: Medium   REF: 362   OBJ: 14.1
   TOP: African-American Rights

4. During the Civil War, Lincoln put forth his plan for bringing Southerners back into the Union in his
   a. Emancipation Proclamation.
   b. Reconstruction Proclamation.
   c. Proclamation of Amnesty and Reconstruction.
   d. Second Inaugural Address.

   ANS: C   DIF: Medium   REF: 362   OBJ: 14.1
   TOP: Lincoln's Presidency

5. The laws passed by newly established Southern legislatures to restrict the freedom of the emancipated slaves were called
   a. Slave Codes.   c. John Crow Laws.
   b. Black Codes.   d. Separate But Equal Laws.

   ANS: B   DIF: Medium   REF: 365–366   OBJ: 14.2
   TOP: African-American Rights

6. The law allowing the federal government to intervene in a state's affairs in order to protect African-Americans was the
   a. Tenure of Office Act.   c. Fifteenth Amendment.
   b. Command of the Army Act.   d. Civil Rights Act.

   ANS: D   DIF: Medium   REF: 368   OBJ: 14.2
   TOP: Constitution

7. The secret army formed by ex-Confederates to preserve their former way of life was the
   a. American Legion.
   c. Sons of Liberty.
   b. Knights of Columbus.
   d. Ku Klux Klan.

   ANS: D   DIF: Medium   REF: 373–374   OBJ: 14.3
   TOP: Racism

8. Of the following, which scandal is NOT associated with the Grant Administration?
   a. Teapot Dome
   c. the Whiskey Frauds
   b. the Salary Grab
   d. Credit Mobilier

   ANS: A   DIF: Medium   REF: 375   OBJ: 14.4
   TOP: Grant's Presidency

9. The 1896 case in which the Supreme Court upheld the legality of segregated facilities was
   a. "McCulloch v. Maryland."
   c. "Brown v. Board of Education."
   b. the Dred Scott Decision.
   d. "Plessy v. Ferguson."

   ANS: D   DIF: Medium   REF: 381   OBJ: 14.5
   TOP: Supreme Court

10. The agricultural system in which a family cultivated land it did not own, keeping a small part of whatever was grown and paying the rest as rent, was known as
    a. peonage.
    c. land leasing.
    b. serfdom.
    d. sharecropping.

    ANS: D   DIF: Medium   REF: 381   OBJ: 14.5
    TOP: Sharecropping

11. "With malice towards none" best expresses whose attitude towards Reconstruction of the South?
    a. Thaddeus Stevens
    c. Charles Sumner
    b. Abraham Lincoln
    d. Horace Greeley

    ANS: B   DIF: Medium   REF: 363   OBJ: 14.1
    TOP: Reconstruction

12. Thaddeus Stevens and Charles Sumner were alike in that they
    a. wanted the federal government to help African-Americans.
    b. led the Radical Republicans in the U.S. Senate.
    c. suffered from physical problems brought on by brutal attacks at the hands of Southerners.
    d. were both from New England.

    ANS: A   DIF: Medium   REF: 362   OBJ: 14.1
    TOP: African-American Rights

13. Lincoln's plan for Reconstruction
    a. looked more to the past than to the future.
    b. looked more to the future than to the past.
    c. excluded Confederate soldiers from participation in state governments.
    d. would have taken generations to complete.

    ANS: B   DIF: Medium   REF: 362   OBJ: 14.1
    TOP: Reconstruction

14. The Wade-Davis bill was
    a. proposed but never passed by Congress.
    b. passed by Congress over Lincoln's veto.
    c. accepted by Lincoln as one approach to Reconstruction.
    d. more forgiving than Lincoln's plan for Reconstruction.

    ANS: C   DIF: Medium   REF: 362–363   OBJ: 14.1
    TOP: Reconstruction

15. Which one of the following is NOT true? Lincoln was assassinated
    a. as part of a larger conspiracy.   c. by a pro-Southern fanatic.
    b. a few days after Lee surrendered.   d. before the war ended.

    ANS: D   DIF: Medium   REF: 363–364   OBJ: 14.1
    TOP: Lincoln's Assassination

16. Lincoln wanted to readmit the Southern states after
    a. one-tenth of the state's voters took an oath of loyalty.
    b. one-half of the state's voters took an oath of loyalty.
    c. one-third of the state's voters took an oath of loyalty.
    d. all of the state's voters took an oath of loyalty.

    ANS: A   DIF: Medium   REF: 362   OBJ: 14.1
    TOP: Post Civil War Reunion

17. Both Thaddeus Stevens and Charles Sumner
    a. were radical Republicans.   c. felt bitter towards the South.
    b. favored the Wade-Davis bill.   d. all of the above

    ANS: D   DIF: Medium   REF: 362–363   OBJ: 14.1
    TOP: African-American Rights

18. Andrew Johnson was like Lincoln in that he
    a. was shrewd in handling opponents.
    b. had been a leader of the Republican party since the 1850s.
    c. often used humor to make a serious point.
    d. had been born in the South to poor parents.

    ANS: D   DIF: Medium   REF: 365   OBJ: 14.2
    TOP: Andrew Johnson

19. Upon taking office as President, Andrew Johnson
    a. told the Southern states exactly what he wanted them to do.
    b. called for a special session of Congress to deal with Reconstruction.
    c. failed to provide firm direction to southerners willing to admit defeat.
    d. fired Secretary of War Stanton.

    ANS: C   DIF: Medium   REF: 365   OBJ: 14.2
    TOP: Johnson's Presidency

© Prentice-Hall, Inc.

20. Of the following, which was NOT a school set up after the Civil War for African-American students of college age?
    a. Sewanee University
    b. Howard University
    c. Atlanta University
    d. Fisk University

    ANS: A   DIF: Medium   REF: 368   OBJ: 14.2
    TOP: Higher Education

21. The Joint Committee of Fifteen was
    a. led by Charles Sumner.
    b. chosen to select the winner of a disputed presidential election.
    c. chosen to create a plan for readmitting the Confederate states.
    d. included only the Radical members of Congress.

    ANS: C   DIF: Medium   REF: 367   OBJ: 14.3
    TOP: Reconstruction

22. In the Southern states during Military Reconstruction, all of the following were true EXCEPT
    a. free public schools were established.
    b. African-Americans dominated most state governments.
    c. state governments were accused of being corrupt.
    d. Republican rule did not last long.

    ANS: B   DIF: Medium   REF: 373   OBJ: 14.3
    TOP: Reconstruction

23. Johnson was impeached mainly because
    a. he was seldom present in Washington.
    b. he refused to follow Lincoln's policies.
    c. he was caught accepting bribes.
    d. he didn't cooperate with the Radical Republicans.

    ANS: D   DIF: Medium   REF: 370   OBJ: 14.3
    TOP: Johnson's Presidency

24. All of the following occurred during Grant's administra- tion EXCEPT
    a. complete withdrawal of federal troops from the South.
    b. major scandals.
    c. economic depression.
    d. the Boston and Chicago fires.

    ANS: A   DIF: Medium   REF: 375–376   OBJ: 14.4
    TOP: Grant's Presidency

25. The electoral commission was set up to resolve the disputed election of 1876 voted in favor of
    a. Rutherford B. Hayes.
    b. Ulysses S. Grant.
    c. Samuel J. Tilden.
    d. the compromise of 1877.

    ANS: A   DIF: Medium   REF: 378   OBJ: 14.4
    TOP: Presidential Elections

26. Of the following, the only provision NOT a part of the compromise of 1877 was that the new President would
    a. appoint a Southerner to his cabinet.
    b. remove the last federal troops from the South.
    c. ban African-Americans from participating in Southern state governments.
    d. support spending for internal improvements in the South.

    ANS: C   DIF: Medium   REF: 378–379   OBJ: 14.4
    TOP: Reconstruction

27. Southern statutes forcing segregation of the races were called
    a. Discrimination laws.   c. Jim Crow laws.
    b. Separate But Equal laws.   d. Uncle Tom laws.

    ANS: C   DIF: Medium   REF: 380   OBJ: 14.5
    TOP: Segregation

28. Segregation in the South provided
    a. new housing for all African-Americans displaced by the war.
    b. public facilities that were used equally by African-Americans and whites.
    c. separate but equal public facilities.
    d. separate but inferior facilities for African-Americans.

    ANS: D   DIF: Medium   REF: 381   OBJ: 14.5
    TOP: Segregation

29. By 1900, large numbers of former slaves were
    a. attending public schools.
    b. serving in Congress.
    c. working in high-paying jobs.
    d. attending public schools AND serving in Congress.

    ANS: A   DIF: Medium   REF: 382   OBJ: 14.5
    TOP: Public Education

30. Which of the following was a result of Reconstruction in the South?
    a. gift of 40 acres of land to each former slave
    b. complete racial integration of public facilities
    c. free public education for African-Americans and whites
    d. beginning of Republican dominance in Southern politics

    ANS: C   DIF: Medium   REF: 382   OBJ: 14.5
    TOP: Reconstruction

31. It would seem most likely that, as a result of the Civil War and Reconstruction, the South would finish the nineteenth century and enter the twentieth century
    a. economically depressed.   c. agriculturally advanced.
    b. racially integrated.   d. politically fragmented.

    ANS: A   DIF: Medium   REF: 381–382   OBJ: 14.5
    TOP: Reconstruction

32. Approximately how many years elapsed between Reconstruction and the next major effort on the part of the federal government to guarantee African-Americans their civil rights?
    a. 10 years
    b. 25 years
    c. 50 years
    d. 90 years

    ANS: D   DIF: Medium   OBJ: 14.5   TOP: Civil Rights

33. Reconstruction resulted in all of the following EXCEPT
    a. free public education in the South.
    b. a strong two-party system in the South.
    c. an increase in white Southerners' fears of blacks.
    d. valuable experience for African-Americans in political life.

    ANS: B   DIF: Medium   REF: 379–382   OBJ: 14.5
    TOP: Reconstruction

34. Lincoln's plan for reuniting the nation after the Civil War differed from the Wade-Davis plan that originated in Congress PRIMARILY because
    a. Lincoln's plan was workable, while the Wade-Davis plan was not.
    b. Lincoln's plan was constitutional, while the Wade-Davis plan was not.
    c. Lincoln's plan would have brought about the speedy return of the Southern states to the Union, while the Wade-Davis plan sought to delay their return.
    d. Lincoln's plan recognized secession as a legal right, while the Wade-Davis plan treated it as a crime.

    ANS: C   DIF: Medium   REF: 362–363   OBJ: 14.1
    TOP: Post Civil War

35. President Johnson's lack of success in dealing with Congress after Lincoln's assassination MOST LIKELY resulted from
    a. the fact that he was a Southerner.
    b. his inexperience in national politics.
    c. the fact that he was a Democrat.
    d. his inability to recognize how deeply Northerners felt about punishment of the South and protection of the emancipated slaves.

    ANS: D   DIF: Medium   REF: 365   OBJ: 14.2
    TOP: Johnson's Presidency

36. "I am for Negro suffrage in every rebel state. If it be just, it should not be denied; if it be necessary, it should be adopted; if it be a punishment to traitors, they deserve it." Of the people listed below, the one MOST LIKELY to have spoken these words was
    a. John Wilkes Booth.
    b. Thaddeus Stevens.
    c. Andrew Johnson.
    d. Abraham Lincoln.

    ANS: B   DIF: Medium   REF: 362   OBJ: 14.2
    TOP: Abolitionist Movement

37. In describing Congress' efforts to develop a Reconstruction program for the South, perhaps the BEST term to use would be
a. reactionary.
b. unsuccessful.
c. bipartisan.
d. charitable.

ANS: B   DIF: Medium   REF: 361–382   OBJ: 14.3
TOP: Reconstruction

38. "I don't care a straw for your newspaper articles; my constituents don't know how to read, but they can't help seeing them .#.#.# pictures." Who would MOST LIKELY have said these words?
a. Horace Greeley
b. Horatio Seymour
c. William Marcy Tweed
d. Andrew Johnson

ANS: C   DIF: Medium   REF: 376–377   OBJ: 14.4
TOP: Presidential Elections / Scandals

ESSAY

1. Which of the following is an example of sample reasoning? Write your answer on a separate sheet of paper and support your answer with a paragraph explaining why you chose it.
A. The Secretary of War, W.W. Belknap, was impeached in 1876.
B. Samuel J. Tilden exposed the corruption of the Tweed Ring.
C. In politics Grant was as gullible as a child.
D. A large number of distillers conspired with Treasury Officers to avoid the tax on whiskey.

ANS:
answer D Students' paragraphs should support their answer.

DIF: Hard   REF: 375   OBJ: 14.0   TOP: Government Scandals

2. Summarize the sentiments and events which mark the period called "Reconstruction." Use either a or b as a topic sentence.
   A. Lee's unconditional surrender gave the North a troublesome new problem—what to do with the conquered South.
   B. The emancipation of slaves created great confusion in the aftermath of the war. What was to be the relationship between blacks and whites?

ANS:
There were two main currents of thought in the post–Civil War North regarding the South. One idea was to forgive the South and to try to bring it back into the Union as quickly as possible. The other idea was to punish the South. Following Lincoln's death, President Johnson tried to admit the former slave states with minimal requirements. But when Congress reconvened in 1865, it refused to seat the Southern representatives. The Radical Republicans held that the Southern states had "committed suicide" and proceeded to treat them as conquered territory. In the South, old notions of a "superior" white race and an "inferior" black race resurfaced in the "Black Codes." The North made an attempt at equal treatment of all citizens. The Radical Republicans produced the Freedman's Bureau to help former slaves adjust to their new lives, passed the Civil Rights Bill and the 14th Amendment, and inaugurated military rule in the South.

DIF: Hard   REF: 365–382   OBJ: 14.0
TOP: Civil War Aftermath / Emancipation

3. Besides punishing the South and protecting African-Americans, what other considerations might have motivated the Radical Republicans in their Reconstruction efforts?

ANS:
Answers will vary but could include the following ideas: The Radical Republicans were motivated by economic and political realities as well as by their desire to punish the South and protect African-Americans. As representatives of a rapidly expanding industrial economy, they wanted a pro-business federal government that would support a high tariff and internal improvements. The Radicals also recognized that their political supremacy would be threatened by a "Solid South" in which white Southerners would be united in the Democratic party, and African-American Southerners would be disenfranchised. It was to the Radicals' political advantage to impede the return of former Confederates to power and to do everything possible to assure a large African-American electorate in the South.

DIF: Hard   REF: 369–375   OBJ: 14.1   TOP: Reconstruction

4. After the Reconstruction period, the Fourteenth Amendment became crucial to the development of American business. Explain what role this Civil War amendment might have played in the growth of corporate America.

ANS:
Answers will vary but could include the following ideas: The Fourteenth Amendment says, "No state shall make or enforce any law which shall abridge the privileges or immunities of citizens of the United States; nor shall any state deprive any person of life, liberty, or property, without due process of law." When the courts later decided that a corporation was a "person" as defined by the Fourteenth Amendment, the power of states to regulate, tax, and otherwise control the corporations within their boundaries was severely limited. Some historians have charged that pro-business Radical Republicans had this interpretation in mind when they wrote the amendment, but there is little evidence to support this accusation.

DIF: Hard   REF: 368–369   OBJ: 14.2   TOP: Constitution

5. Your textbook states: "This was the first time American politicians came near to removing a President during his term of office. If they had succeeded, they would have opened the way for a new kind of dictatorship—a dictatorship of Congress." Do you agree or disagree with this conclusion? Explain your answer.

ANS:
Answers could include the following ideas: Agree—So little of the case against Johnson was based on law and so much on political differences that his removal would have set a precedent for future confrontations between the President and Congress. Just the threat of removal would destroy the balance that the Constitution's framers intended, resulting in a dictatorship of Congress. Disagree—The situation was unique in that the President was clearly at odds with sentiment in the North. Northerners were demanding surrender from the South. The congressional elections of 1866 proved how out of touch Johnson was, and his removal from office might have led to a more responsive executive. History has shown that Congress is reluctant to threaten impeachment, and the two-thirds requirement for conviction is a constitutional safeguard against political vendettas against presidents.

DIF: Hard   REF: 370–371   OBJ: 14.3   TOP: Johnson's Presidency

6. What might be the reasons that Southern whites were able to reestablish racial supremacy in the years during and after Reconstruction?

ANS:
Answers will vary but could include the following ideas: Southern whites were able to reestablish racial supremacy largely through violence, or the threat of violence, and through making certain that African-Americans remained economically dependent on whites. Secret societies like the Ku Klux Klan terrorized African-Americans who exercised their rights to vote or hold public office or who simply seemed too "uppity." Once the federal troops were removed, African-Americans were left virtually defenseless, making it prudent for them to accept second-class citizenship without protest.

DIF: Hard   REF: 373–374, 397–382   OBJ: 14.3
TOP: Racism

7. Given what you know about American politics, what parallels might be drawn between the presidential elections of 1824 and 1876?

ANS:

Answers will vary but could include the following ideas: The presidential elections of 1824 and 1876 were similar in that both were ultimately decided in the House of Representatives, both resulted in the candidate with the largest popular vote losing, and both involved charges of collusion. In 1824, the House selected John Quincy Adams over Andrew Jackson (who had polled more votes), after Adams made what has come to be called a "Corrupt Bargain" with Henry Clay. In 1876, the House voted to accept the electoral commission's selection of Rutherford B. Hayes over Samuel J. Tilden (winner of the most popular votes) after Hayes agreed to the pro-Southern "Compromise of 1877."

DIF: Hard   REF: 223–224, 376–378   OBJ: 14.4
TOP: Presidential Elections

8. How did the term "the New South" originate? Explain how the term is used.

ANS:

Answers will vary but could include the following ideas: The term "New South" came into popular usage in the 1880s. Backers of the New South wanted to replace one-crop (cotton) agriculture with a greater variety of crops and with a more comprehensive use of the land, tapping minerals and forests as well as the soil. Most importantly, those who advocated the New South program wanted to emulate Northern industrialization, and they urged Southerners to build or attract mills and factories that would convert raw materials into manufactured goods.

DIF: Hard   OBJ: 14.5

9. In his classic work "Democracy in America," Alexis de Tocqueville stated his belief that whites were less prejudiced against African-Americans in the South than they were in the North during the 1830s. Why might he have held this belief? How can such a belief help explain the racial violence that occurred in the South during Reconstruction?

ANS:

Answers will vary but could include the following ideas: As de Tocqueville saw it, whites felt comfortable around African-Americans as long as there were clear lines, legal and social, separating the races. Where those lines did not exist or were blurred (i.e., the North), the status of whites vis-a-vis African-Americans was less certain, giving rise to racial fear and hatred. When the lines of demarcation between the races in the South were suddenly altered at the end of the Civil War, a more virulent form of racism surfaced there than had existed previously. In the "Black Codes" and "Jim Crow" laws, white Southerners tried to reestablish the formal lines of racial separation and superiority that seemingly allowed them to live quite contentedly in a biracial society in the antebellum era.

DIF: Hard   REF: 379–382   OBJ: 14.5   TOP: Racism

(page intentionally left blank)

MATCHING

Match each item with the correct statement below.

a. Wounded Knee
b. Chief Joseph
c. Dawes Act
d. Helen Hunt Jackson
e. William Cody

f. Charles Goodnight
g. William Sherman
h. George Custer
i. Homestead Act
j. Samuel Colt

1. Law intended to "Americanize" the Indians.
2. This provided settlers with 160 acres of free land in the West.
3. Wrote "A Century of Dishonor," dramatizing the plight of Native Americans.
4. He invented the six-shooter.
5. Famous scout and buffalo hunter.
6. A Civil War hero who turned Indian fighter.
7. He tried to lead the Nez Perces to Canada.
8. Site of the slaughter of 200 unarmed Native Americans in 1890.
9. He was defeated at Little Big Horn.
10. Western trailblazer who led cattle from Texas to Wyoming.

1. ANS: C   DIF: Easy   REF: 391   OBJ: 15.0
   TOP: Native Americans
2. ANS: I   DIF: Easy   REF: 403–404   OBJ: 15.0
   TOP: Western Expansion / Homestead Act
3. ANS: D   DIF: Easy   REF: 391   OBJ: 15.0
   TOP: Native Americans
4. ANS: J   DIF: Easy   REF: 386   OBJ: 15.0
   TOP: Weapons
5. ANS: E   DIF: Easy   REF: 390   OBJ: 15.0
   TOP: Western Expansion
6. ANS: G   DIF: Easy   REF: 388   OBJ: 15.0
   TOP: Native Americans
7. ANS: B   DIF: Easy   REF: 389   OBJ: 15.0
   TOP: Native Americans
8. ANS: A   DIF: Easy   REF: 389   OBJ: 15.0
   TOP: Native Americans
9. ANS: H   DIF: Easy   REF: 389   OBJ: 15.0
   TOP: Native Americans
10. ANS: F   DIF: Easy   REF: 398   OBJ: 15.0
    TOP: Western Expansion / Cattlemen

MULTIPLE CHOICE

1. Until just before the Civil War, the area between the line of settlement in the East and the Rocky Mountains was marked on maps as the
   a. Great American Plains.
   b. Great American Prairie.
   c. Great American Desert.
   d. Great American Wasteland.

   ANS: C   DIF: Medium   REF: 398   OBJ: 15.1
   TOP: The Great American Desert

2. In 1864, a militia force under Colonel John M. Chivington slaughtered approximately 450
   a. Cheyenne.
   b. Arapaho.
   c. Sioux.
   d. Cheyenne and Arapaho.

   ANS: D   DIF: Medium   REF: 388   OBJ: 15.1
   TOP: Native Americans

3. Custer's opposition at Little Big Horn was led by
   a. Chief Joseph.
   b. Chief Crazy Horse.
   c. Chief Sitting Bull.
   d. Chief Crazy Horse and Chief Sitting Bull.

   ANS: D   DIF: Medium   REF: 389   OBJ: 15.1
   TOP: Native Americans

4. The Battle of Wounded Knee signalled
   a. the beginning of the Indian wars.
   b. the end of the Indian wars.
   c. a change in the government's Indian policy.
   d. a need for a bigger cavalry.

   ANS: B   DIF: Medium   REF: 389   OBJ: 15.1
   TOP: Native Americans

5. An 1887 act that was part of an attempt to adopt a more humane policy toward Native Americans was the
   a. Dawes Act.
   b. Indian New Deal.
   c. Reservation Act.
   d. Indian Fair Treatment Act.

   ANS: A   DIF: Medium   REF: 391   OBJ: 15.1
   TOP: Native Americans

6. The lucky and enterprising miner who made his millions from mines that others had given up was
   a. William Larimer.
   b. John W. Mackay.
   c. Henry Comstock.
   d. Mark Twain.

   ANS: B   DIF: Medium   REF: 394   OBJ: 15.2
   TOP: Western Expansion / Mining

7. The author of the novel "Giants in the Earth," a chronicle of farming in the West, was
   a. Ole Rolvaag.
   b. Fritz Becker.
   c. John Wesley Iliff.
   d. Frederic Remington.

   ANS: A   DIF: Medium   REF: 396   OBJ: 15.3
   TOP: Western Expansion / Farming

8. One of the first trailblazers, who agreed to deliver $40,000 worth of cattle from Texas to Cheyenne, Wyoming, was
   a. Joseph G. McCoy.
   b. Charles Goodnight.
   c. Frederic Remington.
   d. Fritz Becker.

   ANS: B   DIF: Medium   REF: 398   OBJ: 15.3
   TOP: Western Expansion / Cattlemen

9. One "go-getting" cattleman who made the cow town of Abilene boom was
   a. Charles Goodnight.
   b. Joseph G. McCoy.
   c. John Wesley Iliff.
   d. Ole Rolvaag.

   ANS: B   DIF: Medium   REF: 399–400   OBJ: 15.3
   TOP: Western Expansion / Cattlemen

10. The Mormons in Utah developed a new way to raise crops, known as
    a. open range farming.
    b. dry farming.
    c. public domain farming.
    d. sod farming.

    ANS: B   DIF: Medium   REF: 405   OBJ: 15.4
    TOP: Western Expansion / Farming

11. The illegal settlers who first claimed land in the newly opened Indian Territory of Oklahoma were called
    a. Chickasaws.
    b. Okies.
    c. Boomers.
    d. Sooners.

    ANS: D   DIF: Medium   REF: 406   OBJ: 15.4
    TOP: Western Expansion / Sooners

12. A policy of wanting either to eliminate the Native Americans or to make them beg for mercy was undertaken by
    a. General William Tecumseh Sherman.
    b. General George A. Custer.
    c. Captain W. J. Fetterman.
    d. William Cody.

    ANS: A   DIF: Medium   REF: 388   OBJ: 15.1
    TOP: Native Americans

13. United States Indian policy in the 1800s included all of the following EXCEPT
    a. development of the reservation system.
    b. preservation of Native American customs.
    c. broken promises.
    d. broken treaties.

    ANS: B   DIF: Medium   REF: 385–391   OBJ: 15.1
    TOP: Native Americans

14. The first force to endanger the buffalo was the
    a. weather.   c. fence.
    b. farmers.   d. railroad.

    ANS: D   DIF: Medium   REF: 390   OBJ: 15.1
    TOP: Western Expansion / Buffalo

15. One of the primary purposes of the Dawes Act was to
    a. "Americanize" the Indians.
    b. rebuild the Native American nations.
    c. restore Native Americans to their ancestral lands.
    d. encourage the Native American population to increase.

    ANS: A   DIF: Medium   REF: 391   OBJ: 15.1
    TOP: Native Americans

16. Which of the following reasons best explains why the United States government allowed whites
    to take Native American land?
    a. The government wanted permanent settlers in the West to assure U.S. control of the area.
    b. White settlers would be taxpayers, while Indians would not.
    c. White settlers would make better use of the land, advancing civilization.
    d. The government wanted to push the Native Americans as far as possible from the major
       urban centers of the East.

    ANS: C   DIF: Medium   OBJ: 15.1   TOP: Native Americans

17. John Mackay was able to make a considerable fortune from the Comstock Lode because
    a. he used improved mining methods and equipment.
    b. he was its original owner.
    c. Henry Comstock owed him money.
    d. he operated a store near the mine.

    ANS: A   DIF: Medium   REF: 394   OBJ: 15.2
    TOP: Western Expansion / Mining

18. Which of the following is a potential danger involved in the unwritten law that was practiced in
    the West?
    a. punishment of innocent people
    b. repeat offenders
    c. acquittal through legal technicalities
    d. victory of a minority over the wishes of the majority

    ANS: A   DIF: Medium   REF: 394–395   OBJ: 15.2
    TOP: Western Expansion / Law

19. The mining frontier was significant because
    a. the majority of miners made vast fortunes.
    b. it brought peace between the Indian and the white man.
    c. it demonstrated that the western states had few natural resources.
    d. it stimulated the cattle and railroad businesses.

    ANS: D   DIF: Medium   REF: 395   OBJ: 15.2
    TOP: Western Expansion / Mining

20. Which of the following authors did NOT write about the settling of the American West?
    a. Mark Twain
    c. Bret Harte
    b. Henry James
    d. Ole Rolvaag

    ANS: B   DIF: Medium   REF: 396   OBJ: 15.2
    TOP: American Writers

21. Cowboys borrowed all of the following from the Mexicans EXCEPT the
    a. lariat.
    c. big hat.
    b. chaps.
    d. six shooter.

    ANS: D   DIF: Medium   REF: 398   OBJ: 15.3
    TOP: Cowboys

22. In which of the following ways did the growth of railroads NOT contribute to the passing of the frontier?
    a. It split the western buffalo herd and brought hunters west.
    b. It led to the setting up of cow towns.
    c. It sold excess land near railroad tracks to settlers.
    d. It reduced the need for the long cattle drive.

    ANS: D   DIF: Medium   OBJ: 15.3   TOP: Western Expansion

23. The first territory in the United States to grant women the right to vote was
    a. Wyoming.
    c. Kansas.
    b. Montana.
    d. Colorado.

    ANS: A   DIF: Medium   REF: 397   OBJ: 15.3
    TOP: Women's Rights

24. All of the following factors helped bring an end to the open range EXCEPT
    a. hard winters that wiped out herds.
    b. farmers planting crops.
    c. competition from the buffalo for range grass.
    d. fencing off of ranches.

    ANS: C   DIF: Medium   OBJ: 15.3   TOP: Western Expansion

25. Which of the following events happened last?
    a. homesteaders admitted to Oklahoma
    c. gold discovered in the Black Hills
    b. end of the open range
    d. Custer's last stand

    ANS: A   DIF: Medium   REF: 406   OBJ: 15.4
    TOP: Western Expansion

26. What areas had the government promised to the Native Americans, then taken away when settlers moved into it?
    a. Black Hills of South Dakota and the Oklahoma Territory
    b. Oregon and Idaho
    c. Sierra Nevada and the northern Rockies
    d. northern Texas and southern New Mexico

    ANS: A   DIF: Medium   REF: 389, 406   OBJ: 15.4
    TOP: Native Americans

27. Farmers had avoided the Great Plains for all of the following reasons EXCEPT
    a. the grass was long.   c. there was little rain.
    b. trees were rare.   d. the area was different.

    ANS: A   DIF: Medium   REF: 401   OBJ: 15.4
    TOP: Western Expansion / Farming

28. The 1862 Homestead Act provided a 160-acre plot to
    a. anyone working for the government.   c. anyone over 21 years of age.
    b. railroad workers.   d. native-born Americans.

    ANS: C   DIF: Medium   REF: 403   OBJ: 15.4
    TOP: Western Expansion / Homestead Act

29. In order to get free land under the 1862 Homestead Act, a settler had to
    a. be a United States citizen.
    b. be married.
    c. live on and cultivate part of the land.
    d. promise never to move away from, or sell, the land.

    ANS: C   DIF: Medium   REF: 403–404   OBJ: 15.4
    TOP: Western Expansion / Homestead Act

30. Which group actively encouraged Europeans to immigrate to the Great Plains?
    a. the Mormon Church   c. mine owners
    b. the federal government   d. railroad owners

    ANS: D   DIF: Medium   REF: 404   OBJ: 15.4
    TOP: Western Expansion / Immigrants

31. Pioneer farmers needed fencing to
    a. keep in the cattle.   c. protect their land from dust storms.
    b. keep out the cattle.   d. protect their land from poachers.

    ANS: B   DIF: Medium   REF: 404   OBJ: 15.4
    TOP: Western Expansion / Farming

32. Conflicts between farmers and cattle ranchers were mainly about
    a. water.   c. use of railroads.
    b. Indians.   d. land.

    ANS: D   DIF: Medium   REF: 401   OBJ: 15.4
    TOP: Western Expansion

33. A land rush in 1889 brought tens of thousands of settlers to
    a. South Dakota.   c. Kansas.
    b. Nebraska.   d. Oklahoma.

    ANS: D   DIF: Medium   REF: 406   OBJ: 15.4
    TOP: Western Expansion

34. In 1879, Chief Joseph of the Nez Perce published an appeal to the President of the United States. In it he wrote, "If you tie a horse to a stake, do you expect he will grow fat? If you pen an Indian on a small spot of earth and compel him to stay there, he will not be contented nor will he grow and prosper." From this quotation, you can conclude that Chief Joseph probably
    a. favored the confinement of Native Americans on reservations.
    b. believed Native Americans should fight to the death against the United States army.
    c. opposed the confinement of Native Americans on reservations.
    d. believed that Native Americans would never grow and prosper.

    ANS: C   DIF: Medium   REF: 389   OBJ: 15.1
    TOP: Native Americans

35. Of the following "isms," which one most closely matches the attitude underlying the Dawes Act?
    a. communism   c. feudalism
    b. socialism   d. individualism

    ANS: D   DIF: Medium   REF: 391   OBJ: 15.1
    TOP: Native Americans

36. "When dealing with savage men, as with savage beasts, no question of national honor can arise. Whether to fight, to run away, or employ a ruse, is solely a question of expediency." The attitude expressed in this quotation might BEST explain why
    a. whites often broke promises and treaties with the Native Americans.
    b. whites took the Native Americans' land.
    c. whites held the Native Americans in high regard as the "noble savage."
    d. whites believed that the only good Indian was a dead Indian.

    ANS: A   DIF: Medium   OBJ: 15.1   TOP: Native Americans

37. Which of the following did NOT aid the farmers who settled the Great Plains?
    a. the Dawes Act   c. railroads
    b. barbed wire   d. the Homestead Act

    ANS: A   DIF: Medium   REF: 391   OBJ: 15.4
    TOP: Western Expansion / Farming

38. Which of the following were results of the settling of the Great American Desert? I. The buffalo almost completely disappeared. II. Native Americans were pushed onto reservations. III. Crop production on the plains was reduced. IV. New states entered the Union.
    a. I, II, and III   c. I and IV
    b. II, III, and IV   d. I, II, and IV

    ANS: D   DIF: Medium   REF: 386, 387, 390, 405
    OBJ: 15.4   TOP: Western Expansion

SHORT ANSWER

In one or two sentences, define and distinguish between the terms given below.

1. dry farming

   ANS:
   Dry farming is a method of farming developed by the Mormons. By deeply plowing the soil after a rain and firming the topsoil, moisture was trapped in the dry soils of the Great Plains.

   DIF: Hard   REF: 405   OBJ: 15.0
   TOP: Western Expansion / Farming

2. open range

   ANS:
   The open range was western, unfenced land suitable for livestock grazing and part of the public domain. There cattle roamed freely, grazing on buffalo grass.

   DIF: Hard   REF: 401   OBJ: 15.0   TOP: Western Expansion

3. long drive

   ANS:
   The long drive refers to the long trip made by cowboys driving Texas long-horned cattle from Texas through the open range to cattle dealers and the railroads.

   DIF: Hard   REF: 398   OBJ: 15.0   TOP: Cattle

ESSAY

1. Which of the following is not an example of sample reasoning? Write your answer on a separate sheet of paper and support your answer with a paragraph explaining why you chose it.
   A. William Larimer was born and raised in Pennsylvania.
   B. Very few miners got rich in the Cherry Creek gold rush.
   C. The mining towns were wild, but they were not without law.
   D. To survive and raise a family on the Great Plains, a woman had to be many things.

   ANS:
   answer A Students' paragraphs should support their answer.

   DIF: Hard   REF: 393   OBJ: 15.0   TOP: Western Expansion

2. During and after the Civil War, people settled the Great Plains. New American ways of life were invented by a variety of "Go-Getters." Who were they and how did they transform the frontier?

ANS:
Student answers will vary but could include the following ideas: "Go-Getters" of the Great Plains included William Larimer, who laid out the plans for Denver, Colorado; John McKay, who made money from the forsaken mines of Comstock Lode in Nevada, inspiring many others to try mining; John Wesley Iliff, who "struck it rich" selling cattle to westward pioneers, railroad workers, and the military; Charles Goodnight, who developed the "cattle drive" from Texas north and made the "cow town" possible; Joseph McCoy, who built the cow town of Abilene, Kansas into a prosperous city; and Joseph Glidden, the Illinois farmer whose design for barbed wire proved easy to manufacture.

DIF: Hard   REF: 363–401   OBJ: 15.0   TOP: Western Settlers

3. Summarize the U.S. government's treatment of Native Americans from 1820 to 1890.

ANS:
Answers will vary but could include the following ideas: From 1820 to 1890, the U.S. government repeatedly deprived Native Americans of land, pushing them onto increasingly smaller areas. Treaties were often broken for the economic advantage of white settlers, and violence was used against even unarmed Native Americans. The Dawes Act, an attempt at reform, tried to break up the tribes and make the Native Americans conform to the dominant lifestyle.

DIF: Hard   REF: 386–391   OBJ: 15.1   TOP: Native Americans

4. Two Mexican "imports," the horse and longhorn cattle, had an enormous impact on the lives of the Plains Indians. Explain how they first facilitated, and then doomed, the lifestyle of the Plains Indians.

ANS:
Answers will vary but could include the following ideas: Neither the horse nor the longhorn cattle was native to North America. Both were introduced during the Spanish conquests. Over time wild herds of horses drifted northward from Mexico. The Plains Indians quickly became adept horsemen, using the horse to enhance their nomadic lifestyle, especially their ability to seek out and kill buffalo. Not until the latter half of the nineteenth century did the longhorn cattle become commercially significant. But when they did, their raising led to long drives, cow towns, and railroads, all of which contributed to the decline and demise of Indian nomadic life on the Great Plains.

DIF: Hard   REF: 396–401   OBJ: 15.1   TOP: Native Americans

5. Based on your reading of the chapter, describe who the "Go-Getters" were, and how they transformed the frontier.

    ANS:
    Answers will vary but could include the following ideas: Go-Getting miners exploited the mineral wealth of the West and helped develop the land. Go-Getting cowboys invented the cattle drive and thereby created a cattle empire based on Texas longhorns. Go-Getting farmers faced up to the challenges of the treeless plains, using dry farming, sod houses, buffalo chips, windmills, and barbed wire to transform barren lands into productive fields of crops.

    DIF: Hard   REF: 391–401   OBJ: 15.2   TOP: Western Settlers

6. How did the arrival of miners in the West complicate Native American–white relations?

    ANS:
    Answers will vary but could include the following ideas: Prior to the arrival of miners in the West, the vast majority of whites in the region were transients heading to permanent settlements near the Pacific Coast, or isolated individuals who lived off the land as traders and trappers. The miners, however, put up entire communities almost instantaneously. The size and suddenness of these communities posed a threat to white–Native American relations long before the arrival of the ranchers and the farmers.

    DIF: Hard   REF: 395   OBJ: 15.2
    TOP: U.S. / Native American Relations

7. Why has the cowboy remained such an important folk hero in American culture?

    ANS:
    Answers will vary but could include the following ideas: The cowboy, especially as portrayed by Wild West shows, became a romantic figure for an increasingly urbanized and industrialized population. The cowboy was a loner, not tied to any one location or place of employment. He worked outdoors, traveling enormous distances, facing and overcoming all kinds of hazards (weather, Indians, snakes, stampedes). City people saw in the cowboy a degree of freedom and excitement absent from their own lives, and they ignored the hardships of real cowboy life. The cowboy remains a romantic folk hero because of the myth, perpetuated by books, movies, and television.

    DIF: Hard   REF: 396–401   OBJ: 15.3   TOP: Cowboys

© Prentice-Hall, Inc.

8. What evidence does this chapter provide that the law is difficult to enforce in times of rapid social and economic change?

ANS:
Answers will vary but could include the following ideas: The law as embodied in Indian treaties was regularly violated as new economic opportunities demanded the removal or subjugation of the native inhabitants (e.g., the discovery of gold in the Black Hills). The law as it had been practiced in the East operated too slowly and uncertainly to satisfy the needs of mining towns. Thus, vigilante justice arose. In the transformation of the Great Plains from open range to fenced farms, farmers had to seek government assistance in enforcing their property rights against ranchers. Finally, when law-abiding homesteaders arrived in Oklahoma, they found their potential homesites already occupied by "Sooners" who had violated the law to stake claims ahead of the legally designated time.

DIF: Hard   REF: 387–406   OBJ: 15.4
TOP: Western Expansion / Law

9. Evaluate the positive and negative aspects of homesteading on the Great Plains.

ANS:
Answers will vary but could include the following ideas: Positive—Thousands of people became landowners who probably would have remained propertyless were it not for the Homestead Act. Homesteading transformed the vast public domain into a huge crop-producing region that would eventually feed America and much of the world. Negative—Life could be brutal for the homesteading family living in a sod house, facing frequent floods, fires, and freezing temperatures, and trying to save their crops from grasshopper infestations. Many families could not afford to buy the equipment that would make the free land usable, and the lack of water for irrigation required special farming techniques.

DIF: Hard   REF: 396–405   OBJ: 15.4
TOP: Settlers / Homesteaders

10. Compare and contrast the difficulties faced by cowboys, miners, and farmers during their settlement of the West.

ANS:
Answers will vary but could include the following ideas: Miners, cattlemen, and farmers all faced the hostility of the Indians, whose lands they encroached upon, often without much protection from federal troops. They also faced all the dangers of unpredictable, sometimes extreme, weather. In addition, miners had to move from place to place as strikes played out. Cowboys faced the hardships of the cattle drives for which they received very little pay. Farmers were beset by a lack of wood and water, attacks by insects and grassfires, and the hostility of ranchers who wanted continued access to free grasslands.

DIF: Hard   REF: 391–405   OBJ: 15.4   TOP: Western Settlers

(page intentionally left blank)

MATCHING

Match each item with the correct statement below.

a. gauge
b. James Bogardus
c. steel
d. banking
e. Samuel Gompers

f. land grants
g. standard
h. Eli Whitney
i. Frederick Taylor
j. Richard Sears

1. The "father" of scientific management was _____.
2. In the 1880s the _____, or distance between the two railroad tracks, became standardized.
3. Andrew Carnegie made his fortune in the _____ industry.
4. J.P. Morgan made his fortune in the _____ industry.
5. The cast-iron building was first developed by _____.
6. Pioneers in the mail-order business were Montgomery Ward and _____.
7. The American Interchangeable System was organized by _____ and Samuel Colt.
8. In 1883 the United States converted from "sun" time to _____.
9. Federal aid to railroads in the West was in the form of _____.
10. The "father" of national labor unions in the U.S. was _____.

1. ANS: I   DIF: Easy   REF: 428–429   OBJ: 16.0
   TOP: Scientific Management
2. ANS: A   DIF: Easy   REF: 416   OBJ: 16.0
   TOP: Railroads
3. ANS: C   DIF: Easy   REF: 418   OBJ: 16.0
   TOP: Steel
4. ANS: D   DIF: Easy   REF: 418   OBJ: 16.0
   TOP: Banking
5. ANS: B   DIF: Easy   REF: 426   OBJ: 16.0
   TOP: Architecture
6. ANS: J   DIF: Easy   REF: 422–425   OBJ: 16.0
   TOP: Mail Order
7. ANS: H   DIF: Easy   REF: 422   OBJ: 16.0
   TOP: Manufacturing
8. ANS: G   DIF: Easy   REF: 415   OBJ: 16.0
   TOP: Standard Time
9. ANS: F   DIF: Easy   REF: 413   OBJ: 16.0
   TOP: Railroads
10. ANS: E   DIF: Easy   REF: 433–434   OBJ: 16.0
    TOP: Unions

MULTIPLE CHOICE

1. The new time system adopted in 1883 was called
   a. God's time.   c. standard time.
   b. sun time.   d. train time.

   ANS: C   DIF: Medium   REF: 415   OBJ: 16.1
   TOP: Standard Time

2. An organized group of companies that agreed to keep their prices the same and not really compete against each other was known as a
   a. trust.   c. tie-in.
   b. conspiracy.   d. pool.

   ANS: D   DIF: Medium   REF: 417   OBJ: 16.1
   TOP: Pools

3. Sometimes called a pirate, the following person was considered a giant of finance.
   a. George Stephenson   c. Andrew Carnegie
   b. J. Pierpont Morgan   d. John D. Rockefeller

   ANS: B   DIF: Medium   REF: 418   OBJ: 16.1
   TOP: American Business Leaders / J. Pierpont Morgan

4. The Scottish-born steel industrialist was
   a. George Stephenson.   c. Andrew Carnegie.
   b. J. Pierpont Morgan.   d. John D. Rockefeller.

   ANS: C   DIF: Medium   REF: 418   OBJ: 16.1
   TOP: Steel / Carnegie

5. Finding ways to limit competition led to a fortune in the oil business for
   a. George Stephenson.   c. Andrew Carnegie.
   b. J. Pierpont Morgan.   d. John D. Rockefeller.

   ANS: D   DIF: Medium   REF: 416–417   OBJ: 16.1
   TOP: John D. Rockefeller / Oil

6. The Yale professor of chemistry who found valuable uses for the newly found oil was
   a. Billy Smith.   c. Benjamin Silliman, Jr.
   b. George H. Bissell.   d. Edwin L. Drake.

   ANS: C   DIF: Medium   REF: 420   OBJ: 16.2
   TOP: Oil

7. Rockefeller forced the railroads to give him a refund on each barrel of his oil they hauled, a payment known as a
   a. rebate.   c. gratuity.
   b. kickback.   d. tariff.

   ANS: A   DIF: Medium   REF: 421   OBJ: 16.2
   TOP: Rockefeller / Oil

8. A successful and creative figure in the mail-order business, who began by selling jewelry, was
   a. Richard Sears.
   b. James Bogardus.
   c. A. T. Stewart.
   d. Frederick W. Taylor.

   ANS: A DIF: Medium REF: 425 OBJ: 16.3
   TOP: Mail Order

9. The bold, ambitious Irish merchant who built one of the first department stores in New York was
   a. Richard Sears.
   b. Alvah Curtis Roebuck.
   c. A. T. Stewart.
   d. James Bogardus.

   ANS: C DIF: Medium REF: 426 OBJ: 16.4
   TOP: Department Stores

10. The genius who built some of the first cast-iron buildings in America was
    a. Alvah Curtis Roebuck.
    b. Frederick W. Taylor.
    c. A. T. Stewart.
    d. James Bogardus.

    ANS: D DIF: Medium REF: 426 OBJ: 16.4
    TOP: Architecture

11. The nation's hundredth birthday was celebrated on July 4, 1876, with a
    a. Centennial Exposition.
    b. People's Palace.
    c. New World Fair.
    d. Bicentennial Exposition.

    ANS: A DIF: Medium REF: 427 OBJ: 16.4
    TOP: Centennial

12. A standardized system of machine-made fasteners was based on the work of
    a. Eli Whitney.
    b. Eli Terry.
    c. A. T. Stewart.
    d. William Sellers.

    ANS: D DIF: Medium REF: 428 OBJ: 16.5
    TOP: Manufacturing

13. The Massachusetts Supreme Court in "Commonwealth v. Hunt" opened the path for
    a. strikes.
    b. assembly lines.
    c. trusts.
    d. unions.

    ANS: D DIF: Medium REF: 431 OBJ: 16.6
    TOP: Supreme Court

14. Samuel Gompers was the first president of the
    a. Longshoremen's union.
    b. American Federation of Labor.
    c. Congress of Industrial Organizations.
    d. Knights of Labor.

    ANS: B DIF: Medium REF: 434 OBJ: 16.6
    TOP: Unions

15. The first transcontinental railroad was completed in
    a. 1828.   c. 1869.
    b. 1860.   d. 1880.

    ANS: C   DIF: Medium   REF: 413   OBJ: 16.1
    TOP: Railroads

16. Who was MOST responsible for the spread of the free public library?
    a. John D. Rockefeller.   c. J. Pierpont Morgan.
    b. Andrew Carnegie.   d. Samuel Gompers.

    ANS: B   DIF: Medium   REF: 418   OBJ: 16.1
    TOP: American Businessmen

17. In 1889, Andrew Carnegie wrote, "Today the world has goods of excellent quality at such low prices that the poor enjoy what the rich could not before afford. What were the luxuries have become the necessaries of life." Which of the following ideas is most nearly the OPPOSITE of Carnegie's?
    a. The industrial revolution has made a few people richer and the vast majority poorer.
    b. Americans can expect life to improve steadily in the future.
    c. The rich deserve their fortunes because they raise everyone's standard of living.
    d. Mass-produced goods are inferior to handmade goods.

    ANS: A   DIF: Medium   OBJ: 16.1   TOP: Industrial Revolution

18. All of the following were forms of business consolidation EXCEPT
    a. trusts.   c. holding companies.
    b. pools.   d. proprietorships.

    ANS: D   DIF: Medium   REF: 417   OBJ: 16.1
    TOP: Corporations

19. To increase his wealth, John D. Rockefeller
    a. expanded into the steel-making business.
    b. collected rebates from railroads.
    c. sold his refineries to other oil companies.
    d. expanded gasoline usage by selling inexpensive cars.

    ANS: B   DIF: Medium   REF: 421   OBJ: 16.2
    TOP: John D. Rockefeller

20. In the 1800s, oil was used for all the following purposes EXCEPT
    a. synthetics.   c. lubricants.
    b. medicine.   d. fuel for lamps.

    ANS: A   DIF: Medium   REF: 419–420   OBJ: 16.2
    TOP: Oil

21. Mail-order catalogs
    a.   were most popular with urban dwellers.
    b.   made it possible for farm families to enjoy new gadgets and fashions.
    c.   were used as teaching aids.
    d.   were most popular with urban dwellers AND made it possible for farm families to enjoy
         new gadgets.

    ANS: D   DIF: Medium   REF: 425   OBJ: 16.3
    TOP: Mail Order

22. Which was NOT a trademark of Montgomery Ward's style of business?
    a.   good value   c.   trust
    b.   an ironclad guarantee   d.   high-priced goods

    ANS: D   DIF: Medium   REF: 423   OBJ: 16.3
    TOP: Mail Order

23. The construction of buildings of cast iron rather than of stone allowed the building of
    a.   impressive mansions.   c.   theaters.
    b.   public libraries.   d.   department stores.

    ANS: D   DIF: Medium   REF: 427   OBJ: 16.4
    TOP: Architecture

24. All of the following were major factors in the development of department stores EXCEPT
    a.   the merchandising ideas of A.T. Stewart.   c.   the invention of inexpensive plate glass.
    b.   the cast-iron building.   d.   new developments in printing in color.

    ANS: D   DIF: Medium   REF: 426–427   OBJ: 16.4
    TOP: Department Stores

25. The United States marked its hundredth birthday with a display of American-made products at
    a.   Philadelphia.   c.   Washington, D.C.
    b.   New York.   d.   Cleveland.

    ANS: A   DIF: Medium   REF: 427   OBJ: 16.5
    TOP: Centennial

26. One of the industries in America most essential to other industries was the making of
    a.   sewing machines.   c.   machine tools.
    b.   clocks.   d.   window glass.

    ANS: C   DIF: Medium   REF: 427–428   OBJ: 16.5
    TOP: Manufacturing / Machine Tools

27. One of the goals of Frederick W. Taylor was to liberate men and women from
    a.   low wages.   c.   sweat shops.
    b.   industrial accidents.   d.   waste.

    ANS: D   DIF: Medium   REF: 428   OBJ: 16.5
    TOP: Manufacturing

28. Labor unions
    a. did not exist until after the Civil War.
    b. were once viewed as illegal conspiracies.
    c. did not participate in strikes until after 1900.
    d. did not permit African-Americans to join until after 1900.

    ANS: B   DIF: Medium   REF: 431   OBJ: 16.6
    TOP: Unions

29. Both the B & O Railroad strike (1877) and the Homestead strike (1894)
    a. resulted in huge gains for workers.
    b. resulted in violence and death.
    c. were led by railroad workers.
    d. resulted in huge gains for workers AND resulted in violence and death.

    ANS: D   DIF: Medium   REF: 432   OBJ: 16.6
    TOP: Unions

30. The so-called Haymarket Massacre did NOT involve
    a. a meeting of workers, anarchists, and communists.
    b. a bomb.
    c. the death of seven policemen.
    d. coal miners.

    ANS: D   DIF: Medium   REF: 432   OBJ: 16.6
    TOP: Unions

31. Membership in the Knights of Labor rapidly declined after the
    a. Panic of 1873.   c. Haymarket Massacre of 1886.
    b. railroad strike of 1877.   d. Pullman Strike of 1894.

    ANS: C   DIF: Medium   REF: 433   OBJ: 16.6
    TOP: Unions

32. Samuel Gompers' type of unionism was known as
    a. "bread and butter" unionism.   c. industrial unionism.
    b. revolutionary unionism.   d. universal unionism.

    ANS: A   DIF: Medium   REF: 433   OBJ: 16.6
    TOP: Unions

33. Of the following economic changes that took place in the United States during the late 1800s,
    which was NOT caused by the expansion of railroads?
    a. Markets for farmers were expanded.
    b. Owners of businesses had little contact with workers.
    c. Businesses grew in size and number.
    d. Factories received greater supplies of raw materials.

    ANS: B   DIF: Medium   REF: 419   OBJ: 16.1
    TOP: Railroads

34. John D. Rockefeller, J. P. Morgan, and Andrew Carnegie all made fortunes because of their skill in
    a. organizing businesses.
    b. selling goods.
    c. squeezing out competitors.
    d. inventing new products.

    ANS: A   DIF: Medium   REF: 418–421   OBJ: 16.1
    TOP: American Businessmen

35. Between the 1850s and the 1890s, the oil industry changed PRIMARILY because
    a. petroleum had not yet been discovered in the 1850s.
    b. demand increased.
    c. competition decreased.
    d. demand increased AND competition decreased.

    ANS: D   DIF: Medium   REF: 421–422   OBJ: 16.2
    TOP: Oil Industry

36. Mail-order catalogs compared favorably with general stores in all of the following ways EXCEPT
    a. the availability of a variety of goods.
    b. the low prices.
    c. the speed of delivery.
    d. the display of new products.

    ANS: C   DIF: Medium   REF: 422–423   OBJ: 16.3
    TOP: Mail Order

37. When Samuel Gompers replied "More," when asked what American workers wanted, he was most likely indicating that organized labor in the United States
    a. was inherently radical.
    b. was pro-capitalist.
    c. wanted to own the factors of production.
    d. was pro-communist.

    ANS: B   DIF: Medium   REF: 433   OBJ: 16.6
    TOP: Unions

38. All of the following contributed to the rise of trade unions EXCEPT
    a. industrialization.
    b. standardization.
    c. urbanization.
    d. nationalization.

    ANS: D   DIF: Medium   REF: 430–432   OBJ: 16.6
    TOP: Unions

SHORT ANSWER

In one or two sentences, define and distinguish between the terms given below.

1. local time–standard time

ANS:
Local time was based on when the sun was at its zenith in each town and resulted in each town having its clocks set to their own time. Standard time divided the U.S. into four zones within which the time would be exactly the same, eliminating much confusion.

DIF: Hard   REF: 415   OBJ: 16.0   TOP: Local–Standard Time

2. "rule-of-thumb"–scientific management

ANS:
"Rule of thumb" refers to the rough, practical way that early craftsmen did their work without reliance on precise measure. Scientific management relies on precise measure and aims at avoiding waste in all tasks.

DIF: Hard   REF: 428   OBJ: 16.0   TOP: Manufacturing

ESSAY

1. Which of the samples below gives the best support to the following argument? Support your answer with a paragraph explaining why you chose it.
   The new mighty corporations were alarming. These concerns were run by managers who were quite separate from the thousands of stockholders who really owned the business. Most stockholders never even saw the factories of which they were part-owners.
   A. A sample of 50 letters to the editor from the 1880s, most of which said that stockholders had too little control over corporations.
   B. A sample of 300 stockholders in the garment industry from 1870 to 1890 showing that 78 percent of them were not involved in corporate decisions and had never seen the factories they owned.
   C. A sample of 250 stockholders in all major industries from 1872 to 1890 showing that 76 percent of them had neither participated in corporate decisions nor seen the factories they owned.
   D. A sample of 400 stockholders in the meat-packing industry from 1870 to 1900; three quarters of them had neither participated in any decisions nor seen the factories they owned.

ANS:
answer C Students' paragraphs should support their answer.

DIF: Hard   REF: 418–419   OBJ: 16.0   TOP: Corporations

2. Between 1865 and 1900, Go-Getters in the industrial Northeast and Midwest also transformed the nation. Who were they and how did they help establish an American standard of living?

ANS:
Morgan organized railroads in the 1800s and put together the financing for the United States Steel Corporation. Andrew Carnegie build the Carnegie Steel Company and established public libraries. John D. Rockefeller organized the oil industry, and through gifts set up the University of Chicago and other centers of higher learning. Montgomery Ward and Richard Sears transformed the desires and needs of American consumers, and department store pioneer A.T. Stewart changed the concept of the American shopping district. William Sellers' system of measurement and design for screws and nuts became the national and international standard. Frederick W. Taylor's ideas of scientific efficiency brought change to business and industry. Thomas A. Edison's "invention factory" and its products, such as the electric light, the phonograph, and the motion-picture camera, brought both practical and cultural changes. Samuel Gompers organized labor.

DIF: Hard   REF: 413–434   OBJ: 16.0
TOP: American Businessmen

3. Explain how standardization contributed to the growth of the country between 1865 and 1900, using at least two examples.

ANS:
Answers will vary but could include the following ideas: Between 1865 and 1900, screws and bolts, time zones, and railroad gauges all became standardized. Standardization made both transportation and mass production of goods faster and easier, speeding up the economic growth of the country.

DIF: Hard   REF: 413–416   OBJ: 16.1   TOP: Standardization

4. Based on what you have read in the chapter, how did the Go-Getters help establish a new standard of living for Americans between 1865 and 1900?

ANS:
Answers will vary but could include the following ideas: Andrew Carnegie, J. Pierpont Morgan, and John D. Rockefeller used new methods of organization to centralize and expand industries. The huge trusts limited competition but made the United States the world's industrial leader. Edison's invention factory, Taylor's efficiency science, and the mail-order stores of Ward and Sears increased the output and distribution of products. Industrialization caused serious problems, but it did raise the standard of living of most Americans.

DIF: Hard   REF: 413–430   OBJ: 16.2
TOP: American Businessmen

5. Explain the parallels that might be drawn between the mail-order businesses created by Montgomery Ward and Richard Sears and today's televised "home stopping networks."

ANS:
Answers will vary but could include the following ideas: Ward, Sears, and the televised home shopping networks all tapped new technologies to expand the distribution of mass-produced goods. The early mail-order houses used breakthroughs in printing to prepare attractive catalogs in huge quantities. Similarly, television is now being used to reach consumers who—like earlier rural families—may not have easy access to stores and who enjoy seeing products displayed in a way designed to enhance their appeal.

DIF: Hard   REF: 422–425   OBJ: 16.3   TOP: Mail Order

6. Would huge department stores like Stewart's Cast Iron Palace have been feasible before the Civil War? Explain your answer.

ANS:
Answers will vary but could include the following ideas: Stewart's Cast Iron Palace, though begun shortly before the Civil War, had its greatest impact after the war. The construction techniques used by James Bogardus were still experimental. Most importantly, there were few urban centers in America capable of supporting huge department stores before the Civil War. These stores required enormous supplies of mass-produced goods for a population with a good deal of disposable time and money. These requirements could not be met in many places in pre–Civil War America.

DIF: Hard   REF: 425–427   OBJ: 16.4   TOP: Manufacturing

7. Compare how Frederick W. Taylor's approach to management resembled the assembly line approach to manufacturing.

ANS:
Answers will vary but could include the following ideas: Frederick W. Taylor studied processes by breaking down a large procedure into its component steps and then trying to find the most efficient means to complete each step. The assembly line approach to manufacturing sought to break down the assembly of a finished product into component steps and then to assign specific workers to specific steps in order to achieve maximum efficiency.

DIF: Hard   REF: 428–429   OBJ: 16.5   TOP: Manufacturing

8. Describe how improvements in industrial production and efficiency changed the way factory work was organized.

ANS:
Answers will vary but could include the following ideas: Advances in standardization, machine tools, and assembly line production of mass-produced goods led to a depersonalized organization of factory work in which a worker became a function in the process. While this organization greatly enhanced industrial efficiency, it deprived workers of the satisfaction of seeing a job through from start to finish, and it reduced the value of workers in the eyes of employers to that of a commodity to be purchased at the lowest price.

DIF: Hard   REF: 427–430   OBJ: 16.5   TOP: Manufacturing

9. Compare and contrast the Knights of Labor and the American Federation of Labor.

ANS:
Answers will vary but could include the following ideas: The Knights of Labor, unlike the American Federation of Labor, was organized as a centralized industrial union with membership open to all workers. Also unlike the AFL, the Knights did not believe in the strike as an instrument that organized labor should use against management. Members of the American Federation of Labor were trade workers who belonged to independent trade groups which in turn belonged to the AFL; thus, it was not as centrally controlled as the Knights. Only after the merger with the CIO did the union founded by Gompers include industrial workers. Both the Knights and the AFL, however, shared the same belief that American workers had to make a collective response to the forces of industrialization in order to protect themselves.

DIF: Hard   REF: 433–434   OBJ: 16.6   TOP: Unions

10. If Thomas Jefferson could have examined the country in 1900, what aspects of the post–Civil War transformation would he have liked? What aspects would he have disliked? Explain your answer.

ANS:
Answers will vary but could include the following ideas: Jefferson would have been pleased to see the growth of the country, especially the expansion of agriculture into the territory he acquired for the United States in the Louisiana Purchase. He would have liked the advancements made in science and technology, the improvements in farm life, the growth of markets for farm products, and especially the continued existence of American democracy. He would have been dismayed by industrialization, the trend toward monopolization, the masses of propertyless workers, the necessity for collective organizations to protect workers' rights, and the threat to American democracy posed by enormously powerful businesses and businessmen.

DIF: Hard   OBJ: 16.6

(page intentionally left blank)

MATCHING

Match each item with the correct statement below.

a. Theodore Roosevelt
b. Justin Morrill
c. Ida B. Wells-Barnett
d. W.E.B. DuBois
e. Frederick Law Olmstead

f. Woodrow Wilson
g. James Bogardus
h. Frances Willard
i. Jane Addams
j. Frederick Turner

1. Established Hull House.
2. Helped organize National Association for the Advancement of Colored People (NAACP).
3. Helped design Central Park in New York City.
4. Cast-iron buildings.
5. Vetoed literacy test bill.
6. Established land-grant colleges.
7. Organized the Niagara Movement.
8. Women's Christian Temperance Union president—worked for women's suffrage.
9. Frontier thesis.
10. "Gentlemen's agreement" with Japan concerning immigration restrictions.

1. ANS: I   DIF: Easy   REF: 445   OBJ: 17.0
    TOP: Immigration / Education

2. ANS: C   DIF: Easy   REF: 446   OBJ: 17.0
    TOP: African-American Rights

3. ANS: E   DIF: Easy   REF: 455–456   OBJ: 17.0
    TOP: Urbanization

4. ANS: G   DIF: Easy   REF: 454   OBJ: 17.0
    TOP: Architecture

5. ANS: F   DIF: Easy   REF: 444   OBJ: 17.0
    TOP: Discrimination

6. ANS: B   DIF: Easy   REF: 448   OBJ: 17.0
    TOP: Higher Education

7. ANS: D   DIF: Easy   REF: 450   OBJ: 17.0
    TOP: African-American Rights

8. ANS: H   DIF: Easy   REF: 446   OBJ: 17.0
    TOP: Women's Rights

9. ANS: J   DIF: Easy   REF: 442–443   OBJ: 17.0
    TOP: Western Expansion

10. ANS: A   DIF: Easy   REF: 444   OBJ: 17.0
    TOP: Immigration

MULTIPLE CHOICE

1. Because of their ethnic variety, America's cities in the late 1800s could be called
   a. melting pots.
   c. mixing bowls.
   b. misery lanes.
   d. melting pots and mixing bowls.

   ANS: D   DIF: Medium   REF: 437   OBJ: 17.1
   TOP: Immigration

2. The act Congress passed in 1882 to prevent immigration from Asia was called the
   a. Chinese Exclusion Act.
   c. Immigration Restriction Act.
   b. Gentlemen's Agreement.
   d. Literacy Act.

   ANS: A   DIF: Medium   REF: 444   OBJ: 17.1
   TOP: Immigration

3. The importance of higher education for women was stressed by
   a. Matthew Vassar.
   c. Booker T. Washington.
   b. Leland Stanford.
   d. John D. Rockefeller.

   ANS: A   DIF: Medium   REF: 449   OBJ: 17.3
   TOP: Higher Education

4. The founder of Tuskegee Institute in Alabama was
   a. Johns Hopkins.
   c. W.E.B. Du Bois.
   b. Washington Roebling.
   d. Booker T. Washington.

   ANS: D   DIF: Medium   REF: 449   OBJ: 17.3
   TOP: African-American Rights / Education

5. An African-American leader who opposed the philosophy of Tuskegee Institute was
   a. Johns Hopkins.
   c. Booker T. Washington.
   b. Frances Benjamin Johnston.
   d. W.E.B. Du Bois.

   ANS: D   DIF: Medium   REF: 450   OBJ: 17.3
   TOP: African-American Rights

6. A 1905 declaration demanding immediate granting of all human rights for African-Americans
   was issued by the
   a. Niagara Movement.
   c. Urban League.
   b. NAACP.
   d. Wellesley Movement.

   ANS: A   DIF: Medium   REF: 450   OBJ: 17.3
   TOP: African-American Rights

7. The builder of the bridge for the city of St. Louis was
   a. Louis Sullivan.
   c. John Roebling.
   b. James Buchanan Eads.
   d. Washington Roebling.

   ANS: B   DIF: Medium   REF: 450   OBJ: 17.4
   TOP: Bridges

8. The building of the St. Louis bridge depended upon recently perfected watertight working chambers called
   a. suspension spans.
   b. sand chambers.
   c. bedrocks.
   d. caissons.

   ANS: D   DIF: Medium   REF: 451   OBJ: 17.4
   TOP: Bridges

9. The Brooklyn Bridge was planned and begun by
   a. John Roebling.
   b. Washington Roebling.
   c. Emily Warren Roebling.
   d. Currier & Ives.

   ANS: A   DIF: Medium   REF: 451   OBJ: 17.4
   TOP: Bridges

10. The inventor of a brake that made elevators safer was
    a. Henry Bessemer.
    b. William Le Baron Jenney.
    c. James Bogardus.
    d. Elisha Graves Otis.

    ANS: D   DIF: Medium   REF: 453   OBJ: 17.5
    TOP: U.S. Inventors

11. The inventor responsible for the mass-production steel furnace was
    a. Henry Bessemer.
    b. William Le Baron Jenney.
    c. James Bogardus.
    d. Elisha Graves Otis.

    ANS: A   DIF: Medium   REF: 454   OBJ: 17.5
    TOP: U.S. Inventors

12. Andrew Carnegie's steel plant and company town was called
    a. Radburn.
    b. Homestead.
    c. Haymarket.
    d. Pullman.

    ANS: B   DIF: Medium   REF: 455   OBJ: 17.6
    TOP: Company Towns

13. By 1910, the proportion of the population living in American cities who had moved from the farms was
    a. one-tenth.
    b. one-quarter.
    c. one-third.
    d. one-half.

    ANS: C   DIF: Medium   REF: 437   OBJ: 17.1
    TOP: Urbanization

14. The "frontier thesis" contends that the closing of the western frontier was responsible for
    a. a big decrease in immigration in the late 19th century.
    b. low prices for agricultural products.
    c. the Indian Wars.
    d. much of the corruption and discontent of the Guilded Age.

    ANS: D   DIF: Medium   REF: 442–443   OBJ: 17.1
    TOP: Western Expansion

15. Although thought to be an improved, fireproof plan for crowded city buildings, major flaws were found in the
    a. cast-iron building.   c. steel-framed skyscraper.
    b. dumbbell building.   d. narrow-shaft building.

    ANS: B   DIF: Medium   REF: 438–440   OBJ: 17.1
    TOP: Architecture

16. City slums today differ most from city slums in the late 1800s because today's slums
    a. play no role in urban politics.
    b. are ignored by local, state, and federal governments.
    c. are populated by many of the same families generation after generation.
    d. are filled with dirt, disease, and crime.

    ANS: C   DIF: Medium   REF: 438–440   OBJ: 17.1
    TOP: Urbanization

17. Which of the following factors had an equalizing effect upon the immigrants?
    a. schools
    b. various ethnic neighborhoods
    c. foreign language newspapers
    d. various ethnic neighborhoods AND foreign language newspapers

    ANS: A   DIF: Medium   REF: 447   OBJ: 17.1
    TOP: Immigration / Education

18. All of the following were aimed at helping immigrants succeed in America EXCEPT
    a. public schools.   c. "gentlemen's agreements."
    b. land-grant colleges.   d. settlement houses.

    ANS: C   DIF: Medium   REF: 445–448   OBJ: 17.1
    TOP: Immigration

19. One reason for calling cities "mixing bowls" of immigrants rather than "melting pots" is that
    a. there were violent conflicts between immigrants from different countries.
    b. the children of immigrants learned English quickly.
    c. immigrants tended to maintain many aspects of their original culture.
    d. immigrants usually married someone outside their ethnic group.

    ANS: C   DIF: Medium   REF: 437–438   OBJ: 17.1
    TOP: Immigration

20. The Immigration Restriction League
    a. was created by a group of former Klansmen.
    b. urged Congress to deport immigrants from southern Europe.
    c. believed in Anglo-Saxon superiority.
    d. was organized by Jane Addams in Chicago.

    ANS: C   DIF: Medium   REF: 443   OBJ: 17.1
    TOP: Immigration / Discrimination

21. A literacy test bill
    a. was mainly aimed at excluding Irish immigrants.
    b. was passed shortly after the Civil War.
    c. was never passed in Congress.
    d. was vetoed by Presidents Cleveland, Taft, and Wilson.

    ANS: D   DIF: Medium   REF: 444   OBJ: 17.1
    TOP: Discrimination

22. Jane Addams' plan for a settlement house called for the residents to be
    a. the city's poorest and most needy.
    b. abandoned children.
    c. educated, well-to-do young men and women.
    d. uneducated, newly arrived immigrants.

    ANS: C   DIF: Medium   REF: 445   OBJ: 17.2
    TOP: Education

23. Both Vassar and Bryn Mawr
    a. were established by the Morrill Act.
    b. were established by Booker T. Washington.
    c. were settlement houses in Chicago.
    d. were colleges founded for women.

    ANS: D   DIF: Medium   REF: 449   OBJ: 17.3
    TOP: Higher Education

24. The Morrill Act allowed for the establishment of
    a. settlement houses.   c. land-grant colleges.
    b. tenement houses.   d. garden cities.

    ANS: C   DIF: Medium   REF: 448   OBJ: 17.3
    TOP: Higher Education

25. Both Booker T. Washington and W.E.B. Du Bois
    a. were former slaves.
    b. believed education was the key to African-American advancement.
    c. accepted the practice of "separate but equal."
    d. urged African Americans to study history and the humanities.

    ANS: B   DIF: Medium   REF: 449–450   OBJ: 17.3
    TOP: African American Rights

26. The Niagara Movement was organized by
    a. Booker T. Washington.   c. Justin Morrill.
    b. W.E.B. Du Bois.   d. Ida B. Wells-Barnett.

    ANS: B   DIF: Medium   REF: 450   OBJ: 17.3
    TOP: African American Rights

27. Which of the following was NOT a characteristic of the Mississippi River Bridge?
    a. The foundation of one tower went down 123 feet.
    b. It was a suspension bridge.
    c. It used new chromium steel.
    d. It was constructed with the use of caissons.

    ANS: B   DIF: Medium   REF: 450–451   OBJ: 17.4
    TOP: Bridges

28. Both the Brooklyn and St. Louis bridges
    a. were suspension bridges.
    b. took less than a year to build.
    c. lost workers due to "caisson disease."
    d. were suspension bridges AND lost workers due to "caisson disease."

    ANS: C   DIF: Medium   REF: 451   OBJ: 17.4
    TOP: Bridges

29. All of the following were improvements in the functioning of elevators EXCEPT
    a. a brake that would clasp the elevator cage to the sides if the rope broke.
    b. an electric motor.
    c. hydraulic power.
    d. steam power.

    ANS: D   DIF: Medium   REF: 453   OBJ: 17.5
    TOP: Elevators

30. Henry Bessemer is to steel as
    a. Edison is to the electric light.   c. Ford is to the automobile.
    b. Bell is to the telephone.   d. Whitney is to the cotton gin.

    ANS: C   DIF: Medium   REF: 454–455   OBJ: 17.5
    TOP: Industrialists

31. What made the construction of skyscrapers possible?
    a. invention of safe elevators
    b. discovery of a cheaper method to produce steel
    c. the "dumbbell design" for buildings
    d. invention of safe elevators AND discovery of a cheaper method to produce steel

    ANS: D   DIF: Medium   REF: 453–454   OBJ: 17.5
    TOP: Architecture

32. A major invention aiding the building of skyscrapers was the
    a. mass production steel furnace.   c. mass production of wire rope.
    b. mass production of wrought iron.   d. use of caissons to sink foundations.

    ANS: A   DIF: Medium   REF: 454–455   OBJ: 17.5
    TOP: Architecture

33. Ebenezer Howard was responsible for a blueprint for
    a. improved tenement life.
    c. a suburban utopia.
    b. Central Park.
    d. garden apartments.

    ANS: C   DIF: Medium   REF: 456   OBJ: 17.6
    TOP: Suburban Development

34. Immigrants to the United States in the late 1800s settled mostly in the North rather than the South because
    a. there were many more major cities in the North.
    b. educational opportunities were greater in the North.
    c. jobs were more plentiful in the North.
    d. all of the above

    ANS: D   DIF: Medium   REF: 437–438   OBJ: 17.1
    TOP: Immigration

35. All of the following took place between 1860 and 1915 EXCEPT
    a. the urban population increased 700 percent.
    b. a literacy test requirement for immigration went into effect.
    c. the National Association for the Advancement of Colored People was founded.
    d. the Morrill Act was passed.

    ANS: B   DIF: Medium   REF: 437, 446, 448
    OBJ: 17.3   TOP: Urbanization / African-American Rights / Education

36. "No race can prosper till it learns that there is as much dignity in tilling a field as in writing a poem." These words were probably written by
    a. Matthew Vassar.
    c. W.E.B. Du Bois.
    b. Booker T. Washington.
    d. Jane Addams.

    ANS: B   DIF: Medium   REF: 449–450   OBJ: 17.3
    TOP: Education

37. Otis, Bogardus, Jenney, and Bessemer each contributed to the
    a. growth of cities.
    c. Americanization of immigrants.
    b. expansion of railroads.
    d. conflict between labor and management.

    ANS: A   DIF: Medium   REF: 453–455   OBJ: 17.5
    TOP: Urbanization

38. Company towns like Pullman and Homestead probably could not survive today because
    a. industrial workers no longer need to be close to their work sites.
    b. owners and managers of major industries today are less willing to spend money on benefits for their workers.
    c. owners and managers of major industries today cannot exert as much control over the lives of workers.
    d. the growth of suburbs has taken up all the potential land for company towns.

    ANS: C   DIF: Medium   REF: 455   OBJ: 17.6
    TOP: Company Towns

SHORT ANSWER

In one or two sentences, define and distinguish between the terms given below.

1. melting pot

   ANS:
   Melting pot is a term applied to American cities where large numbers of immigrants settled, despite the fact that many strived to keep their ethnic identities.

   DIF: Hard   REF: 437   OBJ: 17.0   TOP: Immigration

2. tenement

   ANS:
   A tenement was a six- or seven-story, poorly ventilated building that poor families squeezed into in the cities.

   DIF: Hard   REF: 438   OBJ: 17.0   TOP: Urban Life

3. "gentlemen's agreement"

   ANS:
   "Gentlemen's agreement" is an expression for any agreement to discriminate when you are ashamed to admit what you are really doing. The term originated after Theodore Roosevelt persuaded the Japanese government to prevent its people from emigrating.

   DIF: Hard   REF: 444   OBJ: 17.0   TOP: Discrimination

4. political boss

   ANS:
   A political boss was a corrupt politician, usually in city government. Bosses often built their political power by providing jobs, money, and advice to recent immigrants.

   DIF: Hard   REF: 441–442   OBJ: 17.0   TOP: Politics

5. oldcomers

   ANS:
   Oldcomers included wealthy, well-educated, and powerful people who lived in the East. Their families had come to America several generations earlier, and they sometimes resented the new wave of immigrants in the late 1800s.

   DIF: Hard   REF: 443   OBJ: 17.0
   TOP: Social Class / Immigration

ESSAY

1. Which of the following is an example of the fallacy of stereotyping? Write your answer on a separate sheet of paper and support your answer with a paragraph explaining why you chose it.
   A. The theory of survival of the fittest is wrong. Actually the poor work hard but don't get rich and the rich don't work hard but keep all the money.
   B. Most industrial leaders worked hard for their money.
   C. Andrew Carnegie worked hard to earn his money. He was from a poor family and started off as a bobbin boy.
   D. Few poor people were able to move up the economic ladder to become rich. Men like Andrew Carnegie were the exception, not the rule.

   ANS:
   answer A Students' paragraphs should support their answer.

   DIF: Hard   OBJ: 17.0   TOP: Social Class

2. Rapid urbanization before the turn of the century brought many problems. Efforts to solve these problems were made through social reforms as well as through triumphs of engineering and urban planning. Use the above paragraph as the conclusion of your essay. Provide the explanations and information that would lead to such a conclusion.

   ANS:
   Turn-of-the-century cities faced many problems, such as overcrowding, tenement houses, dirt, disease, crime, and resistance to new immigration (nativism). Solutions included such as Jane Addams' Hull House in Chicago, the Women's Suffrage and Temperance Movements, the rise of the NAACP and the spread of schooling for a larger segment of Americans, including women, African-Americans, and immigrants. In the cities, engineering triumphs made life more convenient and city living more practical. Examples were large bridges, such as John and Washington Roebling's Brooklyn Bridge of 1883. Elevators also helped the city rise, as did the use of skeleton structures for sky scrapers. To escape the hazards of city life, companies built towns like Pullman, IL. City planners such as Olmsted pioneered in making cities as much as possible like "gardens."

   DIF: Hard   REF: 437–456   OBJ: 17.0   TOP: Urbanization

3. What might have motivated so many people to move from farms to cities in the late 1800s?

   ANS:
   Answers will vary but could include the following ideas: The post–Civil War era was a difficult time for American farmers. They suffered from bouts of severe deflation and other economic ills that eventually fueled the Populist revolt. As a result, many farmers left agriculture and moved to the cities to take jobs in industry. Besides the economic motivation, many American rural families were drawn to the cities by the excitement of urban living and the relative ease of such living when compared to the rigors of prairie farming.

   DIF: Hard   OBJ: 17.1   TOP: Farming

4. Overall, was the effect immigrants had on American life in the late 1800s positive or negative? Explain your answer.

ANS:
Answers will vary but could include the following ideas: Positive—Immigrants injected a new vitality into American life, mixing their own customs and cultures with those already here. They peopled the cities and accounted for much of the labor force in new American factories. Many of them and even more of their descendants made major contributions to the arts, sciences, politics, and other fields. Negative—The immigrants of the late nineteenth century were responsible for most of the ills that we associate with urban slums. Although individually they may have been fine people, collectively they resulted in corrupt political machines, blighted housing, and an economic system that included sweat shops and child labor.

DIF: Hard   OBJ: 17.1   TOP: Immigration

5. Compare and contrast the temperance movement of the late 1800s with today's "Just say no to drugs" campaign.

ANS:
Answers will vary but could include the following ideas: The temperance movement of the late 1800s was largely religious in nature. It saw drunkenness as a sin, but it also viewed drinking as a social problem, especially affecting the immigrant family. Supporters of temperance were appalled at working-class fathers failing to support their families because they spent their paychecks on liquor. Temperance backers also tended to be pro-feminist, seeing wives as the main victims of husbands who drank. The anti-drug movement is not nearly as religious, and it does not see itself as a part of a larger reform movement. Both campaigns relied on songs and other forms of public entertainment to convey the message.

DIF: Hard   REF: 446   OBJ: 17.2
TOP: Temperance Movement

6. Were the social services performed by the settlement houses really necessary? Explain your answer.

ANS:
Answers will vary but could include the following ideas: The social services performed by the settlement houses were necessary in the sense that few other sources of aid and comfort were available to the urban immigrant. The settlement houses provided "Americanization" activities that helped to integrate immigrants into American life while simultaneously helping Americans respect other cultures. The settlement houses also gave a boost to recreational and artistic endeavors at a time when government support for such things did not exist.

DIF: Hard   REF: 444–446   OBJ: 17.2   TOP: Immigration

7. "In all things that are purely social we can be as separate as the fingers, yet one as the hand in all things essential to mutual progress." How might this sentence from Booker T. Washington be used to support the majority position in "Plessy v. Ferguson"?

ANS:
Answers will vary but could include the following ideas: A year before "Plessy v. Ferguson," Washington announced that he, as the leading African-American spokesman of his day, would be content with separate but equal status in social matters. The majority decision validated Jim Crow laws mandating racial separation, and it took more than fifty years for that decision to be overturned, even longer for African-Americans to overcome the second-class citizenship that Booker T. Washington had found acceptable.

DIF: Hard   REF: 380–381   OBJ: 17.3
TOP: African-American Rights

8. How did Americans obtain greater educational opportunities in the late 1800s?

ANS:
Answers will vary but could include the following ideas: Americans obtained greater educational opportunities in the late 1800s through the expansion of the free public school system, the growth of high schools, and new laws requiring children to attend school. New colleges resulted from the Morrill Act; and, since these colleges were funded in large part by state governments, they provided opportunities for higher education to immigrants and others who otherwise would have been denied a college education. Immigrants also found educational opportunities in the settlement houses.

DIF: Hard   REF: 444–450   OBJ: 17.3   TOP: Education

9. What modern architectural achievement affects our daily lives as much as William Le Baron Jenney's skyscraper affected the lives of city dwellers in the late 1800s? Explain your answer.

ANS:
Answers will vary but could include the following ideas: One contemporary architectural achievement that has made an impact comparable to that of Jenney's skyscraper is the suburban shopping mall. The mall has redefined shopping practices, strengthened the American commitment to the automobile, seriously diminished the economies of downtown shopping areas, and become a focal point for entertainment activities.

DIF: Hard   REF: 454–455   OBJ: 17.4   TOP: Architecture

10. Based on your reading of the chapter, why might workers have disliked living in company towns?

ANS:
Answers will vary but could include the following ideas: Company towns often offered poor living conditions: crowded apartments and inadequate facilities. Most importantly, these towns were a money-making vehicle for the company owners who used the towns to control their workers. Rents were higher and services were costlier in company towns than in neighboring towns. Workers were pressured into living in the towns where they were spied upon and not allowed to use facilities for anything construed as anti-company activity. The town newspapers were pro-company, and so were government officials, store owners, etc.

DIF: Hard   REF: 455   OBJ: 17.5   TOP: Company Towns

MATCHING

Match each item with the correct statement below.

a. Hayes
b. Populist
c. Cleveland
d. Bryan
e. McKinley

f. spoils system
g. filibuster
h. civil service
i. Garfield
j. Arthur

1. Mark Hanna staged his successful campaign against Bryan.
2. Assumed the Presidency upon Garfield's death.
3. Civil War veteran from Ohio; he was a "dark horse" candidate for President.
4. Elected to two nonconsecutive terms.
5. Practice of rewarding party loyalists with government jobs.
6. Farmers organized this political party that demanded sweeping reforms.
7. Talking endlessly to delay vote on Senate bill.
8. Made unsuccessful bids for the Presidency in 1896, 1900, and 1908.
9. The whole body of government employees holding regular jobs.
10. Many questioned the fairness of the vote count which put him into office.

1. ANS: E   DIF: Easy   REF: 476   OBJ: 18.0
2. ANS: J   DIF: Easy   REF: 462   OBJ: 18.0
   TOP: U.S. Presidents
3. ANS: I   DIF: Easy   REF: 461   OBJ: 18.0
   TOP: Presidential Elections
4. ANS: C   DIF: Easy   REF: 463–464   OBJ: 18.0
   TOP: U.S. Presidents
5. ANS: F   DIF: Easy   REF: 460   OBJ: 18.0
   TOP: Spoils System
6. ANS: B   DIF: Easy   REF: 471   OBJ: 18.0
   TOP: Political Parties
7. ANS: G   DIF: Easy   REF: 466   OBJ: 18.0
   TOP: Filibuster
8. ANS: D   DIF: Easy   REF: 476   OBJ: 18.0
   TOP: Presidential Elections
9. ANS: H   DIF: Easy   REF: 462   OBJ: 18.0
   TOP: U.S. Government / Civil Service
10. ANS: A   DIF: Easy   REF: 459   OBJ: 18.0
    TOP: Presidential Elections

MULTIPLE CHOICE

1. When inflation occurs, there is
   a. a rise in the supply of money.
   b. lifting of the general level of prices.
   c. dissatisfaction among debtors.
   d. a rise in the supply of money AND lifting of the general level of prices.

   ANS: D   DIF: Medium   REF: 459   OBJ: 18.1
   TOP: Economics

2. Roscoe Conkling was
   a. a New York State boss and senator.
   b. editor of "Harper's Weekly."
   c. an influential opponent of the spoils system.
   d. BOTH editor of "Harper's Weekly" AND an influential opponent of the spoils system.

   ANS: A   DIF: Medium   REF: 460   OBJ: 18.1
   TOP: Politicians

3. James A. Garfield was shot by
   a. Roscoe Conkling.   c. Chester Arthur.
   b. Charles Guiteau.   d. W. S. Hancock.

   ANS: B   DIF: Medium   REF: 462   OBJ: 18.1
   TOP: Garfield's Presidency

4. Senator Shelby M. Cullom of Illinois oversaw passage of
   a. the Interstate Commerce Act.   c. a bill that increased tariffs.
   b. a national veterans' pension plan. d. the Pendleton Act.

   ANS: A   DIF: Medium   REF: 464   OBJ: 18.2
   TOP: Railroads

5. A powerful leader in the House of Representatives, responsible for the passage of much important legislation during Harrison's term was
   a. Shelby M. Cullom.   c. Henry Cabot Lodge.
   b. Grover Cleveland.   d. John Sherman.

   ANS: C   DIF: Medium   REF: 466   OBJ: 18.2
   TOP: Harrison's Presidency

6. "Granges" were
   a. small farms.
   b. grain elevators.
   c. laws regulating railroad rates.
   d. local lodges of the Patrons of Husbandry.

   ANS: D   DIF: Medium   REF: 469   OBJ: 18.3
   TOP: Farming

7. A fiery orator who won many Kansas farmers over to the Populist cause was
   a. General James B. Weaver.   c. Mary Elizabeth Lease.
   b. Tom Watson.   d. Jacob Coxey.

   ANS: C   DIF: Medium   REF: 471   OBJ: 18.3
   TOP: Political Parties

8. An "army" of 500 workers was led on a march from Ohio to Washington by
   a. Jacob Coxey.   c. Tom Watson.
   b. James B. Weaver.   d. Jerry Simpson.

   ANS: A   DIF: Medium   REF: 474   OBJ: 18.3
   TOP: Labor Unions

9. William McKinley's campaign was managed by
   a. Mark Hanna.   c. Tom Watson.
   b. James B. Weaver.   d. Theodore Roosevelt.

   ANS: A   DIF: Medium   REF: 476   OBJ: 18.4
   TOP: Presidential Elections

10. The presidents who served between 1876 and 1892 could be characterized as
    a. bold.   c. elitists.
    b. timid.   d. radicals.

    ANS: B   DIF: Medium   OBJ: 18.1   TOP: U.S. Presidents

11. The administration of Rutherford B. Hayes was marked by
    a. depression.
    b. violence.
    c. controversy within the Republican party.
    d. all of the above

    ANS: D   DIF: Medium   REF: 459–460   OBJ: 18.1
    TOP: Hayes's Presidency

12. The period between 1865 and 1900 is sometimes called the Gilded Age because
    a. money was based on the gold standard.
    b. the great wealth of some people hid widespread corruption.
    c. buildings were often trimmed in gold.
    d. many people supported the unlimited coining of silver.

    ANS: B   DIF: Medium   REF: 458   OBJ: 18.1
    TOP: Gilded Age

13. Deflation in the Gilded Age was characterized by
    a. falling prices.
    b. increased purchasing power of the dollar.
    c. debts being more difficult to pay.
    d. all of the above

    ANS: D   DIF: Medium   REF: 459   OBJ: 18.1
    TOP: Gilded Age / Economics

14. The term "free silver" meant
    a. paper money free of any silver backing.
    b. unlimited coining of silver dollars.
    c. a changeover to all silver currency.
    d. an elimination of all silver currency.

    ANS: B   DIF: Medium   REF: 459   OBJ: 18.1
    TOP: Economics

15. President Hayes
    a. favored the spoils system.
    b. wanted to abolish the spoils system.
    c. wanted to avoid the issue of the spoils system.
    d. opposed a civil service system.

    ANS: B   DIF: Medium   REF: 460   OBJ: 18.1
    TOP: Hayes's Presidency

16. Half-breeds were Republicans who did NOT
    a. support business interests.
    b. want civil service reform.
    c. want a hands-off policy toward the South.
    d. support Roscoe Conkling for President.

    ANS: D   DIF: Medium   REF: 461   OBJ: 18.1
    TOP: Political Parties

17. "Solid South" refers to
    a. consistent Democratic voting in the Southeast for many years.
    b. consistent Republican voting in the Southeast for many years.
    c. unanimous opposition to protective tariffs in the southern states.
    d. the large number of presidential candidates who came from the southern states between 1865 and 1900.

    ANS: A   DIF: Medium   REF: 461   OBJ: 18.1
    TOP: Voting / Political Parties

18. The Pendleton Act
    a. established a nonpartisan Civil Service Commission.
    b. prohibited appointment to certain government jobs for political reasons.
    c. made it illegal to assess jobholders to support the party.
    d. all of the above

    ANS: D   DIF: Medium   REF: 462   OBJ: 18.1
    TOP: Government Jobs

19. The Populists' presidential candidate in 1892 was
    a. "Sockless Jerry" Simpson.   c. Albert Gorman.
    b. Tom Watson.   d. General James B. Weaver

    ANS: D   DIF: Medium   REF: 472   OBJ: 18.3
    TOP: Presidential Elections

20. In order to restore the nation's gold reserve, President Cleveland enlisted help from banker
    a. Ben Tillman.
    c. William Wilson.
    b. J. Pierpont Morgan.
    d. Andrew W. Mellon.

    ANS: B   DIF: Medium   REF: 474   OBJ: 18.3
    TOP: Cleveland's Presidency / Economics

21. The nicknames "Great Commoner" and "Prairie Avenger" were applied to
    a. Grover Cleveland.
    c. William Jennings Bryan.
    b. Ben Tillman.
    d. William McKinley.

    ANS: C   DIF: Medium   REF: 475   OBJ: 18.4
    TOP: Farming / Economics

22. The phrases "crown of thorns" and "cross of gold" were used by
    a. William McKinley.
    c. Grover Cleveland.
    b. Mark Hanna.
    d. William Jennings Bryan.

    ANS: D   DIF: Medium   REF: 476   OBJ: 18.4
    TOP: Farming / Economics

23. Both the Interstate Commerce Act and the Sherman Antitrust Act were
    a. eventually declared unconstitutional.
    b. early attempts by government to regulate big business.
    c. vigorously enforced by U.S. Presidents during the Gilded Age.
    d. supported by railroad owners.

    ANS: B   DIF: Medium   REF: 464, 467   OBJ: 18.2
    TOP: Government Regulation

24. In the first ten years of its existence, the Sherman Antitrust Act was
    a. used to break up the Standard Oil Company.
    b. successful in breaking up many trusts.
    c. used against organized labor.
    d. used to ban rebates by railroads.

    ANS: C   DIF: Medium   REF: 474   OBJ: 18.2
    TOP: Government Regulation

25. The major issue in the campaign of 1888 was
    a. the tariff.
    c. silver.
    b. the trusts.
    d. civil service.

    ANS: A   DIF: Medium   REF: 464–466   OBJ: 18.2
    TOP: Presidential Elections

26. Which of the following groups favored a high tariff?
    a. business leaders
    c. labor leaders
    b. farmers
    d. business leaders AND labor leaders

    ANS: D   DIF: Medium   REF: 464   OBJ: 18.2
    TOP: Tariffs

27. The decision in the case of "Munn v. Illinois"
    a. allowed a state to set maximum rates for grain storage.
    b. denied a state's right to set maximum rates for grain storage.
    c. allowed banks to foreclose farm mortgages.
    d. denied banks' rights to foreclose farm mortgages.

    ANS: A   DIF: Medium   REF: 470–471   OBJ: 18.3
    TOP: Farming

28. To block action on the tariff bill, southern Senators used the technique of
    a. mudslinging.   c. czar rule.
    b. waving the bloody shirt.   d. filibuster.

    ANS: D   DIF: Medium   REF: 466   OBJ: 18.2
    TOP: Tariffs

29. The Populists wanted
    a. free coinage of silver.
    b. an income tax.
    c. government control of railroads, telephone, and telegraph.
    d. all of the above

    ANS: D   DIF: Medium   REF: 471   OBJ: 18.3
    TOP: Political Parties

30. The organization called Patrons of Husbandry was an
    a. antitrust organization.   c. organization of farmers.
    b. anti-tariff organization.   d. organization of silver miners.

    ANS: C   DIF: Medium   REF: 469   OBJ: 18.3
    TOP: Farming

31. In 1894, a court injunction
    a. ordered Pullman strikers to go back to work.
    b. declared Coxey's march illegal.
    c. ordered the Pullman Company to dismiss its strikebreakers.
    d. ordered federal troops to work as strikebreakers.

    ANS: A   DIF: Medium   REF: 474   OBJ: 18.3
    TOP: Unions / Strikes

32. Which of the following quotations is INCORRECTLY paired with the person who said it?
    a. Charles Guiteau—"I am a Stalwart and Arthur is President now."
    b. James Blaine—"To the victors belong the spoils."
    c. Mary Lease—"Farmers should raise less corn and more hell."
    d. William Jennings Bryan—"You shall not crucify mankind upon a cross of gold."

    ANS: B   DIF: Medium   REF: 462, 471, 476
    OBJ: 18.4   TOP: Quotations

33. Which group most strongly supported free coinage of silver?
    a. factory workers   c. retired people
    b. farmers   d. Southern bankers

    ANS: B   DIF: Medium   REF: 459   OBJ: 18.4
    TOP: Farming / Economics

34. William Jennings Bryan believed that the nation's ills could be cured with
    a. the gold standard.   c. an income tax.
    b. free silver.   d. government ownership of farms.

    ANS: B   DIF: Medium   REF: 475–476   OBJ: 18.4
    TOP: Economics

35. The fatal weakness of William Jennings Bryan was his failure to
    a. appeal to city people.
    b. appeal to factory workers.
    c. communicate his ideas.
    d. appeal to city people and factory workers.

    ANS: D   DIF: Medium   REF: 476   OBJ: 18.4
    TOP: Economics

36. In which of the following ways did the spoils system work against good government? I. There
    was frequent turnover in government jobs. II. There was never "new blood" in government
    because jobs were held for life. III. Many unqualified people held government jobs. IV. Many
    government workers were more loyal to party interests than to what was good for the people.
    a. I and III   c. I, II, and III
    b. I and IV   d. I, III, and IV

    ANS: D   DIF: Medium   REF: 460   OBJ: 18.1
    TOP: U.S. Government

37. "The lessons of paternalism ought to be unlearned and the better lesson taught that while the
    people should patriotically and cheerfully support their government, its functions do not include
    the support of the people." This quotation shows that Grover Cleveland would probably best be
    labeled a political
    a. conservative.   c. reactionary.
    b. liberal.   d. novice.

    ANS: A   DIF: Medium   REF: 463   OBJ: 18.2
    TOP: Cleveland's Presidency

38. "Every contract, combination . . . , or conspiracy in restraint of trade or commerce among the
    several States, or with foreign nations, is hereby declared to be illegal." This sentence most
    likely appeared in the
    a. Pendleton Act.
    b. Interstate Commerce Act.
    c. "Pollock v. Farmers' Loan and Trust Company" decision.
    d. Sherman Antitrust Act.

    ANS: D   DIF: Medium   REF: 467   OBJ: 18.2
    TOP: U.S. Trade

39. Farmers' Alliances were formed as a result of which of the following? I. a decrease in rural population II. falling prices for farm goods III. a period of prosperity for farmers IV. rising costs for transportation and storage of grain
    a. I and II
    b. I and III
    c. II and III
    d. II and IV

    ANS: D   DIF: Medium   REF: 470–471   OBJ: 18.2
    TOP: Farming

40. It is an OPINION rather than a fact that
    a. McKinley ran a "front porch" campaign for President in 1896.
    b. the change of only 19,000 votes would have given Bryan an electoral college majority in 1896.
    c. Bryan could have won the election of 1896 by broadening his appeal beyond the free silver issue.
    d. Mark Hanna tried to convince voters that Bryan was a dangerous radical.

    ANS: C   DIF: Medium   REF: 476   OBJ: 18.4
    TOP: Presidential Elections

ESSAY

1. Which is NOT a weakness of the following piece of evidence? Write your answer on a separate sheet of paper and support your answer with a paragraph explaining why you chose it. Representative William McKinley said that the bill he sponsored was "protective in every paragraph and American in every line and word."
   A. It is not primary.
   B. McKinley is making himself look good—he has a reason to distort.
   C. There is no other evidence supporting it here.
   D. All are weaknesses of this evidence.

   ANS:
   answer A
   Students' paragraphs should support their answer.

   DIF: Hard   OBJ: 18.0

2. Present three specific examples to contribute to an argument supporting the following claim: The glitter of the Gilded Age, between 1865 and 1900, covered a "multitude of sins."

   ANS:
   Student answers will vary but could include these ideas: Labor strife developed into the railway strike of 1877, the Homestead Strike of 1892, the miner's strike in Idaho, and the Pullman Strike of 1894. Deflation led to falling prices, especially farm prices, which made it difficult for farmers to repay loans or to pay high western-railroad shipping rates. The "spoils system" (also known as patronage hiring) was a challenge to good government. Coxey's Army demonstrated against the plight of the poor in 1894. Unfair transportation rates led to the Interstate Commerce Act of 1887, and monopolies such as the Standard Oil, E.C. Knight, and American Tobacco companies led to the Sherman Anti-Trust Act of 1890.

   DIF: Hard   REF: 458–475   OBJ: 18.0   TOP: Gilded Age

3. What effect does a balance in Congress between the two national political parties have on the federal government?

ANS:
Answers will vary but could include the following ideas: Party balance makes Presidents fearful of taking strong initiatives. They try to "play it safe" and not lose current support by offending members of Congress. In times of national crisis, party balance may well lead to a rebellion within a party or to formation of a third party in order to voice concerns that timid Presidents and politicians are avoiding.

DIF: Hard   REF: 459   OBJ: 18.1
TOP: Politics / Political Parties

4. Why were there so many one-term presidencies during the Gilded Age?

ANS:
Answers will vary but could include the following ideas: With the exception of Grover Cleveland (the only two-term President during the Gilded Age), the men who won the office were neither personally engaging nor leaders with a distinctive political ideology. As a result, they never developed a large popular following that would have put them into office for a second term.

DIF: Hard   OBJ: 18.1   TOP: Presidential Elections / Gilded Age

5. "The glitter of the Gilded Age covered a multitude of sins." Give three examples that support this statement.

ANS:
Answers will vary but could include the following ideas: Until the passage of the Pendleton Act, unqualified party hacks continued to fill government jobs. Monopolies thrived despite passage of the Sherman Antitrust Act. Farmers and workers suffered economic decline in an age of supposed prosperity.

DIF: Hard   REF: 458–475   OBJ: 18.1   TOP: Gilded Age

6. How were the presidential elections of 1884 and 1888 similar and how were they different?

ANS:
Answers will vary but could include the following ideas: Similarities—Cleveland was the Democratic candidate for President in both; Cleveland won the popular vote in both; New York was the decisive state in both; the tariff was the main issue of party disagreement. Differences—An incumbent ran in 1888 but not in 1884; Republicans bought votes in 1888; New York went Democratic in 1884 and Republican in 1888; Democrat Cleveland won in 1884 while Republican Harrison won in 1888.

DIF: Hard   REF: 463–468   OBJ: 18.2   TOP: Presidential Elections

7. Explain the Supreme Court's thinking in ruling against the Sherman Antitrust Act in "United States v. E. C. Knight Company."

ANS:
Answers will vary but could include the following ideas: The Supreme Court said that manufacturing (that occurred within a state's boundaries) could not be regulated by Congressional control over interstate commerce. By drawing a sharp distinction between manufacturing and commerce—"Commerce succeeds to manufacture and is not a part of it"—the court in an 8-1 decision allowed most monopolies to escape the regulations of the Sherman Antitrust Act. A manufacturing monopoly was thus beyond the control of the federal government.

DIF: Hard   REF: 467   OBJ: 18.2   TOP: Supreme Court

8. Who were the Populists, and what did they want?

ANS:
Answers will vary but could include the following ideas: The Populists created a political party in the late 1800s and early 1890s to protest what seemed to them the exploitation of the poor by the rich. To some extent, the party involved labor organizations, but its strength lay with the farmers who belonged to agrarian associations in the West and South. According to the party's platform in 1892, the Populists wanted free and unlimited coinage of silver, government ownership of transportation and communication lines, a graduated income tax, direct election of U.S. Senators, adoption of the secret ballot, restrictions on ownership of land to American citizens, restrictions on immigration, a shorter working day for industrial laborers, and other reforms.

DIF: Hard   REF: 471–472   OBJ: 18.3   TOP: Political Parties

9. What were the arguments of the proponents of the free coinage of silver, and how did they present their arguments?

ANS:
Answers will vary but could include the following ideas: In a period of declining prices for farm products, free coinage of silver seemed to hold the prospect of raising prices generally (inflation) and making debts easier to pay. Another group of proponents of the free coinage of silver—western silver miners—were not so much interested in an inflated currency as they were in driving up the price of silver by creating a huge government demand for their metal. The agricultural proponents presented their arguments—most vividly in Bryan's "Cross of Gold" speech—as a moral crusade to save the American family farm, which they saw as the centerpiece of American civilization.

DIF: Hard   REF: 459–460, 467, 475–476   OBJ: 18.4
TOP: Farming / Economics

10. If the Populists had been successful on the free silver issue, would the result likely have been prosperity for America's farmers? Explain why or why not.

ANS:
Answers will vary but could include the following ideas: The problems plaguing the American farmer in the decades following the Civil War were far more complicated than the farmers thought. Their belief that an inflated currency would bring prosperity was overly optimistic. A solution to overproduction, international competition, and other aspects of the agricultural problem did not rest in free and unlimited coining of silver.

DIF: Hard   REF: 459–460, 467, 475–476   OBJ: 18.4
TOP: Farming / Economics

(page intentionally left blank)

MATCHING

Match each item with the correct statement below.

a. Walter Reed
b. Open Door
c. jingoes
d. Alfred Thayer Mahan
e. William Seward

f. anti-imperialists
g. arbitration
h. Dupuy DeLome
i. Matthew Perry
j. neutrality

1. He helped prove that yellow fever was transmitted by mosquitoes.
2. A naval officer and scholar, he convinced many of the need for a powerful navy.
3. He was the American naval commander who opened up Japan for trade.
4. Not taking sides in a dispute.
5. The idea that all countries were to have equal trading opportunities in China.
6. Having a third party make a decision in a dispute.
7. As Secretary of State, he negotiated the purchase of Alaska from Russia
8. He was the Spanish ambassador to the United States who criticized President McKinley.
9. Don't mind fighting a war to advance their nation's interests.
10. Those who opposed the United States becoming an empire.

1. ANS: A   DIF: Easy   REF: 516   OBJ: 19.0
   TOP: Cuba
2. ANS: D   DIF: Easy   REF: 508   OBJ: 19.0
   TOP: U.S. / Foreign Trade
3. ANS: I   DIF: Easy   REF: 505   OBJ: 19.0
   TOP: U.S. / Japanese Relations
4. ANS: J   DIF: Easy   OBJ: 19.0   TOP: Neutrality
5. ANS: B   DIF: Easy   REF: 517–518   OBJ: 19.0
   TOP: U.S. / Foreign Trade
6. ANS: G   DIF: Easy   REF: 507   OBJ: 19.0
   TOP: Arbitration
7. ANS: E   DIF: Easy   REF: 506   OBJ: 19.0
   TOP: U.S. Expansion / Alaska
8. ANS: H   DIF: Easy   REF: 512   OBJ: 19.0
   TOP: U.S. / Spanish Relations
9. ANS: C   DIF: Easy   REF: 513   OBJ: 19.0
10. ANS: F   DIF: Easy   REF: 514   OBJ: 19.0

MULTIPLE CHOICE

1. Which of the following individuals did President Tyler send to China to secure special privileges?
   a. Matthew C. Perry
   b. William Seward
   c. Caleb Cushing
   d. Charles Sumner

   ANS: C   DIF: Medium   REF: 505   OBJ: 19.1
   TOP: U.S. / Chinese Relations

2. The firm, skillful, adventurous naval officer who secured the opening of two Japanese ports to American ships was
   a. Matthew C. Perry.
   b. William Seward.
   c. Caleb Cushing.
   d. Charles Sumner.

   ANS: A   DIF: Medium   REF: 505   OBJ: 19.1
   TOP: U.S. Foreign Relations

3. The Senate was persuaded by the eloquent _____ to approve the Alaska treaty.
   a. William Seward
   b. Charles Sumner
   c. James G. Blaine
   d. Charles Francis Adams

   ANS: B   DIF: Medium   REF: 506   OBJ: 19.1
   TOP: U.S. Expansion / Alaska

4. The purchase of Alaska was sometimes called
   a. "Seward's Stupidity."
   b. "Seward's Folly."
   c. "Seward's Icebox."
   d. "Seward's Folly" and "Seward's Icebox."

   ANS: D   DIF: Medium   REF: 506   OBJ: 19.1
   TOP: U.S. Expansion / Alaska

5. The author of "The Influence of Sea Power upon History" was
   a. Alfred Thayer Mahan.
   b. Henry Cabot Lodge.
   c. Theodore Roosevelt.
   d. Albert J. Beveridge.

   ANS: A   DIF: Medium   REF: 508–509   OBJ: 19.2
   TOP: U.S. / Foreign Trade

6. President Cleveland's Secretary of State, who felt that the United States had the right to intervene in Latin America, was
   a. Richard Olney.
   b. Theodore Roosevelt.
   c. Albert J. Beveridge.
   d. Alfred Thayer Mahan.

   ANS: A   DIF: Medium   REF: 510   OBJ: 19.2
   TOP: U.S. / Latin American Relations

7. The "Yellow Kid" cartoon series was created by
   a. William Randolph Hearst.
   b. Richard F. Outcault.
   c. Joseph Pulitzer.
   d. Valeriano Weyler.

   ANS: B   DIF: Medium   REF: 512   OBJ: 19.3
   TOP: U.S. / Cuban Relations

8. Passed in 1898 and pledging that the United States would not exercise sovereignty in Cuba, but largely ignored until 1903, was the
   a. Platt Amendment.
   b. Teller Amendment.
   c. Santiago Treaty.
   d. Havana Treaty.

   ANS: B   DIF: Medium   REF: 516–517   OBJ: 19.3
   TOP: U.S. / Cuban Relations

9. The amendment that became a "permanent treaty with Cuba" in 1903 was the
    a. Foraker Amendment.
    b. Pacification Amendment.
    c. Teller Amendment.
    d. Platt Amendment.

    ANS: D   DIF: Medium   REF: 517   OBJ: 19.3
    TOP: U.S. / Cuban Relations

10. A rebellion in China against foreign intervention was called the
    a. Boer Rebellion.
    b. Yellow Rebellion.
    c. Open Door Rebellion.
    d. Boxer Rebellion.

    ANS: D   DIF: Medium   REF: 518   OBJ: 19.3
    TOP: U.S. / Chinese Relations

11. Early efforts by the United States to annex Hawaii and to buy Cuba, Alaska, and Lower California were bedeviled by the issue of
    a. national debt.
    b. Constitutional prohibitions.
    c. slavery.
    d. xenophobia.

    ANS: C   DIF: Medium   REF: 505   OBJ: 19.1
    TOP: U.S. Expansion

12. One of the major reasons the United States purchased Alaska was to
    a. search for gold.
    b. drill for oil.
    c. force Britain out of Canada.
    d. establish military bases.

    ANS: C   DIF: Medium   REF: 506   OBJ: 19.1
    TOP: U.S. Expansion

13. The Treaty of Kanagawa opened trade between the United States and
    a. China.
    b. Japan.
    c. Siam.
    d. the Philippines.

    ANS: B   DIF: Medium   REF: 505   OBJ: 19.1
    TOP: U.S. / Foreign Trade

14. The United States entered a joint protectorate with Germany over
    a. Alaska.
    b. Mexico.
    c. Chile.
    d. Samoa.

    ANS: D   DIF: Medium   REF: 508   OBJ: 19.1
    TOP: U.S. / German Relations

15. American sailors were interested in the strategically located South Pacific harbor of
    a. Pago Pago.
    b. Valparaiso.
    c. Tutuila.
    d. Canton.

    ANS: A   DIF: Medium   REF: 508   OBJ: 19.1
    TOP: U.S. / South Pacific

16. Alfred T. Mahan, in explaining what was necessary to keep the United States strong in the modern world, put forward the idea that
    a. the United States must sell its products on all continents.
    b. the nation needed a powerful navy.
    c. the United States should build a canal across the Isthmus of Panama.
    d. all of the above

    ANS: D   DIF: Medium   REF: 508–509   OBJ: 19.2
    TOP: U.S. Foreign Policy

17. All of the following individuals were in favor of American expansion EXCEPT
    a. Henry Cabot Lodge.   c. Albert J. Beveridge.
    b. Theodore Roosevelt.   d. Grover Cleveland.

    ANS: D   DIF: Medium   REF: 509   OBJ: 19.2
    TOP: U.S. Expansion

18. In 1893, American settlers, assisted by marines from the cruiser "Boston", overthrew the
    a. leader of Venezuela.   c. queen of Hawaii.
    b. emperor of Mexico.   d. Spanish government in Cuba.

    ANS: C   DIF: Medium   REF: 509   OBJ: 19.2
    TOP: U.S. Expansion / Hawaii

19. Which Latin American nation requested United States intervention in the late 1800s?
    a. Chile   c. Colombia
    b. Venezuela   d. Panama

    ANS: B   DIF: Medium   REF: 510   OBJ: 19.2
    TOP: U.S. / Latin America

20. The Venezuelan boundary dispute was settled by
    a. the Spanish-American War.
    b. an arbitration tribunal in Santiago.
    c. an arbitration tribunal in Paris.
    d. a treaty between the United States and Venezuela.

    ANS: C   DIF: Medium   REF: 510   OBJ: 19.2
    TOP: U.S. / Latin America

21. Americans favored overseas expansion in the late 1800s for all of the following reasons EXCEPT
    a. spreading Christianity and democracy.
    b. acquiring bases for U.S. security.
    c. acquiring new markets for trade.
    d. halting the spread of communism.

    ANS: D   DIF: Medium   OBJ: 19.2   TOP: U.S. Expansion

© Prentice-Hall, Inc.

22. The U.S. battleship "Maine"
    a. was shattered by an explosion while in Havana Harbor.
    b. led the attack on Spanish warships in the Philippines.
    c. led the attack on Spanish warships near Santiago, Cuba.
    d. was the flagship when the U.S. fleet sailed around the world.

    ANS: A   DIF: Medium   REF: 512   OBJ: 19.3
    TOP: Spanish-American War

23. Most of the credit for the American victory in the Spanish-American War was earned by
    a. the Army.   c. the Rough Riders.
    b. the Navy.   d. the Navy and the Rough Riders.

    ANS: D   DIF: Medium   REF: 513   OBJ: 19.3
    TOP: Spanish-American War

24. Compared to the Civil War and the American Revolution, the Spanish-American War was
    a. much longer.
    b. much costlier in terms of U.S. casualties.
    c. much less costly in terms of U.S. casualties.
    d. less significant in terms of the relationship of the United States to the world.

    ANS: C   DIF: Medium   REF: 513   OBJ: 19.3
    TOP: Spanish-American War

25. All of the following developments led to war with Spain in 1898 EXCEPT
    a. the sinking of the MAINE.
    b. the Yellow Press.
    c. the DeLome letter.
    d. Spanish interference with American trade.

    ANS: D   DIF: Medium   REF: 512   OBJ: 19.3
    TOP: Spanish-American War

26. Both the Platt and Teller amendments
    a. gave Cubans the right to establish their own constitution.
    b. called for Spanish evacuation of Cuba.
    c. forbade United States military intervention in Cuba.
    d. required that Cuba reimburse U.S. businessmen for damage done to their sugar
       plantations.

    ANS: A   DIF: Medium   REF: 516–517   OBJ: 19.3
    TOP: U.S. / Cuban Relations

27. Which of the following is true of U.S. foreign relations from 1865 to 1900?
    a. The United States tried to eliminate European influence in the Americas.
    b. The United States abandoned the Monroe Doctrine.
    c. U.S. interest in Latin America was limited to trade.
    d. The United States helped several countries in Latin America and Asia to win full
       independence.

    ANS: A   DIF: Medium   OBJ: 19.3   TOP: U.S. Foreign Relations

28. Puerto Rico
    a. willingly came under U.S. rule.
    b. benefited from roads and schools built by the United States.
    c. once had government established by the Foraker Act of 1900.
    d. willingly came under U.S. rule AND benefited from roads and schools built by the United States.

    ANS: D   DIF: Medium   REF: 515–516   OBJ: 19.3
    TOP: U.S. / Puerto Rico

29. After the Boxer Rebellion, the Chinese
    a. cut off relations with the United States.
    b. believed that relations with the United States were strained.
    c. were friendly to and impressed by the United States.
    d. were cautious in dealing with the United States.

    ANS: C   DIF: Medium   REF: 518   OBJ: 19.3
    TOP: U.S. / Chinese Relations

30. In its race for empire, the United States had, by 1900,
    a. acquired colonial outposts.
    b. committed itself to preserving Chinese independence and territorial integrity.
    c. become one of the world's great powers.
    d. all of the above

    ANS: D   DIF: Medium   OBJ: 19.3   TOP: U.S. Expansion

31. The United States applied the Monroe Doctrine in all of the following situations EXCEPT
    a. opening Japanese ports to U.S. ships.
    b. settling the Venezuelan boundary dispute.
    c. passing the Platt Amendment.
    d. urging the removal of French troops from Mexico.

    ANS: A   DIF: Medium   OBJ: 19.1   TOP: U.S. Foreign Policy

32. The settlement of the "Alabama" claims is important as an example of
    a. the power of the "Yellow Press."
    b. early U.S. involvement in Asia.
    c. a "splendid little war."
    d. the peaceful settlement of an international dispute.

    ANS: D   DIF: Medium   REF: 507   OBJ: 19.1
    TOP: U.S. British Relations

33. "Whether they will or not, Americans must now begin to look outward. The growing production of the country demands it." The main idea of this statement by Alfred T. Mahan is probably that
    a. the United States must look abroad to find new markets for its products.
    b. the United States should always avoid entangling alliances.
    c. the United States must look abroad to find new suppliers of manufactured goods.
    d. Americans are too eager to give up isolationism and expand abroad.

    ANS: A   DIF: Medium   REF: 508   OBJ: 19.2
    TOP: U.S. Foreign Policy

34. "That the United States hereby disclaims any disposition or intention to exercise sovereignty, jurisdiction, or control over said Island except for the pacification thereof, and asserts its determination, when that is accomplished, to leave the government in control of the Island to its people." This quotation probably was a part of the

a. Monroe Doctrine.
b. Foraker Act.
c. Teller Amendment.
d. Platt Amendment.

ANS: C   DIF: Medium   REF: 516   OBJ: 19.3
TOP: U.S. / Cuban Relations

35. It is a FACT rather than an opinion that

a. the rebellions in the Philippines and China were patriotic uprisings like the American Revolution.
b. it was inevitable that the United States would join the race for empire in the 1800s.
c. the United States acquired new territory after the Spanish-American War.
d. American expansion in the late 1800s violated the principles of the Declaration of Independence and the Constitution.

ANS: C   DIF: Medium   REF: 513–514   OBJ: 19.3
TOP: Spanish-American War

ESSAY

1. Which of the following is an example of proof by evidence? Write your answer on a separate sheet of paper and support your answer with a paragraph explaining why you chose it.

A. The Venezuelan boundary dispute was settled peacefully.
B. Senator Beveridge believed that America would profit by expanding overseas. He said, "The trade of the world must and shall be ours."
C. The battleship "Maine" was sent to Havana harbor to protect American lives.
D. The U.S. Army was unprepared for the Spanish-American War. It was undersupplied and disorganized.

ANS:
answer B Students' paragraphs should support their answers.

DIF: Hard   REF: 509   OBJ: 19.0   TOP: U.S. Trade Overseas

2. Briefly explain how American foreign policy changed between 1860 and 1900. Then identify the point of view and chief role of three of the following individuals in regard to those changes. William H. Seward, Alfred Thayer Mahan, Joseph Pulitzer, William Jennings Bryan, John Hay

ANS:
Student answers will vary but could include these ideas: United States foreign policy changed from near isolationism to direct interventionism during the years from 1860 to 1900. Much of the impetus for contact with other countries was commercial, some was military (security), some was national pride, and some may have been political maneuvering (as in the Declaration of War with Spain). Seward was one of the first of U.S. expansionists. He bought Alaska. Mahan was a proponent of big powerism for the U.S. His book, The Influence of Sea Power on History (1890), made a great impact. Pulitzer was a "war hawk" who drummed up support for war against Spain through his newspapers. Bryan was an Anti-Imperialist who wanted the U.S. to leave foreign nations to their own devices. John Hay desired equal commercial treatment for the U.S. in foreign markets, espousing the Open Door policy.

DIF: Hard   OBJ: 19.0   TOP: U.S. Foreign Policy

3. What reasons were the United States likely to have had for wanting to expand trade with China and Japan before 1850?

ANS:
Answers will vary but could include the following ideas: Although Japan vigorously resisted trade with the United States prior to 1854, Americans had been trading with China from the time of the American Revolution. The voyage from the United States to China was long and hazardous, but the potential for profit was enormous. American ships brought U.S. products such as animal pelts and farm machinery to trade for silk, tea, spices, and other Chinese products. By 1820, the China trade was worth $20 million per year. By 1850, Americans were very eager to open other Chinese ports besides Canton and to have an opportunity to trade with Japan.

DIF: Hard   OBJ: 19.1   TOP: U.S. Trade - Japan & China

4. What possible precedent might the United States and Britain have cited when they decided to peacefully negotiate their differences over the "Alabama" claims?

ANS:
Answers will vary but could include the following ideas: The British and the Americans might have cited Jay's Treaty of 1794 as a precedent for the peaceful negotiation of differences when both countries were on the verge of war. The United States was angry over continued British presence in the Old Northwest and over interference with U.S. shipping including the impressment of U.S. sailors. Although Jay's Treaty did not deal with impression, and Britain continued to violate U.S. shipping rights, war fever cooled in both countries. The "Alabama" claims used this precedent as a foundation for peaceful resolution of differences between Britain and the United States.

DIF: Hard   OBJ: 19.1   TOP: U.S. / British Relations

5. Compare and contrast the ways in which the United States acquired what would later become the 49th and 50th states, Alaska and Hawaii.

ANS:
Answers could include the following: The U.S. acquisitions of Alaska and Hawaii were difficult and involved actions that were not in keeping with a high standard of rectitude. Alaska was acquired as a purchase from Russia for $7.2 million. There was, however, opposition to "Seward's Folly,"and the Russian minister to the United States had to bribe members of Congress in order to secure approval. Attempts to annex Hawaii began in 1854. There were a great many Americans on the Hawaiian islands, but annexation was made impossible by the sectional conflict in the United States. When Queen "Lil" tried to retake control from the American residents in the 1890s ("Hawaii for the Hawaiians" was her motto), she was overthrown by pro-annexation forces. Although Grover Cleveland rejected annexation on the basis of the unjust deposition of the queen, Hawaii was annexed in the pro-expansion fervor of the Spanish-American War.

DIF: Hard   REF: 506, 509–510   OBJ: 19.2
TOP: U.S. History - Alaska & Hawaii

6. Would Alfred T. Mahan have been likely to have been a supporter of the United Nations? Explain why or why not.

ANS:
Answers will vary but could include the following ideas: Alfred T. Mahan would not have been likely to be a supporter of the United Nations. Mahan, along with his contemporaries Henry Cabot Lodge and Theodore Roosevelt, was not a believer in international cooperation. Instead, he believed that nations should and do pursue their own national interests, that the United States' national interest lay in expansion, and that war was an instrument that the United States should use to advance its national interest.

DIF: Hard   REF: 508–509   OBJ: 19.2   TOP: U.S. / Foreign Policy

7. In what ways did the belief that sea power determined a nation's military strength influence American foreign policy?

ANS:
Answers will vary but could include the following ideas: Believers in the notion that sea power determined a nation's military strength could argue that a powerful navy made a nation great in both peace and war. In times of peace, the navy would protect foreign markets, and foreign markets were considered necessary to support the industrial production of a great nation. In terms of foreign policy during peacetime and wartime, the protection of markets by sea demanded refueling ports under American control all over the globe. In times of war, the navy would provide the first line of defense to America's enormous coastlines along the Atlantic, Pacific, and Caribbean coasts. Again, in terms of foreign policy, these coastal areas would have to be kept free from hostile governments or governments that, through their own lack of stability, might invite the intervention of foreign powers.

DIF: Hard   REF: 508–509   OBJ: 19.2
TOP: U.S. Foreign Policy / Naval

8. Discuss U.S. entry into the War of 1812 and into the Spanish-American War in terms of the influences of War Hawks and of the jingoes, respectively.

ANS:
Answers will vary but could include the following ideas: There was substantial opposition in the United States both to the War of 1812 and to the Spanish-American War. In both cases, the anti-war position was overcome by pro-expansionist sentiment. The War Hawks were mostly southern and western members of the House of Representatives who wanted to annex Canada. The jingoes included the Yellow Press as well as members of the government who wanted to annex Cuba and assert U.S. might in world affairs.

DIF: Hard   OBJ: 19.3   TOP: War of 1812 / Spanish-American War

9. Compare and contrast the Teller and the Platt Amendments.

ANS:
Answers will vary but could include the following ideas: Both the Teller and Platt amendments dealt with U.S. relations with Cuba. The Teller Amendment, attached to the declaration of war against Spain, said that the United States had no interest in taking over or controlling Cuba and would leave the island in control of its people when the war was over. The Platt Amendment rejected this hands-off policy, asserting that the United States would oversee and approve all Cuban treaties with foreign powers and would intervene if necessary to protect Cuban independence. In effect, the Platt Amendment made Cuba a U.S. protectorate.

DIF: Hard   OBJ: 19.3   TOP: U.S. / Cuban Relations

10. Identify the point of view and chief role of each of the three following individuals with regard to changes in American foreign policy between 1860 and 1900: William H. Seward, Alfred Thayer Mahan, Joseph Pulitzer, William Jennings Bryan, and John Hay.

ANS:
Answers could include the following: Seward was a strong supporter of U.S. expansion. He engineered the purchase of Alaska in the hope that U.S. possession of that territory would force the British out of Canada. Mahan argued in an influential book on naval power that the United States must find new markets overseas and that it must have a powerful navy to protect foreign markets. Joseph Pulitzer, through his newspaper, the "New York World," clamored for U.S. intervention in Cuba; the newspaper's sensationalist stories helped stir up jingoistic feelings on the eve of the Spanish-American War. William Jennings Bryan opposed U.S. imperialism, believing that the acquisition of new territory by force was at odds with the nation's ideals. John Hay, Secretary of State under McKinley, wanted to expand U.S. trade with China and insisted upon an "Open Door" policy that granted every nation equal commercial treatment in China.

DIF: Hard   REF: 506–509, 511–512, 515–518   OBJ: 19.3
TOP: U.S. / Foreign Policy

MATCHING

Match each item with the correct statement below.

a.	socialism	f.	Upton Sinclair
b.	William McKinley	g.	William H. Taft
c.	capitalism	h.	William Gorgas
d.	Pancho Villa	i.	Theodore Roosevelt
e.	Woodrow Wilson	j.	nonpartisan

1. Public ownership of the means of production and distribution.
2. Assassinated by Leon Czolgosz in 1898.
3. Mexican bandit who raided and killed American citizens.
4. Offered America a "Square Deal."
5. Reestablished the practice of delivering annual messages to Congress in person.
6. Private ownership of the means of production and distribution.
7. Exposed unsanitary conditions in the meatpacking industry in "The Jungle."
8. Only American to serve as President and as Chief Justice.
9. Fought yellow fever by destroying mosquito-breeding places in Panama.
10. Not favoring any political party.

1. ANS: A   DIF: Easy   REF: 526   OBJ: 20.0
   TOP: Socialism
2. ANS: B   DIF: Easy   REF: 521   OBJ: 20.0
   TOP: McKinley's Presidency
3. ANS: D   DIF: Easy   REF: 544   OBJ: 20.0
   TOP: Mexican History
4. ANS: I   DIF: Easy   REF: 521   OBJ: 20.0
   TOP: T. Roosevelt's Domestic Programs
5. ANS: E   DIF: Easy   REF: 537   OBJ: 20.0
   TOP: Wilson's Presidency
6. ANS: C   DIF: Easy   REF: 526   OBJ: 20.0
   TOP: Capitalism
7. ANS: F   DIF: Easy   REF: 524   OBJ: 20.0
   TOP: T. Roosevelt's Reform Programs
8. ANS: G   DIF: Easy   REF: 536   OBJ: 20.0
   TOP: William Taft
9. ANS: H   DIF: Easy   REF: 541–542   OBJ: 20.0
   TOP: Panama
10. ANS: J   DIF: Easy   REF: 527   OBJ: 20.0
    TOP: Nonpartisan

MULTIPLE CHOICE

1. The energetic president of the United Mine Workers was was
   a. Leon Czolgosz.
   b. John Mitchell.
   c. George F. Baer.
   d. John L. Lewis.

   ANS: B   DIF: Medium   REF: 522   OBJ: 20.1
   TOP: Coal Mining

2. After his election in 1904, Roosevelt made one of his first goals the strengthening of the
   a. Northern Securities Company.
   b. Interstate Commerce Commission.
   c. U.S. Army.
   d. Public Land Office.

   ANS: B   DIF: Medium   REF: 524   OBJ: 20.1
   TOP: T. Roosevelt's Domestic Programs

3. The Hepburn Act was a major step toward regulating business in that it
   a. gave the ICC power over pipelines, ferries, terminals, and bridges.
   b. forbade railroad rebates and free passes.
   c. allowed the ICC to lower rates if shippers complained.
   d. all of the above

   ANS: D   DIF: Medium   REF: 524   OBJ: 20.1
   TOP: T. Roosevelt's Reform Programs

4. The 1902 act that furthered Theodore Roosevelt's conservation program was the
   a. Hepburn Act.
   b. Newlands Reclamation Act.
   c. Forest Homestead Act.
   d. National Conservation Act.

   ANS: B   DIF: Medium   REF: 524–525   OBJ: 20.1
   TOP: T. Roosevelt's Reform Programs

5. Roosevelt's nickname for reform journalists and novelists was
   a. "progressives."
   b. "muckrakers."
   c. "mudslingers."
   d. "agitators."

   ANS: B   DIF: Medium   REF: 529   OBJ: 20.2
   TOP: T. Roosevelt

6. The Danish immigrant photographer who published shocking pictures of starving children in American slums was
   a. George Luks.
   b. Jacob Riis.
   c. Gustavus Myers.
   d. John Spargo.

   ANS: B   DIF: Medium   REF: 531   OBJ: 20.2
   TOP: Photographers

7. The Progressives who struck out on their own, thinking Taft was a "tool of the interests," were called
   a. "insurgents."
   b. "muckrakers."
   c. "nationalists."
   d. "revolutionaries."

   ANS: A   DIF: Medium   REF: 533   OBJ: 20.3
   TOP: Progressive Movement

8. The Underwood-Simmons bill reformed
   a. the income tax.
   b. the tariff.
   c. election procedures.
   d. banking procedures.

   ANS: B   DIF: Medium   REF: 538   OBJ: 20.4
   TOP: Wilson's Reform Policies

9. The Clayton Antitrust Act of 1914 prevented
   a. interlocking directorates.
   b. runs on banks.
   c. stock speculation.
   d. unfair shipping rates.

   ANS: A   DIF: Medium   REF: 539   OBJ: 20.4
   TOP: Wilson's Reform Policies

10. The revolutionary general who seized ruling power in Mexico was
    a. Pancho Villa.
    b. Emiliano Zapata.
    c. Victoriano Huerta.
    d. Francisco Madero.

    ANS: C   DIF: Medium   REF: 543   OBJ: 20.5
    TOP: Mexican History

11. It was Teddy Roosevelt's feeling that
    a. all trusts should be broken up.
    b. good trusts should be regulated, not broken up.
    c. bad trusts should be broken up.
    d. good trusts should be regulated, not broken up AND bad trusts should be broken up.

    ANS: D   DIF: Medium   REF: 524   OBJ: 20.1
    TOP: T. Roosevelt's Presidency

12. In his enforcement of the Sherman Antitrust Act, Theodore Roosevelt
    a. believed that trusts were inherently evil and should be destroyed.
    b. felt that the courts should distinguish between good and bad trusts.
    c. managed to eliminate virtually all major trusts.
    d. felt that the courts should distinguish between good and bad trusts AND managed to eliminate virtually all major trusts.

    ANS: B   DIF: Medium   REF: 523–524   OBJ: 20.1
    TOP: T. Roosevelt's Presidency

13. All of the following were accomplished during Theodore Roosevelt's administrations EXCEPT
    a. the breaking up of the Northern Securities Company.
    b. the completion of the Panama Canal.
    c. the passage of the Pure Food and Drug Act.
    d. the passage of the Newlands Reclamation Act.

    ANS: B   DIF: Medium   REF: 523–525   OBJ: 20.1
    TOP: T. Roosevelt's Presidency

14. Theodore Roosevelt experienced success in all of the following during his administration EXCEPT
    a. breaking up trusts.   c. conserving public lands.
    b. settling labor disputes.   d. establishing a federal reserve system.

    ANS: D   DIF: Medium   REF: 522–525   OBJ: 20.1
    TOP: T. Roosevelt's Presidency

15. The Seventeenth Amendment allowed
    a. women to vote.   c. an income tax.
    b. direct election of senators.   d. recall, initiative, and referendum.

    ANS: B   DIF: Medium   REF: 529   OBJ: 20.2
    TOP: Constitution

16. Most reformers of the early 20th century
    a. wanted less government interference in business affairs.
    b. had little regard for the plight of the poor.
    c. were first-generation immigrants with little money.
    d. were professionals from old American families.

    ANS: D   DIF: Medium   REF: 527   OBJ: 20.2
    TOP: Reformers

17. Theodore Roosevelt's reform program was based on
    a. a strong national government that would regulate business.
    b. breaking up trusts.
    c. restoration of individualism.
    d. breaking up trusts AND restoration of individualism.

    ANS: A   DIF: Medium   OBJ: 20.3
    TOP: T. Roosevelt's Reform Programs

18. The Sixteenth Amendment is the
    a. women's suffrage amendment.
    b. prohibition amendment.
    c. direct election of senators amendment.
    d. income tax amendment.

    ANS: D   DIF: Medium   REF: 534   OBJ: 20.3
    TOP: Constitution

19. The scandal connected with a sale of public land that lost Taft the Progressive support that he had retained was called the
    a. Morgan-Guggenheim affair.
    b. Payne-Aldrich affair.
    c. Ballinger-Pinchot affair.
    d. Mann-Elkins affair.

    ANS: C   DIF: Medium   REF: 533   OBJ: 20.3
    TOP: Taft Scandals

20. Which of the following is NOT an accurate description of Woodrow Wilson?
    a. an author and scholar
    b. a persuasive speaker
    c. a rugged outdoorsman
    d. a devout, religious man

    ANS: C   DIF: Medium   REF: 536–537   OBJ: 20.4
    TOP: Woodrow Wilson

21. Which of the following is incorrectly paired?
    a. Theodore Roosevelt—"New Nationalism"
    b. William H. Taft—"dollar diplomacy"
    c. Woodrow Wilson—"Square Deal"
    d. William McKinley—"watchful waiting"

    ANS: C   DIF: Medium   REF: 536, 542–543
    OBJ: 20.4   TOP: U.S. Presidents

22. The Underwood-Simmons bill
    a. lowered tariff rates.
    b. raised tariff rates.
    c. included an income tax with high rates.
    d. raised tariff rates AND included an income tax with high rates.

    ANS: A   DIF: Medium   REF: 537–538   OBJ: 20.4
    TOP: Wilson's Reform Policies

23. The Federal Trade Commission, established in 1914, regulated
    a. banking procedures.
    b. business practices.
    c. stock market manipulations.
    d. railroad operations.

    ANS: B   DIF: Medium   REF: 539   OBJ: 20.4
    TOP: Federal Trade Commission

24. "Speak softly and carry a big stick" was the motto of
    a. William Howard Taft.
    b. Woodrow Wilson.
    c. Theodore Roosevelt.
    d. William Jennings Bryan.

    ANS: C   DIF: Medium   REF: 540   OBJ: 20.5
    TOP: T. Roosevelt

25. Theodore Roosevelt received the Nobel Peace Prize for
    a. ending a war between China and Japan.
    b. ending a war between Japan and Russia.
    c. building the Panama Canal.
    d. formulating the Roosevelt Corollary.

    ANS: B   DIF: Medium   REF: 540   OBJ: 20.5
    TOP: T. Roosevelt

26. The Root-Takahira Agreement of 1908 provided that Japan
    a. be allowed to annex Korea.
    b. be allowed to pursue its own interests in Manchuria.
    c. not meddle with U.S. colonies in the Pacific.
    d. all of the above

    ANS: D   DIF: Medium   REF: 540   OBJ: 20.5
    TOP: U.S. / Japanese Relations

27. Woodrow Wilson's foreign policy in Mexico
    a. was basically consistent with the Roosevelt Corollary.
    b. was radically different from that of Theodore Roosevelt.
    c. helped stabilize the government of Victoriano Huerta.
    d. revealed a desire to annex Mexico to the United States.

    ANS: A   DIF: Medium   REF: 543–544   OBJ: 20.5
    TOP: Wilson's Foreign Policy

28. Before 1903, Panama was a province of
    a. Cuba.   c. Venezuela.
    b. Ecuador.   d. Colombia.

    ANS: D   DIF: Medium   REF: 541   OBJ: 20.5
    TOP: Panama

29. The Roosevelt Corollary extended the U.S. foreign policy first presented in
    a. the Open Door policy.   c. the Monroe Doctrine.
    b. Washington's Farewell Address.   d. the Manifest Destiny Doctrine.

    ANS: C   DIF: Medium   REF: 542   OBJ: 20.5
    TOP: T. Roosevelt's Foreign Policy

30. The phrase "dollar diplomacy" best characterizes the foreign policy of
    a. Theodore Roosevelt.
    b. William Howard Taft.
    c. Woodrow Wilson.
    d. William Howard Taft and Woodrow Wilson.

    ANS: D   DIF: Medium   REF: 542–543   OBJ: 20.5
    TOP: Taft / Wilson Foreign Policy

31. All of the following were examples of Theodore Roosevelt applying the "big stick" policy EXCEPT
    a. building the Panama Canal.
    b. sending the "Great White Fleet" around the world.
    c. intervening in the Dominican Republic.
    d. sending troops into Mexico to overthrow Huerta.

    ANS: D   DIF: Medium   REF: 540–542   OBJ: 20.5
    TOP: T. Roosevelt's Foreign Policy

32. Theodore Roosevelt and Franklin Roosevelt were alike in that they both believed in an economic system based on
    a. socialism.
    b. wealth being concentrated in the hands of a few.
    c. capitalism.
    d. the equal distribution of wealth throughout the society.

    ANS: C   DIF: Medium   REF: 526   OBJ: 20.1
    TOP: Capitalism

33. For the most part, the Progressive movement did NOT draw its strength from
    a. professionals.   c. small towns.
    b. big cities.   d. merchants.

    ANS: C   DIF: Medium   REF: 527   OBJ: 20.2
    TOP: Progressive Movement

34. Which of the following individuals was NOT a muckraker?
    a. Finley Peter Dunne   c. Ida Tarbell
    b. Lincoln Steffens   d. John Spargo

    ANS: A   DIF: Medium   REF: 529–531   OBJ: 20.2

35. "Constitutions are checks upon the hasty action of the majority. They are the self-imposed restraints of a whole people upon a majority of them to secure sober action and a respect for the rights of the minority." This statement best characterizes the political philosophy of
    a. Theodore Roosevelt.   c. William Howard Taft.
    b. William Jennings Bryan.   d. Woodrow Wilson.

    ANS: D   DIF: Medium   REF: 536, 539–540
    OBJ: 20.3   TOP: Woodrow Wilson

36. Which of the following contributed to the insurgent revolt of Progressive Republicans?
        I. Taft's signing of the Payne-Aldrich tariff; II. Taft's signing of the Mann-Elkins Act; III. Taft's firing of Gifford Pinchot IV. Taft's support of the income tax amendment
    a. I and II   c. I and IV
    b. I and III   d. II, III, and IV

    ANS: B   DIF: Medium   REF: 532–533   OBJ: 20.3
    TOP: Progressive Movement

37. A cartoon in 1912 commented on the presidential election with an animal "equation." The cartoon showed a Republican elephant divided by a Bull Moose equaling a Democratic donkey. The cartoonist's opinion was probably that
    a.   Roosevelt split the Republican vote and made Wilson the winner.
    b.   Wilson's political philosophy put him somewhere in the middle between Roosevelt's radicalism and Taft's conservatism.
    c.   Wilson would accomplish as much as Roosevelt and Taft added together.
    d.   The Bull Moose party could not have survived without the help of the Republican party.

    ANS: A   DIF: Medium   REF: 534–536   OBJ: 20.3
    TOP: Presidential Elections

38. "The masters of the government of the United States are the combined capitalists and manufacturers of the United States." This statement by Woodrow Wilson most likely means that Wilson saw big business as
    a.   needing to be regulated.
    b.   needing to be broken into smaller units.
    c.   a potential threat to democratic institutions.
    d.   entitled to respect because of its formidable power.

    ANS: C   DIF: Medium   REF: 537–540   OBJ: 20.4
    TOP: Wilson's Presidency

39. "In the Western Hemisphere the adherence of the United States to the Monroe Doctrine may force the United States, however reluctantly, in flagrant cases of wrongdoing or impotence, to the exercise of an international police power." This sentence is most likely a part of the
    a.   Root-Takahira Agreement   c.   Open Door policy.
    b.   U.S.-Colombia treaty of 1921.   d.   Roosevelt Corollary.

    ANS: D   DIF: Medium   REF: 542   OBJ: 20.5
    TOP: T. Roosevelt's Foreign Policy

ESSAY

1. What is the main point of the following passage? Write your answer on a separate sheet of paper and support your answer with a paragraph explaining why you chose it.
        Theodore Roosevelt had a clear view of the new role he wanted for the United States. Although he distrusted the power of large corporations, he loved power for the nation and for himself. He wanted the United States to hold the center of the world stage. For all practical purposes he was his own Secretary of State. Though he never shrank from a good fight, he saw himself as a champion of peace. His motto was "speak softly and carry a big stick." Still, he seemed to enjoy bellowing while waving his big stick at home and abroad.
    A. Theodore Roosevelt knew what he wanted.
    B. Theodore Roosevelt wanted power for the United States and for himself.
    C. Theodore Roosevelt was his own Secretary of State.
    D. Theodore Roosevelt never shrank from a good fight.

    ANS:
    answer b Students' paragraphs should support their answer.

    DIF: Hard   REF: 540–542   OBJ: 20.0
    TOP: T. Roosevelt's Presidency

2. In the opening years of the 1900s, especially during the administrations of Teddy Roosevelt and Woodrow Wilson, the reformers were so successful that the period came to be called the "Progressive Era." In an essay, cite at least five examples to document this claim.

ANS:
On the federal level, Progressive Era reformers were successful in attacking the trusts and big business in such actions as the coal strike, the Northern Securities case, the Meat Inspection Act, the Pure Food and Drug Act, and the Employers' Liability Act. They initiated wide-scale conservation efforts through the Newlands Reclamation Act of 1902, increased setting-aside of forests in reserves, and the formation of a Forest Service. They more equably distributed the nation's wealth through income and inheritance taxes. In the cities reformers brought new forms of management. In the states they passed laws on child labor, compulsory insurance, women's hours, and prohibition. Other reforms included the initiative, referendum, and recall, women's suffrage, and banking and business regulations, such as the Federal Reserve Act of 1913, the Clayton Antitrust Act of 1914, and the creation of the Federal Trade Commission in 1914.

DIF: Hard   REF: 523–526, 528–529, 538–540   OBJ: 20.0
TOP: Reform / T. Roosevelt / Wilson Presidencies

3. "The great virtue of my radicalism lies in the fact that I am perfectly ready, if necessary, to be radical on the conservative side." Starting with this statement by Theodore Roosevelt, give at least two examples of actions taken by him during his presidency that could be considered radical in the defense of conservative principles.

ANS:
Answers will vary but could include the following ideas: Roosevelt's radicalism rested in his means, not in his goals. His goals were to preserve American democracy and free enterprise in an age of economic upheaval. To achieve these conservative goals, he introduced an activist presidency, utilizing the power of his office far more than had other peacetime Presidents. Thus, his threat to send the army into the coal mines, his trustbusting in the Northern Securities case, and his attacks on "the malefactors of great wealth" were intended to preserve rather than to overthrow basic American institutions.

DIF: Hard   REF: 522–531   OBJ: 20.1
TOP: T. Roosevelt's Presidency

4. In what ways did Theodore Roosevelt's view of when the government should get involved in the economy and in the everyday life of the country's people represent a departure from previous Presidents' views?

ANS:
Answers will vary but could include the following ideas: Presidents before Theodore Roosevelt generally saw the federal government taking only a very small role in the economy and the everyday life of the country's people. Early in the nineteenth century, most Presidents believed that government intervention in the economy was at the root of inequities in American life. Lincoln, of course, assumed tremendous presidential power during the Civil War, but postwar Presidents were generally timid. Roosevelt was a departure in that he saw his role as protector of the public interest, demanding powerful action during peacetime. He took responsibility for checking misbehavior by big business, ensuring that the public received pure foods and medicines, conserving the nation's natural resources, etc.

DIF: Hard   REF: 522–531   OBJ: 20.1
TOP: T. Roosevelt's Presidency

5. It has been said that the Progressives believed that the truth is often shrouded in secrecy. Explain what role the muckrakers played in digging out the truth and in contributing to the reforms of the Progressive Era.

ANS:
Answers will vary but could include the following ideas: An example of the Progressive attitude would be Charles Beard's examination of the financial interests of the Founding Fathers in the belief that the key to understanding behavior lay not in public statements but in private endeavors. The muckrakers looked for the seamy side of life in the belief that the underside of America provided a more accurate view of the country. They also believed that exposing these things—the corruption of big business, the exploitation of women and children, and the evils of urban political machines—would lead to corrective action.

DIF: Hard   REF: 524, 529–531   OBJ: 20.2
TOP: Progressive Movement

6. Explain why the form of government that involves direct primary, initiative, referendum, recall, and a city manager would be much more useful to professionals, intellectuals, and white-collar workers than to the urban poor, landless sharecroppers, and factory workers.

ANS:
Answers will vary but could include the following ideas: The Progressive reforms were much more appealing to middle-class and upper middle-class Americans than they were to the working poor in urban and rural areas. For the most part, the Progressive reforms were not economic reforms that would directly benefit economically deprived segments of the population. The city-manager form of government and the direct primary were attempts to break the control of urban political machines. The initiative, referendum, and recall allowed people who had the time for and interest in political activism to have a greater say in policy-making. Americans whose main goal was providing subsistence for themselves and for their families were not generally backers of the Progressive movement.

DIF: Hard   OBJ: 20.2   TOP: Progressive Reform

7. The Progressive party was a rarity in that it was a third party with a realistic chance of winning a presidential election. Cite at least two other examples of third party participation in a presidential election either before or after 1912.

ANS:
Answers will vary but could include the following ideas: The earliest third party to run a presidential candidate was the Anti-Masonic party in 1832. The Free Soil party ran Martin Van Buren for President on an antislavery platform in 1848 and played a pivotal role in the outcome of the election. Millard Fillmore ran in the election of 1856 as the candidate of the Know-Nothing party. The Constitutional Union party split the Democratic vote in the election of 1860. The Populist party made its greatest impact in the presidential elections of 1892 and 1896. The Prohibition party dates from 1872, and the Socialist party from 1901. Twentieth-century third party efforts include the Dixiecrats in 1948 and George Wallace's American Independent party in 1968 and in 1972.

DIF: Hard   OBJ: 20.3
TOP: Progressive Movement / Presidential Elections

8. Compare and contrast Theodore Roosevelt and Woodrow Wilson in terms of their personalities, policies, philosophies, and accomplishments.

ANS:
Answers could include the following: Roosevelt and Wilson were educated men from affluent families. Both were scholars and authors. Roosevelt was energetic and outgoing; Wilson, quiet and reserved. Both espoused Progressive policies. Roosevelt believed in a strong government to regulate business and protect the well-being of the people. Wilson was uncomfortable with big business and a government that could control and regulate corporations. He wanted to break up trusts and restore competition between smaller enterprises; Roosevelt wanted to break only those that behaved badly, allowing those not bent on eliminating competitors to survive. Roosevelt's accomplishments included trustbusting of a few monopolies to set an example, conservation of natural resources, and regulatory legislation. Wilson's accomplishments were banking and tariff reform, the Clayton Antitrust Act, and the Federal Trade Commission.

DIF: Hard   OBJ: 20.4   TOP: U.S. Presidents / Wilson, T. Roosevelt

9. One historian has concluded, "In terms of enacting reform legislation, Woodrow Wilson's first term ranks as one of the most successful in American history." Do you agree or disagree with this statement? Cite specific pieces of legislation to support your position.

ANS:
Answers will vary but could include the following ideas: Agree— Wilson's first term saw the enactment of a lower tariff benefiting American consumers; the Federal Reserve Act, which provided a stable currency and reduced the chance of runs on local banks; the Clayton Antitrust Act, which put teeth into the earlier Sherman Antitrust Act; and the Federal Trade Commission to monitor business practices.   Disagree—Although many reform measures were passed during Woodrow Wilson's first term, his administration cannot be ranked as one of the most successful because he ignored so many pressing problems: he did nothing to benefit African-Americans, the urban poor, or the women's suffrage movement; and he did little to help farmers, factory workers, and child laborers until late in his first term when he realized that his reelection in 1916 necessitated additional reforms.

DIF: Hard   REF: 521–531, 535–544   OBJ: 20.4
TOP: Wilson's Reform Policies

© Prentice-Hall, Inc.

MATCHING

Match each item with the correct statement below.

a.   nationalist
b.   Henry Ford
c.   William J. Bryan
d.   Zimmermann Note
e.   Henry Cabot Lodge

f.   pacifist
g.   George Creel
h.   "Lusitania"
i.   Liberty loans
j.   Fourteen Points

1.   Wilson's proposals for the peace treaty after World War I.
2.   Wilson's Secretary of State who was strongly opposed to the war.
3.   As head of the Committee on Public Information, he sold the war to America.
4.   He and William Borah headed Senate opposition to the U.S. joining the League of Nations.
5.   An American industrialist who sent a "peace ship" to Europe to end the war.
6.   One who is opposed to war.
7.   Britain intercepted this message from Germany proposing an alliance with Mexico.
8.   Person with strong loyalty to his country and who advocates its independence.
9.   British liner sunk by Germany without warning, killing 128 Americans.
10. Method by which the United States raised funds to pay for war.

1.   ANS: J   DIF: Easy   REF: 555–556   OBJ: 21.0
     TOP: Wilson's Foreign Policy
2.   ANS: C   DIF: Easy   REF: 552   OBJ: 21.0
     TOP: Wilson's Administration
3.   ANS: G   DIF: Easy   REF: 566   OBJ: 21.0
     TOP: WWI Propaganda
4.   ANS: E   DIF: Easy   REF: 569–570   OBJ: 21.0
     TOP: League of Nations
5.   ANS: B   DIF: Easy   REF: 549   OBJ: 21.0
     TOP: WWI
6.   ANS: F   DIF: Easy   REF: 553   OBJ: 21.0
     TOP: Pacifist
7.   ANS: D   DIF: Easy   REF: 555   OBJ: 21.0
     TOP: WWI Espionage
8.   ANS: A   DIF: Easy   OBJ: 21.0   TOP: Nationalist
9.   ANS: H   DIF: Easy   REF: 552   OBJ: 21.0
     TOP: WWI
10. ANS: I   DIF: Easy   REF: 563   OBJ: 21.0
     TOP: WWI Economics

MULTIPLE CHOICE

1. World War I was precipitated by the assassination of
    a. Archduke Francis Ferdinand.   c. Czar Nicholas.
    b. Kaiser Wilhelm.   d. the King of Serbia.

    ANS: A   DIF: Medium   REF: 547   OBJ: 21.1
    TOP: WWI

2. Warlike statements were made by Germany's leader,
    a. Archduke Francis Ferdinand.   c. Czar Nicholas.
    b. Kaiser Wilhelm.   d. Paul von Hindenburg.

    ANS: B   DIF: Medium   REF: 550   OBJ: 21.1
    TOP: U.S. / German Relations

3. Wilson's 1918 program for the future of the world came to be known as the
    a. Armed Neutrality Program.   c. American Plan.
    b. Fourteen Points.   d. Preparedness Plan.

    ANS: B   DIF: Medium   REF: 555–556   OBJ: 21.1
    TOP: Wilson's Foreign Policy

4. On the southern front, the American advance against Germany was led by
    a. Colonel Edward House.   c. General Douglas MacArthur.
    b. General John J. Pershing.   d. Colonel Theodore Roosevelt.

    ANS: B   DIF: Medium   REF: 559   OBJ: 21.2
    TOP: WWI / U.S. / Germany

5. To mobilize money for the war effort, the United States government instituted a program of
    a. Liberty Tariffs.   c. Liberty Loans.
    b. Liberty Taxes.   d. Liberty Stamps.

    ANS: C   DIF: Medium   REF: 563   OBJ: 21.3
    TOP: WWI Economics

6. Created in 1918 to arbitrate labor disputes was the
    a. United States Employment Service.   c. War Industries Board.
    b. National War Labor Board.   d. National Labor Relations Board.

    ANS: B   DIF: Medium   REF: 565   OBJ: 21.3
    TOP: Labor

7. With a stated purpose to "sell the war to America," President Wilson created the
    a. Council of Defense.   c. Department of War Education.
    b. Committee on Public Information.   d. Federal Bureau of Information.

    ANS: B   DIF: Medium   REF: 566   OBJ: 21.3
    TOP: WWI Propaganda

8. The Espionage Act of 1917 gave the President the power to
   a. censor.
   b. ration.
   c. impose martial law.
   d. deport aliens.

   ANS: A   DIF: Medium   REF: 566   OBJ: 21.3
   TOP: Civil Liberties

9. "The Big Four" included
   a. France, Spain, Germany, and England.
   b. France, Germany, Italy, and the United States.
   c. France, England, Italy, and the United States.
   d. the United States, England, France, and Spain.

   ANS: C   DIF: Medium   REF: 567   OBJ: 21.4
   TOP: WWI

10. Opposition to joining the League of Nations was led by
    a. William E. Borah.
    b. Henry Cabot Lodge.
    c. William Jennings Bryan.
    d. William E. Borah and Henry Cabot Lodge

    ANS: D   DIF: Medium   REF: 569–570   OBJ: 21.4
    TOP: League of Nations

11. The spark that began World War I was ignited in
    a. the northern Atlantic.
    b. northeastern Europe.
    c. southeastern Europe.
    d. Vienna.

    ANS: C   DIF: Medium   REF: 547   OBJ: 21.1
    TOP: WWI

12. The first declaration of war involved
    a. Serbia declaring against Bosnia.
    b. Russia declaring against Serbia.
    c. Bosnia declaring against Italy.
    d. Austria-Hungary declaring against Serbia.

    ANS: D   DIF: Medium   REF: 547   OBJ: 21.1
    TOP: WWI

13. All of the following explain the outbreak of World War I in Europe in 1914 EXCEPT
    a. nationalism.
    b. imperialism.
    c. militarism.
    d. industrialism.

    ANS: D   DIF: Medium   OBJ: 21.1   TOP: WWI

14. America tended to favor the Allies because of all the following EXCEPT
    a. language and cultural ties to Great Britain.
    b. reports of German atrocities coming from England.
    c. the huge numbers of Irish and German immigrants in the United States.
    d. the militaristic goals of Kaiser Wilhelm.

    ANS: C   DIF: Medium   REF: 549–550   OBJ: 21.1
    TOP: WWI

15. Of the following, all are main reasons why the United States entered World War I EXCEPT
    a. unrestricted submarine warfare by Germany.
    b. financial ties between America and the Allies.
    c. American fears that Germany would help Mexico.
    d. Wilson's belief that the world must be made safe for democracy.

    ANS: C   DIF: Medium   REF: 551–552, 555
    OBJ: 21.1   TOP: WWI

16. In 1916, Wilson did not campaign on his record of
    a. keeping the country out of war.
    b. enacting Progressive reforms.
    c. launching a preparedness program.
    d. establishing the Fourteen Points program.

    ANS: D   DIF: Medium   REF: 552–553   OBJ: 21.1
    TOP: Presidential Elections

17. Wilson's Fourteen Points
    a. were noble and idealistic.
    b. had little impact on the rest of the world.
    c. emphasized the need for secret diplomacy.
    d. were the idea of Bernard Baruch.

    ANS: A   DIF: Medium   REF: 555–556   OBJ: 21.1
    TOP: Wilson's Foreign Policy

18. Soldiers who fought in the trenches often suffered from
    a. a sense of isolation.
    b. enemy propaganda.
    c. the effects of poison gas.
    d. a sense of isolation and the effects of poison gas.

    ANS: D   DIF: Medium   REF: 537   OBJ: 21.2
    TOP: WWI

19. Paris was defended and saved from the Germans by the
    a. American Peacekeeping Force.   c. American Expeditionary Force.
    b. League of Nations Army.   d. American/British Military Corps.

    ANS: C   DIF: Medium   REF: 559   OBJ: 21.2
    TOP: WWI / Paris

20. World War I was the bloodiest war in history because of
    a. the lack of trained medical personnel.   c. the development of new weapons.
    b. the use of naval blockades.   d. its length.

    ANS: C   DIF: Medium   REF: 556   OBJ: 21.2
    TOP: WWI

21. The purpose of the Selective Service Act of 1917 was to
    a. fill essential jobs in vital industries.
    b. retrain workers and convert factories for wartime production.
    c. select qualified women to take over jobs held by men sent to war.
    d. register men for the military.

    ANS: D   DIF: Medium   REF: 561   OBJ: 21.3
    TOP: WWI

22. The Selective Service Act of 1917 provided for
    a. the registration of men between ages 21 and 31 for the draft.
    b. hiring substitutes to replace those not wishing to be drafted.
    c. draft dodgers to be tried for treason.
    d. drafting of women for medical and clerical jobs.

    ANS: A   DIF: Medium   REF: 561   OBJ: 21.3
    TOP: WWI

23. Gains made by labor during World War I included all of the following EXCEPT
    a. shorter hours.   c. increased wages.
    b. the right to belong to a union.   d. the right to strike.

    ANS: D   DIF: Medium   REF: 566   OBJ: 21.3
    TOP: Labor Unions

24. All of the following were curtailed during the war EXCEPT the freedom of
    a. speech.   c. assembly.
    b. the press.   d. religion.

    ANS: D   DIF: Medium   REF: 566   OBJ: 21.3
    TOP: Civil Liberties

25. In the mobilization effort, women
    a. entered the Selective Service rolls.   c. took over jobs previously held by men.
    b. joined the Nurse Corps.   d. all of the above

    ANS: D   DIF: Medium   REF: 561, 565   OBJ: 21.3
    TOP: WWI / Women

26. The war affected farmers by
    a. causing a drop in prices for crops.
    b. causing a rise in prices for crops.
    c. making them cut back on their acreage.
    d. causing a drop in prices for crops and making them cut back on their acreage.

    ANS: D   DIF: Medium   REF: 564   OBJ: 21.3
    TOP: WWI / Farming

27. In the mobilization effort, decisions about what goods should be produced were made by the
    a. War Industries Board.   c. Selective Service.
    b. Committee on Public Information. d. War Department.

    ANS: A   DIF: Medium   REF: 565   OBJ: 21.3
    TOP: WWI / Economics

28. In his role as economic leader during the war, Bernard Baruch was
    a. weak.   c. ruthless.
    b. idealistic.   d. ineffective.

    ANS: C   DIF: Medium   REF: 565   OBJ: 21.3
    TOP: WWI / Economics

29. As a result of the war,
    a. a labor shortage existed.
    b. wages rose.
    c. union membership declined.
    d. a labor shortage existed and wages rose.

    ANS: D   DIF: Medium   REF: 565   OBJ: 21.3
    TOP: WWI / Economics

30. During the war, civil liberties in America were
    a. expanded.   c. unaffected.
    b. diminished.   d. respected.

    ANS: B   DIF: Medium   REF: 566   OBJ: 21.3
    TOP: Civil Liberties

31. To the other members of the "Big Four," Woodrow Wilson was
    a. irritating and self-righteous.
    b. too vengeful in his plans for peace.
    c. a model of moral leadership.
    d. irritating and self-righteous and too vengeful in his plans for peace.

    ANS: A   DIF: Medium   REF: 567   OBJ: 21.4
    TOP: Woodrow Wilson / Foreign Relations

32. What Americans feared most in Wilson's peace plan was the
    a. demand for German reparations.
    b. demand for American reparations.
    c. promise to respect and preserve League members against external aggression.
    d. promise to actively restore war-ravaged countries to their pre-war status.

    ANS: C   DIF: Medium   REF: 569   OBJ: 21.4
    TOP: Wilson's Peace Plan

33. When the Senate refused to ratify the Treaty of Versailles, Wilson
    a. agreed to compromise.
    b. appealed directly to the American people.
    c. returned to Europe to renegotiate the treaty.
    d. abandoned hope for a League of Nations.

    ANS: B   DIF: Medium   REF: 570   OBJ: 21.4
    TOP: Wilson's Presidency

34. To Wilson, the election of 1920 was
    a. a chance to be the first U.S. President to win a third term.
    b. a referendum on the League of Nations.
    c. a referendum on the Progressive Era.
    d. all of the above

    ANS: B   DIF: Medium   REF: 570   OBJ: 21.4
    TOP: Presidential Elections

35. The major reason for American opposition to the League of Nations was
    a. fear of being required to get involved in future Europeans wars.
    b. Wilson's failure to promote the League to the public.
    c. the desire of Americans to punish the Central Powers.
    d. the high financial costs of joining the League.

    ANS: A   DIF: Medium   REF: 569   OBJ: 21.4
    TOP: League of Nations

36. Because of statements by Kaiser Wilhelm, many Americans came to see Germany as
    a. idealistic.   c. militaristic.
    b. the center of European culture.   d. an enemy of colonialism.

    ANS: C   DIF: Medium   REF: 550   OBJ: 21.1
    TOP: U.S. / German Relations

37. "I can't keep the country out of war. Any little German lieutenant can put us into war at any time by some calculated outrage." When he made this statement, President Wilson meant that
    a. American public opinion would demand a declaration of war if Germany continued to violate American neutrality rights.
    b. he had been forced to lie to the American people about keeping the country out of war in the election campaign of 1916.
    c. he felt inferior to German military officers.
    d. American democratic institutions were under attack by Germany.

    ANS: A   DIF: Medium   REF: 551–555   OBJ: 21.1
    TOP: U.S. / German Relations

38. Which of the following supported neutrality most strongly early in the war?
    a. Theodore Roosevelt   c. John J. Pershing
    b. William Jennings Bryan   d. Henry Cabot Lodge

    ANS: B   DIF: Medium   REF: 552   OBJ: 21.1
    TOP: WWI / U.S. Involvement

39. The fifth of Wilson's Fourteen Points called for "a free, open-minded, and absolutely impartial adjustment of all colonial claims." Which action at the Paris Conference contradicted this goal?
   a. the establishment of Poland, Czechoslovakia, and Yugoslavia
   b. the demand for war reparations
   c. the parceling out of German colonies among the Allies
   d. the inclusion of Article 10 in the plan for the League of Nations

   ANS: C   DIF: Medium   REF: 567   OBJ: 21.4
   TOP: Wilson's Foreign Policy

40. Which provision of the Treaty of Versailles created the most bitterness in Germany after World War I?
   a. loss of its colonies to the Allies
   b. the amount of reparations Germany was assessed
   c. Germany's exclusion from the League of Nations
   d. the division of Germany into two zones

   ANS: B   DIF: Medium   REF: 567–568   OBJ: 21.4
   TOP: Post WWI Germany

ESSAY

1. Which of the following is an example of reasoning by eliminating alternatives? Write your answer on a separate sheet of paper and support your answer with a paragraph explaining why you chose it.
   A. Of course, a nation geared to peace could not all at once meet the demands of war.
   B. The Sedition Act of 1918 was wrong. How could the United States fight a war for freedom and democracy overseas but not allow free speech at home?
   C. The key factor in the defeat of the League of Nations in the United States could not have been Senator Henry Cabot Lodge's opposition to it. President Wilson could have gotten Senate approval by agreeing to Lodge's reservations.

   ANS:
   answer C Students' paragraphs should support their answer.

   DIF: Hard   REF: 569–570   OBJ: 21.0   TOP: League of Nations

2. Summarize the causes and effects of United States involvement in World War I.

   ANS:
   Despite its large Central-European immigrant population in 1917, the country had a distinctly pro-British orientation. The language and a majority of customs and laws were British. Thus, even when Britain began violating United States neutral shipping rights, Americans protested far less than when Germany used submarine warfare. Trade with the Allies escalated, creating a strong interest in preserving Allied economies, while trade with Germany declined. For many Americans, the Zimmerman Note was the "last straw." Direct effects of United States involvement included the prevention of the fall of Paris to Germany, the destruction of the German supply line, and the eventual defeat of the Axis. Indirect effects included the expansion of government involvement in rationing, travel, employment, railroads, etc.

   DIF: Hard   OBJ: 21.0   TOP: WWI / U.S. Involvement

3. Based on what you have read in the chapter, explain why Woodrow Wilson won reelection by such a narrow margin in 1916 after a very successful first term.

ANS:
Answers will vary but could include the following ideas: Despite a very successful first term, Woodrow Wilson faced several severe obstacles when he ran for reelection: (1) the opposition candidate, Charles Evans Hughes, was quite capable; (2) Wilson had won in 1912 only because the Republican vote was divided between Roosevelt and Taft; (3) Wilson did not possess the kind of personal charm that appealed to the masses of voters; (4) the Republicans had almost a lock on the presidency since the Civil War, losing only to Grover Cleveland; and (5) Americans may have been tiring of reform, particularly of the lofty principled variety that Wilson preached.

DIF: Hard   REF: 552–554   OBJ: 21.1   TOP: Presidential Elections

4. Create a persuasive argument for the United States entering World War I on the side of the Central Powers.

ANS:
Answers will vary but could include the following ideas: The United States in 1917 was no longer the land of transplanted Englishmen. The country contained many immigrants whose roots went back to the countries composing the Central Powers; immigrants with Irish roots, moreover, had good reason to hate Britain. Except for the extremely brief war with Spain in 1898, the only sustained military conflicts the United States had experienced with a European country consisted of two wars with Britain. Britain had violated America's neutral shipping rights during the Napoleonic Wars, had supplied ships to the Confederacy during the Civil War, and again had violated neutral shipping rights since the outbreak of World War I.

DIF: Hard   OBJ: 21.1   TOP: WWI / U.S. Involvement

5. Explain how changes in technology affected the course of World War I.

ANS:
Answers will vary but could include the following ideas: World War I witnessed a host of technological changes. Airplanes and tanks made their first combat appearance, although planes were not yet equipped for heavy bombing raids, and tanks were neither numerous nor sufficiently armored to have a major impact on the war. Poison gas was also used, but lack of effective control made it often as dangerous to one's own troops as to the enemy. As the rifle forced a new type of warfare on the participants in the Civil War, the machine gun led directly to the trench war that dominated World War I. Although not a new weapon, the machine gun had never been so dominant before.

DIF: Hard   REF: 556–560   OBJ: 21.2   TOP: WWI Technology

6. Explain the significance of propaganda during World War I.

ANS:
Answers will vary but could include the following ideas: Propaganda played a crucial part in the war from the opening days of World War I. The British demonstrated that they realized the importance of propaganda when they cut the transatlantic cable connecting the United States and Germany so that all news from Europe would be channeled through England. The British then proceeded to highlight German atrocities for American consumption in order to mold public opinion against the Central Powers. Then immediately following U.S. entry into the war, President Wilson appointed the Committee on Public Information to "sell the war to America." The Creel Committee effectively worked up a war hysteria so that Americans would come to hate everything German.

DIF: Hard   REF: 540–550, 566   OBJ: 21.2
TOP: WWI Propaganda

7. How might the U.S. experience in World War I have contributed to a strong preference for isolationism in America when conflict in Europe again raged in the 1930s?

ANS:
Answers will vary but could include the following ideas: Many Americans came away from World War I believing that thousands of American men had died needlessly in a war that really was of no concern to the United States. Others were convinced that our participation in World War I was part of a plot by U.S. financiers to protect their overseas investments. Such beliefs bred a strong sense of isolationism, which President Franklin Roosevelt had to battle in order to aid the Allies in the years before Pearl Harbor.

DIF: Hard   OBJ: 21.3   TOP: WWI

8. Should Presidents whose programs or policies are blocked by Congressional opposition appeal directly to the American people for support? Evaluate the wisdom of such an appeal being used as a political strategy. Use Wilson's experience with the Treaty of Versailles as a starting point for your discussion.

ANS:
Answers could include the following: Presidents have often sought to rally public support for their programs and policies by appealing to the people when Congressional opposition is significant. Examples include President Nixon's appeal to the "silent majority" for support of his policy in Southeast Asia and President Reagan's call for continuing financial aid to the Nicaraguan Contras. To be effective, the President must convince the American people that he understands and represents their interests as a nation better than Congress does. It is doubtful that this was the case as President Wilson tried to win support for the Treaty of Versailles with its League of Nations. The American people were in no mood in 1919 to enter another bloodbath on behalf of a threatened member of the League. Wilson probably misgauged public opinion and therefore his use of the direct appeal was not politically astute.

DIF: Hard   OBJ: 21.4   TOP: Wilson's Presidency

9. Explain the disagreements between Wilson and the other Allied leaders at the Peace Conference at Paris.

ANS:
Answers will vary but could include the following ideas: Wilson arrived in Paris with the Fourteen Points that he hoped would lay the foundation for a just peace in Europe. The leaders of France, Britain, and Italy thought Wilson naive and would not tolerate Wilson's generosity to the defeated Central Powers. They insisted on stripping Germany of its colonies and imposing massive reparations for war damages. Wilson grudgingly assented to their demands in return for their inclusion of the League of Nations in the Treaty of Versailles.

DIF: Hard   REF: 567–570   OBJ: 21.4   TOP: WWI

10. How did Europe change as a result of World War I?

ANS:
Answers will vary but could include the following ideas: The war changed the map of Europe. Germany, Russia, and Austria-Hungary all lost territory. New nations appeared in Eastern Europe, including Poland, Latvia, Lithuania, Estonia, Czechoslovakia, and Yugoslavia. In Russia, revolutions had overthrown both the czar and the short-lived provisional government, resulting in Communist rule. Throughout Europe, millions of people, soldiers and civilians, had been killed, and in Germany the seeds of another world-wide conflict were already planted due to the vindictive Treaty of Versailles.

DIF: Hard   REF: 547–570   OBJ: 21.4   TOP: WWI / Europe

(page intentionally left blank)

MATCHING

Match each item with the correct statement below.

a.	A. Mitchel Palmer	f.	education
b.	disarmament	g.	Charles Lindbergh
c.	Calvin Coolidge	h.	Albert Fall
d.	Andrew Mellon	i.	Nicola Sacco
e.	Bolsheviks	j.	budget

1. Secretary of the Treasury _____ was a millionaire banker who served under three Presidents.
2. Wilson's Attorney General, _____, believed the whole country was threatened by Communists and anarchists.
3. _____ was one of two immigrants executed for murder despite the lack of solid evidence against them.
4. The 1921 Washington naval conference was the first successful _____ conference in history.
5. Radical Communists led by V.I. Lenin, who seized power in Russia, were called _____.
6. In 1927 his solo flight over the Atlantic made _____ a national hero.
7. In 1928 the United States spent more money on _____ than all the rest of the world combined.
8. As governor, _____ gained attention by using the National Guard to break the 1919 Boston police strike.
9. Harding set up a bureau to draw up a federal _____ to guide Congress in spending money.
10. Secretary of the Interior _____ was involved in the Teapot Dome scandal.

1. ANS: D   DIF: Easy   REF: 583   OBJ: 22.0
   TOP: Harding's Staff
2. ANS: A   DIF: Easy   REF: 578–579   OBJ: 22.0
   TOP: Communism / Red Scare
3. ANS: I   DIF: Easy   REF: 580–581   OBJ: 22.0
   TOP: Discrimination / Sacco & Vonzetti
4. ANS: B   DIF: Easy   REF: 584   OBJ: 22.0
   TOP: Disarmament
5. ANS: E   DIF: Easy   REF: 577   OBJ: 22.0
   TOP: Russian History
6. ANS: G   DIF: Easy   REF: 593   OBJ: 22.0
   TOP: Charles Lindbergh
7. ANS: F   DIF: Easy   REF: 593   OBJ: 22.0
   TOP: Education
8. ANS: C   DIF: Easy   REF: 577   OBJ: 22.0
   TOP: Labor Unions
9. ANS: J   DIF: Easy   REF: 584–585   OBJ: 22.0
   TOP: Harding's Presidency / Budget
10. ANS: H   DIF: Easy   REF: 587   OBJ: 22.0
    TOP: Harding Scandals

MULTIPLE CHOICE

1. The Massachusetts governor who called out the National Guard to keep order during a police strike was
   a. Herbert Hoover.
   c. Charles Lynch.
   b. Calvin Coolidge.
   d. A. Mitchell Palmer.

   ANS: B   DIF: Medium   REF: 577   OBJ: 22.1
   TOP: Labor Unions

2. All of those who wanted to cut down immigration from certain countries were called
   a. restrictionists.
   c. xenophobes.
   b. isolationists.
   d. anarchists.

   ANS: A   DIF: Medium   REF: 580   OBJ: 22.1
   TOP: Immigration

3. The poet who described the postwar world as "The Wasteland" was
   a. T. S. Eliot.
   c. F. Scott Fitzgerald.
   b. Sinclair Lewis.
   d. Eugene O'Neill.

   ANS: A   DIF: Medium   REF: 582   OBJ: 22.1
   TOP: Poets

4. The movement to discourage the use of intoxicating liquors was known as the
   a. restrictionist movement.
   c. sobriety movement.
   b. temperance movement.
   d. suffrage movement.

   ANS: B   DIF: Medium   REF: 582   OBJ: 22.1
   TOP: Prohibition

5. Prohibition became law in 1919 with ratification of the
   a. Eighteenth Amendment.
   c. Twentieth Amendment.
   b. Nineteenth Amendment.
   d. Twenty-first Amendment.

   ANS: A   DIF: Medium   REF: 582   OBJ: 22.1
   TOP: Constitution / Prohibition

6. Women were granted the right to vote with the ratification of the
   a. Eighteenth Amendment.
   c. Twentieth Amendment.
   b. Nineteenth Amendment.
   d. Twenty-first Amendment.

   ANS: B   DIF: Medium   REF: 582   OBJ: 22.1
   TOP: Constitution / Women's Rights

7. The "Five Power Treaty," the "Nine Power Treaty," and the "Four Power Treaty" were agreed upon at the
   a. Versailles Conference.
   c. London Conference.
   b. Washington Conference.
   d. Teheran Conference.

   ANS: B   DIF: Medium   REF: 584   OBJ: 22.2
   TOP: U.S. / Foreign Affairs

8. Industrialists were given tariff protection by the
   a. Budget and Accounting Act.
   b. Fordney-McCumber Act.
   c. Comptroller General Act.
   d. General Accounting Act.

   ANS: B   DIF: Medium   REF: 585   OBJ: 22.2
   TOP: Harding's Domestic Programs

9. The first solo nonstop flight from New York to Paris was made by
   a. Charles A. Lindbergh.
   b. Ferdinand Morton.
   c. Frederick W. Taylor.
   d. Amelia Earhart.

   ANS: A   DIF: Medium   REF: 593   OBJ: 22.4
   TOP: Charles Lindbergh

10. Bold use of the assembly line in his factories can be credited to
    a. Henry Ford.
    b. J. P. Morgan.
    c. Andrew Carnegie.
    d. John D. Rockefeller.

    ANS: A   DIF: Medium   REF: 594–595   OBJ: 22.4
    TOP: Automobile Manufacturing

11. The U.S. faced all the following problems after World War I except
    a. violent labor strikes.
    b. urban racial riots.
    c. bomb scares.
    d. food shortages.

    ANS: D   DIF: Medium   REF: 577–578   OBJ: 22.1
    TOP: Post WWI / U.S.

12. Evidence of a forthcoming decline of unions in the 1920s was shown in a
    a. police strike.
    b. coal strike.
    c. steel strike.
    d. all of the above

    ANS: D   DIF: Medium   REF: 577–578   OBJ: 22.1
    TOP: Labor Unions

13. All of the following factors contributed to the "Red Scare" EXCEPT
    a. the presence of Communist party members in the United States.
    b. fears over the election of a Catholic as President.
    c. the Russian Revolution.
    d. bomb scares and actual bombings.

    ANS: B   DIF: Medium   REF: 578–580   OBJ: 22.1
    TOP: Communism / Red Scare

14. Both the Ku Klux Klan and the Immigration Restriction League
    a. used terror and violence to achieve their goals.
    b. believed in white supremacy.
    c. worked mostly through the courts and Congress to achieve their goals.
    d. hid their identity by wearing white sheets.

    ANS: B   DIF: Medium   REF: 580   OBJ: 22.1
    TOP: Immigration / Discrimination

15. The National Origins Act of 1924
    a. required that all immigrants be able to read.
    b. required that all immigrants be able to speak English.
    c. raised immigrations quotas.
    d. reduced immigrations quotas.

    ANS: D   DIF: Medium   REF: 580   OBJ: 22.1
    TOP: Immigration

16. Sacco and Vanzetti were accused of
    a. holding up a shoe factory.   c. killing a guard.
    b. killing a paymaster.   d. all of the above

    ANS: D   DIF: Medium   REF: 580–581   OBJ: 22.1
    TOP: Discrimination

17. Which of the following contributed most to the growth of organized crime during the 1920s?
    a. formation of the U.S. Communist party
    b. race riots in America's cities
    c. rise of the anarchist movement
    d. passage of the Eighteenth Amendment

    ANS: D   DIF: Medium   REF: 582   OBJ: 22.1
    TOP: Organized Crime

18. In the 1920s, which of the following countries was probably the strongest military power?
    a. Great Britain   c. Germany
    b. the Soviet Union   d. Japan

    ANS: A   DIF: Medium   REF: 584   OBJ: 22.2
    TOP: British History 1920s

19. Harding's foreign policy was primarily one of
    a. interventionism.   c. world leadership.
    b. noninvolvement.   d. imperialism.

    ANS: B   DIF: Medium   REF: 584   OBJ: 22.2
    TOP: Harding's Presidency / Foreign Policy

20. Harding's domestic program favored
    a. lower tariffs.   c. less government spending.
    b. higher taxes.   d. all of the above

    ANS: C   DIF: Medium   REF: 584   OBJ: 22.2
    TOP: Harding's Presidency / Domestic Policy

21. Regarding war debts, Harding felt that
    a. only those nations that were able should pay.
    b. all war debts should be cancelled.
    c. no war debts should be cancelled.
    d. the United States should not help any nation repay its war debts.

    ANS: C   DIF: Medium   REF: 586   OBJ: 22.2
    TOP: Harding's Presidency / War Debts

22. A new era in planning federal spending was begun with the passage of the
   a. Budget and Accounting Act.
   b. Fordney-McCumber Act.
   c. Comptroller General Act.
   d. General Accounting Act.

   ANS: A   DIF: Medium   REF: 584–585   OBJ: 22.2
   TOP: Harding's Domestic Programs

23. Under Coolidge's administration, regulatory agencies
   a. battled with the Supreme Court.
   b. clamped down on industry.
   c. helped the businesses that they were supposed to regulate.
   d. battled with the President.

   ANS: C   DIF: Medium   REF: 590   OBJ: 22.3
   TOP: Coolidge's Presidency / Business

24. The purpose of the McNary-Haugen bill was to
   a. break up monopolies in the steel industry.
   b. aid farmers.
   c. aid coal miners.
   d. control stock prices.

   ANS: B   DIF: Medium   REF: 590   OBJ: 22.3
   TOP: Farming

25. In the election of 1928, Al Smith
   a. opposed the repeal of Prohibition.
   b. received a plurality of votes in major cities.
   c. attacked Hoover's religion.
   d. attracted the vote of Southern Democrats.

   ANS: B   DIF: Medium   REF: 591–592   OBJ: 22.3
   TOP: Presidential Election

26. Both Harding and Coolidge
   a. did a lot to help the farmer.
   b. vetoed bonus bills for veterans.
   c. had great admiration for American business.
   d. vetoed bonus bills for veterans AND had great admiration for American business.

   ANS: C   DIF: Medium   REF: 589   OBJ: 22.3
   TOP: Harding / Coolidge Presidency

27. The first "shopping center" was built in 1922 in
   a. Cincinnati.
   b. St. Louis.
   c. Kansas City.
   d. Philadelphia.

   ANS: C   DIF: Medium   REF: 592   OBJ: 22.4
   TOP: Shopping Center

28. The "Roaring Twenties" were characterized by
    a. jazz, ragtime, and blues.
    b. speakeasies.
    c. flappers.
    d. all of the above

    ANS: D   DIF: Medium   REF: 593   OBJ: 22.4
    TOP: Life in the 1920's

29. All of the following were associated with jazz music of the '20s EXCEPT
    a. H. L. Mencken
    b. Louis Armstrong.
    c. "Duke" Ellington.
    d. Bessie Smith.

    ANS: A   DIF: Medium   REF: 592   OBJ: 22.4
    TOP: The Jazz Age

30. Factory production innovations in effect by the twenties included
    a. "scientific management."
    b. electric power.
    c. the assembly line.
    d. all of the above

    ANS: D   DIF: Medium   REF: 594   OBJ: 22.4
    TOP: 1920s Industry

31. All of the following took place during the "Roaring Twenties" EXCEPT
    a. the election of a Roman Catholic to the Presidency.
    b. the election of women to state offices.
    c. mass production of the Model T.
    d. the first talking movies.

    ANS: A   DIF: Medium   REF: 590, 592, 595
    OBJ: 22.4   TOP: The 1920s

32. Which of the following reasons was most likely the primary motivation behind passage of the
    National Origins Act?
    a. The United States was becoming overcrowded.
    b. White Anglo-Saxon Protestants wanted to bar immigrants of different racial, ethnic, and
        religious backgrounds.
    c. Immigrants had proven themselves to be a threat to democracy.
    d. Congress felt that it had to retaliate against countries that did not allow Americans to
        migrate.

    ANS: B   DIF: Medium   REF: 580   OBJ: 22.1
    TOP: Immigration / Discrimination

33. Which of the following nations probably approved of the Nine Power Treaty while disapproving
    of the National Origins Act?
    a. China
    b. Great Britain
    c. Japan
    d. the Soviet Union

    ANS: A   DIF: Medium   REF: 580, 584   OBJ: 22.2
    TOP: U.S. / Chinese Relations

34. "Well, boys, I'll tell you what I think. The convention will be deadlocked. After the other candidates have failed, we'll get together in some hotel room, oh, about 2:11 in the morning, and some 15 men, bleary-eyed with lack of sleep, will sit down around a big table and when that time comes Senator Harding will be selected." This prediction by Harry M. Daugherty probably indicated that
    a. the Republican party in 1920 was determined to nominate its most qualified candidate.
    b. the direct primary had proven itself as an effective means for party members to choose their candidate.
    c. despite the reforms of the Progressive era, party professionals were still very powerful.
    d. the Republican convention of 1920 was rigged by Harding supporters.

    ANS: C   DIF: Medium   OBJ: 22.2   TOP: Presidential Elections

35. "Perhaps one of the most important accomplishments of my administration has been minding my own business." The President most likely to have described his term in office this way would have been
    a. Woodrow Wilson.   c. Calvin Coolidge.
    b. Warren G. Harding.   d. Herbert Hoover.

    ANS: C   DIF: Medium   REF: 588–589   OBJ: 22.3
    TOP: Coolidge's Presidency

36. The automobile probably had all of the following effects on American society during the 1920s EXCEPT
    a. increasing consumer borrowing.
    b. increasing commuting distance to jobs.
    c. decreasing church attendance.
    d. decreasing parent-child conflicts.

    ANS: D   DIF: Medium   REF: 595–596   OBJ: 22.4
    TOP: Automobile

37. "We'll show the world we are prosperous, even if we have got to go broke to do it." The point of this comment about the 1920s by humorist Will Rogers is probably that
    a. few Americans cared about living well except to impress others.
    b. Americans were working hard to end the economic depression of the 1920s.
    c. Americans saw prosperity at home as an essential part of military strength.
    d. many Americans were borrowing money or buying on time to acquire the new products of the 1920s.

    ANS: D   DIF: Medium   REF: 596   OBJ: 22.4
    TOP: 1920s Economy

ESSAY

1. Which of the following is NOT an example of proof by evidence? Write your answer on a separate sheet of paper and support your answer with a paragraph explaining why you chose it.
    A. The most sensational of the scandals in the Harding administration was the attempted theft of the national oil reserves.
    B. President Harding was hurt by the friends in his administration. He once said that he had no trouble with his enemies—it was his friends who kept him walking the floors at night.
    C. The worst riot in the summer of 1919 ocurred in Chicago, where a dispute at the beach set off six days and nights of rioting. Hundreds were injured and police records show that 15 whites and 23 African Americans were killed.
    D. President Harding wanted nothing to do with the League of Nations. As he put it, "We seek no part in directing the destinies of the Old World."

    ANS:
    Answer a Students' paragraphs should support their answer.

    DIF: Hard   REF: 587   OBJ: 22.0   TOP: Harding's Presidency

2. In an essay, supply five specific examples that together illustrate the following characterization: "The Twenties was an age of conflict, confusion, excitement, and experiment."

    ANS:
    Students' answers will vary but could include these ideas: In America the Twenties was an age of conflict and confusion. Prohibition laws conflicted with, yet caused the need for speakeasies and bathtub gin. Rising hemlines and bobbed hair conflicted with, and rebelled against, old-fashioned attitudes toward women. Racial friction became evident as the Ku Klux Klan reorganized. The country was alarmed by a "Red Scare." The Twenties was also a time of excitement and experiment. Advertising led consumers into the convenience of installment buying. New products abounded, movies talked, radios and phonographs (playing jazz) became commonplace. Automobile prices dropped so much that many could afford one. National heroes, such as Charles Lindberg and Babe Ruth, and the "flapper" crowded pages of national magazines. Other experiments included the assembly line, new roles for women, and scientific management.

    DIF: Hard   REF: 580–596   OBJ: 22.0   TOP: "The Jazz Age"

3. What might account for the large number of race riots in northern cities in 1919?

ANS:
Answers will vary but could include the following ideas: In the years immediately prior to World War I, huge numbers of African-Americans, about a half million, had moved to northern cities from the South into formerly all-white neighborhoods, and that migration continued during the war. They were drawn to the northern industrial centers where they accepted the worst jobs at the lowest pay. Nonetheless, many white workers resented having to work with African-Americans, and racial tensions rose. African-American civilians were made more militant in defense of their rights by a war being fought to "make the world safe for democracy," and African-American soldiers came back from Europe expecting to find improved conditions. The greater African-American presence in northern cities led to a greater number of conflicts over jobs, housing, etc. The riots of 1919 thus grew out of fertile soil for racial violence.

DIF: Hard   REF: 578   OBJ: 22.1
TOP: Post WWI Racial Tension

4. What possible reasons could explain why the Prohibition Amendment was ratified by two-thirds of the states and then was so flagrantly violated throughout the 1920s?

ANS:
Answers will vary but could include the following ideas: Temperance groups had long sought a ban on the manufacture and sale of alcoholic beverages, but national Prohibition came about only when the country entered World War I. Liquor then seemed a menace to America's fighting efficiency; it seemed to compromise America's high ideals; and it seemed too German (many Germans were involved in the distilling and brewery industries). The Prohibition Amendment was quickly ratified in the moral fervor created by Wilsonian rhetoric and national mobilization. The reaction against this moral frenzy just a few years later included a desire for alcoholic beverages and a disregard for the law that banned them.

DIF: Hard   REF: 582   OBJ: 22.1   TOP: Prohibition

5. Compare Harding and the scandals associated with his administration with Ulysses S. Grant and the scandals that tarnished Grant's terms as President.

ANS:
Answers will vary but could include the following ideas: Both Harding and Grant were ill-prepared and ill-equipped to administer the office of President. Although neither was personally corrupt, both brought into their administrations men whose greed exceeded their commitment to the nation's good. Both Harding and Grant tended to be too trusting and too willing to delegate responsibility. Both were taken by surprise when talk of scandal in their administrations surfaced.

DIF: Hard   OBJ: 22.2   TOP: Harding / Grant Presidency

6. How was the cause of world peace advanced in the 1920s?

   ANS:
   Answers will vary but could include the following ideas: The Washington Conference in 1921 resulted in three treaties that attempted to limit the naval arms race that threatened to develop after World War I. In the Nine Power Treaty, the Western powers and Japan agreed to respect China's integrity. In the Four Power Treaty, the United States, Britain, France, and Japan agreed to respect one another's Pacific possessions. Later in the decade, the Kellogg-Briand Pact also attempted to advance the cause of world peace.

   DIF: Hard   REF: 584   OBJ: 22.2
   TOP: Post WWI Foreign Relations

7. Explain why the Progressive party attracted so much support in the election of 1924.

   ANS:
   Answers will vary but could include the following ideas: The Progressive party received almost 5 million votes in 1924, the largest number ever for a third party. The large turnout in support of Robert M. La Follette's presidential bid reflected significant dissatisfaction with the two major parties, both of which had become decidedly conservative. Running on a platform that called for government ownership of railroads, credit and other aid for farmers, and social legislation as well as other laws to protect workers, La Follette received the bulk of his support from farmers, organized labor, and socialists.

   DIF: Hard   OBJ: 22.3   TOP: Presidential Elections

8. How did the life of the average American improve during the 1920s?

   ANS:
   Answers will vary but could include the following ideas: For most Americans, but not for farmers, the 1920s was a boom period. The economy grew, and people bought new products like cars, radios, phonographs, and refrigerators. The growing economy provided plenty of jobs, and wages grew too, although not as rapidly as industrial output. Health and education improved. And new forms of entertainment, especially radio and the movies, made life more exciting.

   DIF: Hard   REF: 590, 592–596   OBJ: 22.4
   TOP: 1920s Economy

© Prentice-Hall, Inc.

9. The decade of the 1920s was filled with many fads—flagpole sitting, mah-jong, crossword puzzles, marathon dancing, etc. What possible conclusions can be drawn about a society in which one fad follows close on the heels of another?

ANS:
Answers could include the following: Most American people were not interested in questions of public policy during the 1920s. Instead of and in part as a reaction to the demands of the Progressive era and World War I, they turned their attention to fad games and contests and to professional sports. Although business held center stage, there was a strong demand for entertainment, and the continuing fads helped meet that demand. In addition, the 1920s witnessed tremendous growth in the mass media, with newspapers and radio delivering word of every trend to millions of Americans simultaneously. It was the decade of "ballyhoo" in which the media, influenced by the burgeoning advertising industry, gave events an inappropriate importance. Mass production and mass circulation of ideas to a public wanting to enjoy itself led to a nation of faddists.

DIF: Hard   OBJ: 22.4   TOP: U.S. Society in 1920s

(page intentionally left blank)

MATCHING

Match each item with the correct statement below.

a. debt moratorium
b. Black Tuesday
c. Andrew Mellon
d. speculation
e. margin

f. expropriation
g. New Deal
h. Bonus Army
i. dividends
j. Japan

1. The practice of buying and selling stock to make quick profits.
2. A group of unemployed veterans who demanded benefits and were driven out of Washington, D.C., by the army.
3. Name given to the New York Stock Exchange's worst day, October 29, 1929, when prices fell sharply.
4. Purchasing stock by putting a small amount down and borrowing the rest on the value of the stock itself.
5. Share of a company's profits paid to stockholders.
6. The nation that seized Manchuria (1931) and bombed Shanghai (1932).
7. Name for the Mexican government's takeover of all oil properties in their nation.
8. Hoover's Secretary of the Treasury, who favored taking no government action to end the depression.
9. Franklin D. Roosevelt's program to help get the nation out of the depression.
10. Name for Hoover's one-year postponement of Allied war-loan payments to the United States.

1. ANS: D   DIF: Easy   REF: 600   OBJ: 23.0
   TOP: Stock Market
2. ANS: H   DIF: Easy   REF: 606   OBJ: 23.0
   TOP: Great Depression / Bonus Army
3. ANS: B   DIF: Easy   REF: 602   OBJ: 23.0
   TOP: The Great Crash
4. ANS: E   DIF: Easy   REF: 600   OBJ: 23.0
   TOP: Stock Market
5. ANS: I   DIF: Easy   REF: 600   OBJ: 23.0
   TOP: Stock Market
6. ANS: J   DIF: Easy   REF: 612   OBJ: 23.0
   TOP: Japanese History
7. ANS: F   DIF: Easy   REF: 610   OBJ: 23.0
   TOP: Mexican History
8. ANS: C   DIF: Easy   REF: 603   OBJ: 23.0
   TOP: Hoover's Administration
9. ANS: G   DIF: Easy   REF: 613   OBJ: 23.0
   TOP: FDR's New Deal
10. ANS: A   DIF: Easy   REF: 609   OBJ: 23.0
    TOP: Debt Moratorium

MULTIPLE CHOICE

1. Putting down a small amount of cash to buy shares of a stock is known as
   a. percentage buying.   c. buying on margin.
   b. mania buying.   d. buying on time.

   ANS: C   DIF: Medium   REF: 600   OBJ: 23.1
   TOP: Stock Market

2. The acting president of the New York Stock Exchange in 1929 was
   a. J. P. Morgan.   c. David Rockefeller.
   b. Andrew Mellon.   d. Richard Whitney.

   ANS: D   DIF: Medium   REF: 601   OBJ: 23.2
   TOP: Stock Market

3. In the spring of 1929, relief to farmers began with the creation of the
   a. Farm Bureau.
   b. Federal Farm Board.
   c. Agricultural Adjustment Administration.
   d. Farm Security Administration.

   ANS: B   DIF: Medium   REF: 604   OBJ: 23.2
   TOP: Farming

4. In 1930 duties were boosted on a thousand items by the
   a. Hawley-Smoot Tariff Act.   c. McNary-Haugen Tariff Act.
   b. Federal Revenue Tariff Act.   d. Hoover-Hawley Tariff Act.

   ANS: A   DIF: Medium   REF: 604   OBJ: 23.2
   TOP: U.S. Economics

5. Shantytowns of the suddenly poor and displaced were known as
   a. Hoovervilles.   c. Dust Bowls.
   b. Bust Towns.   d. Povertyvilles.

   ANS: A   DIF: Medium   REF: 606   OBJ: 23.2
   TOP: The Great Depression

6. In 1932 a march on Washington was made by a group of unemployed veterans called
   a. Coxey's Army.   c. the Bonus Army.
   b. Hoover's Army.   d. the Bogus Army.

   ANS: C   DIF: Medium   REF: 606   OBJ: 23.2
   TOP: The Great Depression / Bonus Army

7. A postponement of war payments owed to the United States was called a debt
   a. moratorium.   c. relief.
   b. hiatus.   d. default.

   ANS: A   DIF: Medium   REF: 609   OBJ: 23.3
   TOP: Debt Moratorium

8. Coolidge's shrewd and able ambassador to Mexico was
   a. Frank Kellogg.
   b. Charles A. Lindbergh.
   c. John Nance Garner.
   d. Dwight W. Morrow.

   ANS: D   DIF: Medium   REF: 611   OBJ: 23.3
   TOP: Coolidge's Administration

9. A trade boycott against another nation is one type of economic
   a. sanction.
   b. expropriation.
   c. confiscation.
   d. appropriation.

   ANS: A   DIF: Medium   REF: 612   OBJ: 23.3
   TOP: Economics

10. The Democratic candidate for President in 1932 was
    a. Alfred E. Smith.
    b. John Nance Garner.
    c. Franklin D. Roosevelt.
    d. Herbert Hoover.

    ANS: C   DIF: Medium   REF: 613   OBJ: 23.4
    TOP: Presidential Elections

11. All of the following are true about Herbert Hoover's background EXCEPT that he was
    a. an engineer.
    b. raised on a farm.
    c. a Catholic.
    d. a millionaire.

    ANS: C   DIF: Medium   REF: 599   OBJ: 23.1
    TOP: Herbert Hoover

12. When the United States entered World War I, Hoover headed the
    a. Committee on Public Information.
    b. General Accounting Office.
    c. Federal Trade Commission.
    d. Food Administration.

    ANS: D   DIF: Medium   REF: 599   OBJ: 23.1
    TOP: Herbert Hoover

13. Hoover believed that the government should
    a. take no role in business.
    b. be as large and powerful as possible.
    c. assure fairness in business.
    d. take from the rich and give to the poor.

    ANS: C   DIF: Medium   REF: 600   OBJ: 23.1
    TOP: Herbert Hoover

14. In his refusal to modify his political beliefs in the face of a national economic crisis, Herbert Hoover most resembled
    a. Grover Cleveland.
    b. William McKinley.
    c. Franklin Roosevelt.
    d. Richard Nixon.

    ANS: A   DIF: Medium   REF: 607–608   OBJ: 23.1
    TOP: Herbert Hoover

15. As a result of stock market gambling,
    a.   Americans borrowed heavily to bet on stocks.
    b.   businesses put their cash into margin loans rather than into new machines and factories.
    c.   the connection between the real value of companies and their stock prices was reduced.
    d.   all of the above

    ANS: D   DIF: Medium   REF: 600   OBJ: 23.1
    TOP: Stock Market

16. All of the following have been advanced as causes of the Great Depression EXCEPT
    a.   the stock market crash
    b.   the uneven distribution of income.
    c.   the high unemployment of the 1920s.
    d.   high tariffs and other disruptions of world trade.

    ANS: C   DIF: Medium   OBJ: 23.2   TOP: The Great Depression

17. Hoover's methods for dealing with the depression included all of the following EXCEPT
    a.   tax cuts.   c.   higher tariffs.
    b.   direct relief payments.   d.   a limited program of public works.

    ANS: B   DIF: Medium   REF: 604, 607   OBJ: 23.2
    TOP: Hoover's Presidency / Domestic Policy

18. To ease the suffering caused by the stock market crash, Hoover tried all of the following
    EXCEPT
    a.   cutting his own salary.
    b.   lowering income taxes.
    c.   asking cities, states, and charities to feed the hungry.
    d.   asking businesses to lower wages and cut production.

    ANS: D   DIF: Medium   REF: 604   OBJ: 23.2
    TOP: Hoover's Presidency

19. In response to the farmers' plight, the government
    a.   bought great amounts of wheat and cotton.
    b.   ordered a reduction in crops.
    c.   forced up prices for agricultural products.
    d.   encouraged farmers to grow more crops.

    ANS: A   DIF: Medium   REF: 604   OBJ: 23.2
    TOP: Hoover's Presidency / Domestic Policy

20. The stock market "crash" refers to
    a.   the failure of people to repay loan for stock bought on the margin.
    b.   the huge drop in the value of stocks.
    c.   the inflated value of many stocks.
    d.   millions of shares of stock being traded in one day.

    ANS: B   DIF: Medium   REF: 602–603   OBJ: 23.2
    TOP: Stock Market

21. All of the following were effects of the depression EXCEPT
    a. millions of unemployed people.   c. fewer marriages.
    b. malnutrition in children.   d. increased college enrollments.

    ANS: D   DIF: Medium   REF: 606   OBJ: 23.2
    TOP: The Great Depression

22. In 1932 the percentage of unemployed was about
    a. 10 percent.   c. 25 percent.
    b. 20 percent.   d. 35 percent.

    ANS: C   DIF: Medium   REF: 606   OBJ: 23.2
    TOP: The Great Depression

23. Testifying before a House subcommittee on the depression, an Oklahoma newspaper editor said,
    "While Oregon sheep raisers fed mutton to the buzzards, I saw men picking for meat scraps in
    the garbage cans in the cities of New York and Chicago." The unstated main idea of the
    quotation is that
    a. Oregon sheep raisers are thoughtless and selfish.
    b. the depression has affected only those living in cities.
    c. the poverty of the depression exists amid the plenty of a rich country.
    d. the depression is a result of bad transportation policies.

    ANS: C   DIF: Medium   REF: 603   OBJ: 23.2
    TOP: The Great Depression

24. Hoover opposed direct government relief for individuals MAINLY because he believed that
    a. the costs would bankrupt the nation.
    b. the character of the American people would be damaged.
    c. the economy was about to recover.
    d. private charity would rescue those in need.

    ANS: B   DIF: Medium   REF: 608   OBJ: 23.2
    TOP: Hoover's Presidency / Domestic Policy

25. The purpose of the Reconstruction Finance Corporation was to save from bankruptcy
    a. large corporations.   c. insurance companies.
    b. banks.   d. all of the above

    ANS: D   DIF: Medium   REF: 608   OBJ: 23.2
    TOP: Hoover's Presidency / Domestic Policy

26. As a result of the worldwide depression, many Europen nations
    a. gave up the gold standard.   c. borrowed heavily from the USSR.
    b. went bankrupt.   d. increased trade with the United States.

    ANS: A   DIF: Medium   REF: 609   OBJ: 23.3
    TOP: World Economics

27. In 1928 a renunciation of war was signed in Paris in the
    a. Four Power Pact.   c. Stimson-Morrow Pact.
    b. Briand-Mussolini Pact.   d. Kellogg-Briand Pact.

    ANS: D   DIF: Medium   REF: 609   OBJ: 23.3
    TOP: Pre WWII Foreign Affairs

28. The purpose of the London naval conference was frustrated by inclusion of
    a. a default clause.   c. an escalator clause.
    b. a non-aggression clause.   d. a moratorium clause.

    ANS: C   DIF: Medium   REF: 610   OBJ: 23.3
    TOP: Pre WWII Foreign Affairs

29. Hoover's intention toward Latin America was to
    a. strictly enforce peace on U.S. terms.
    b. follow Theodore Roosevelt's policies.
    c. cut off all relations with revolutionary governments.
    d. improve relations and respect the governments in power.

    ANS: D   DIF: Medium   REF: 611   OBJ: 23.3
    TOP: Hoover's Foreign Policy

30. The agreements of the Nine Power Treaty and the hopes of the Kellogg-Briand Pact were
    shattered by the aggressive acts of
    a. Japan.   c. Russia.
    b. Mexico.   d. China.

    ANS: A   DIF: Medium   REF: 612   OBJ: 23.3
    TOP: Pre WWII Japan

31. The 1932 Republican platform favored
    a. more government involvement in business.
    b. abolition of Prohibition.
    c. letting the nation's problems be solved by natural forces.
    d. breaking with tradition.

    ANS: C   DIF: Medium   REF: 613   OBJ: 23.4
    TOP: Presidential Elections

32. The 1932 Democratic platform favored
    a. the repeal of Prohibition.
    b. government withdrawal from the free enterprise system.
    c. fairer distribution of the products of industry.
    d. the repeal of Prohibition and fairer distribution of the products of industry.

    ANS: D   DIF: Medium   REF: 613   OBJ: 23.4
    TOP: Presidential Elections

33. In the election of 1932, Franklin D. Roosevelt favored
    a.   a more equal distribution of income.
    b.   the repeal of Prohibition.
    c.   less government intervention in the economy.
    d.   a more equal distribution of income AND the repeal of Prohibition.

    ANS: D   DIF: Medium   REF: 613   OBJ: 23.4
    TOP: Presidential Elections

34. Which is the correct chronological order of presidential administrations?
    a.   Harding, Coolidge, Hoover, Franklin Roosevelt
    b.   Hoover, Coolidge, Harding, Franklin Roosevelt
    c.   Hoover, Harding, Coolidge, Franklin Roosevelt
    d.   Coolidge, Harding, Hoover, Franklin Roosevelt

    ANS: A   DIF: Medium   OBJ: 23.4   TOP: U.S. Presidents

35. If Herbert Hoover wrote a book in which he explained his political beliefs, the title would most
    likely have been
    a.   "Let Them Eat Cake."
    b.   "American Collectivism."
    c.   "American Individualism."
    d.   "The Failure of the Free Enterprise System."

    ANS: C   DIF: Medium   REF: 600   OBJ: 23.1
    TOP: Herbert Hoover

36. Which of the following was NOT a cause of the Great Depression?
    a.   industrial overproduction   c.   excessive stock speculation
    b.   unequal distribution of wealth   d.   government overspending

    ANS: D   DIF: Medium   REF: 601–603   OBJ: 23.2
    TOP: The Great Depression

37. Buying stocks on margin contributed to the Great Crash because
    a.   margin buying discouraged investors from taking risks.
    b.   as prices fell, stockholders either had to sell their stock or pay more cash.
    c.   margin buying appealed only to rich investors.
    d.   all of the above

    ANS: B   DIF: Medium   REF: 600   OBJ: 23.2
    TOP: The Great Crash

38. All of the following were attempts to ease world tensions EXCEPT the
    a.   Kellogg-Briand Pact.
    b.   German and Austrian debt moratorium.
    c.   creation of Manchukuo.
    d.   abandonment of the Roosevelt Corollary.

    ANS: C   DIF: Medium   REF: 612   OBJ: 23.3
    TOP: Pre WWII Foreign Affairs

39. Which of the following lists of events is in correct chronological order?
    a. German and Austrian debt moratorium, Kellogg-Briand Pact signed, London Naval Conference
    b. Lindbergh makes nonstop flight to Mexico City, Mussolini brings fascism to Italy, Kellogg-Briand Pact signed
    c. Manchukuo set up, League of Nations declares Japan an outlaw nation, Shanghai bombed
    d. Stimson abandons the Roosevelt Corollary, Kellogg-Briand Pact signed, London Naval Conference

    ANS: C   DIF: Medium   REF: 612   OBJ: 23.3
    TOP: Pre WWII Foreign Affairs

40. It is a FACT rather than an opinion that
    a. many people blamed Herbert Hoover for the depression.
    b. Hoover did not care about the plight of ordinary people.
    c. Hoover was wrong to recognize any "de facto" government.
    d. the depression would not have happened if Hoover had not been President.

    ANS: A   DIF: Medium   REF: 613   OBJ: 23.4
    TOP: Hoover's Presidency / The Great Depression

41. Hoover called Franklin D. Roosevelt "a chameleon on a plaid" because Roosevelt
    a. was too radical.
    b. had strong support among garment workers.
    c. said different things to different political constituencies.
    d. had set forth a detailed blueprint for recovery from the depression.

    ANS: C   DIF: Medium   REF: 614   OBJ: 23.4
    TOP: Presidential Elections

ESSAY

1. Which of the following is the WEAKEST example of reasoning by eliminating alternatives? Write your answer on a separate sheet of paper and support your answer with a paragraph explaining why you chose it.
   A. Declining industries in the 1920s could not have been an important cause of the Great Depression, since it is normal for industries to decline in a changing economy. These declining industries were more than made up for by other expanding industries.
   B. The stock market crash couldn't have been the main cause of the Great Depression. The slowdown after it was mild. Not until nearly a year later did the economy drop into a depression. There have been many stock crashes in American history, but not all of them resulted in a depression, and none in a depression of this magnitude.
   C. Overproduction couldn't have been the main cause of the Great Depression because overproduction is not that important. When companies overproduce they know that eventually they will have to cut production and lay off workers, so they plan ahead.

   ANS:
   answer C Students' paragraphs should support their answer.

   DIF: Hard   OBJ: 23.0   TOP: The Great Depression

2. What three main flaws in the American economy led to the events that began the Great Depression?

ANS:
Student answers will vary but could include these ideas: One main flaw in the American economy that led to the Depression was the unequal distribution of wealth. Only a few rich families control-led most of the wealth of the nation. After the crash, wealthy citizens, fearing further loss, refused to spend their money to help the economy. High tariffs kept other countries from trading with the U.S. Previously, loans and investments from the U.S. had enabled other countries to buy American products and pay war debts. After the crash, U.S. loans and investments stopped, and other nations could not pay debts or buy products. More factories were closed. Unemployment rose even higher. The stock market itself was a problem. It provided a forum for speculation (buying on margin). When the market fell, people did not realize that only the prices of stocks had dropped, not the value of the nation's product. Investors lost confidence.

DIF: Hard   REF: 603, 609   OBJ: 23.0   TOP: The Great Depression

3. How did speculation and margin buying affect the stock market?

ANS:
Answers will vary but could include the following ideas: Speculation changed the buying and selling of stocks from informed investments to wild gambles. Stock buyers did not seek to be owners of profitable companies so much as to be transient holders of securities that someone else would buy at a higher price in the very near future. These buyers sought to exert the greatest leverage in their purchases by putting only a small amount of cash down and financing the balance on credit (margin). The result of these practices (speculation and margin buying) was to push stock prices upward way beyond the level appropriate to the value of the underlying companies. When the speculation at last ran its course, prices started to tumble, and brokers demanded additional cash to cover past purchases. Unable or unwilling to come up with the cash, stockholders sold their shares for whatever they could get, accelerating the stock market slide.

DIF: Hard   REF: 600–603   OBJ: 23.1   TOP: Stock Market

4. What underlying economic flaws did the Great Crash reveal?

ANS:
Answers will vary but could include the following ideas: The Great Crash revealed that too much investment was based on speculation and borrowed money. When the crash frightened wealthy people into stopping their spending and investing, it also showed that the unequal distribution of wealth could paralyze industrial output by stalling consumer purchases. Most importantly, the sudden disappearance of millions of dollars in declining stock values shook the confidence of the American people in their own economy, leading to runs on banks and other economic ills.

DIF: Hard   REF: 603–606   OBJ: 23.2   TOP: The Great Crash

5. What actions did Hoover take to deal with the economic crisis?

ANS:
Answers will vary but could include the following ideas: Hoover used the Agricultural Marketing Act to keep farm prices high, persuaded Congress to cut taxes and create the Reconstruction Finance Corporation to pump money into the economy, urged private charities and local governments to aid the needy, encouraged business leaders to keep workers and maintain industrial output, and had Congress pass the Federal Home Loan Bank Act to prevent residential mortgage foreclosure.

DIF: Hard   REF: 603–608   OBJ: 23.2
TOP: Hoover's Economic Policies

6. Explain Hoover's attitude toward aid to the destitute during the depression.

ANS:
Answers will vary but could include the following ideas: Although criticized as uncaring, Hoover was deeply distressed by the suffering that took place during the depression. He urged charities, local governments, and businesses to do their utmost to help the homeless and hungry. His one grave error in regard to the destitute was to call in federal troops when the Bonus Army camped near the White House; the eviction of the squatters, however, was a decision made by General Douglas MacArthur who disobeyed Hoover's order. Although personally sympathetic with the plight of the poor, Hoover would not abandon his individualistic ideology that banned direct government aid to those who were suffering. Even when the magnitude of the problem dwarfed efforts by charities and local governments to alleviate distress, Hoover refused to consider a federal government "safety net."

DIF: Hard   REF: 603–608   OBJ: 23.2
TOP: Hoover's Presidency / Poverty

7. What events in the 1920s and early 1930s foreshadowed the outbreak of World War II?

ANS:
Answers will vary but could include the following ideas: The Kellogg-Briand Pact of the late 1920s actually encouraged German and Italian aggression a decade later because the Fascist and Nazi governments regarded the peaceful nations as timid, a view that was reinforced by the response to Japanese aggression in Manchuria. The failure of all of the participating nations in the 1930 London naval conference to agree upon limits on warships also foreshadowed a build-up of armaments throughout the following decade.

DIF: Hard   REF: 609–613   OBJ: 23.3
TOP: Pre WWII Foreign Affairs

8. How did the United States practice "dollar diplomacy" in relation to Latin America during the Coolidge years?

ANS:
Answers will vary but could include the following ideas: Dollar diplomacy began in earnest during the administration of William Howard Taft, who urged American businesses to invest beyond U.S. borders. During and after Taft's term, American troops were dispatched to Latin America to protect U.S. business interests. Coolidge pulled the troops out of the Dominican Republic but sent them back to Nicaragua. He lodged a protest over Mexico's expropriation of American oil properties but stopped short of using military force to resolve the issue. Hoover advanced this move toward a good neighbor policy in Latin America.

DIF: Hard   REF: 610–611   OBJ: 23.3
TOP: Coolidge's Presidency / Foreign Affairs

9. Compare and contrast the platforms of the Republican and Democratic parties in 1932.

ANS:
Answers will vary but could include the following ideas: The Republican and Democratic platforms of 1932 were quite similar in several respects. Both called for reduced government spending, a balanced budget, U.S. participation in an international monetary conference, and veterans' pensions for service-connected disabilities. They disagreed about the tariff; Republicans wanted to continue the protective tariff while Democrats wanted a competitive tariff for revenue. Republicans wanted to revise the Prohibition Amendment while the Democrats wanted to repeal it. Republicans called for maintenance of the gold standard and restricted immigration. Democrats called for aid to farmers, banking and financial reforms, federal regulation of securities transactions, and control of rates charged by interstate utility companies.

DIF: Hard   OBJ: 23.4   TOP: Presidential Elections

10. What actions might Herbert Hoover have cited during the 1932 presidential campaign to show that he was trying to end the depression?

ANS:
Answers will vary but could include the following ideas: Hoover could and did cite his use of the Agricultural Marketing Act to help farmers and the pump-priming activities of the Reconstruction Finance Corporation and Federal Home Loan Bank. He had created national emergency relief organizations to coordinate the efforts of state and local agencies. He had requested funds for construction of public works, and he had used the prestige of his office in efforts to convince businesses to maintain payrolls and production.

DIF: Hard   OBJ: 23.4   TOP: Hoover's Presidency

11. Is it fair to blame Herbert Hoover for the depression?

ANS:
Answers will vary but could include the following ideas: The Democrats, of course, blamed Hoover for the depression, but it seems clear that the speculative mania that induced the stock market crash preceded his inauguration as President, and it is doubtful that any President could have done much to curb the excessive speculation. To some extent, Hoover contributed to the underlying weaknesses of the American economy while he was Secretary of Commerce. He failed to see patterns of overproduction and underconsumption emerging, and he did nothing to correct the unequal distribution of wealth or the inability of wages to keep pace with worker productivity. As President, Hoover can legitimately be blamed for his refusal to provide direct relief, for his insistence that the depression had to be cured on a worldwide basis, for his unfounded promises that recovery was at hand, and for his inability to inspire the confidence needed to offset the fear that was consuming the American people.

DIF: Hard   OBJ: 23.4
TOP: Hoover's Presidency / The Great Depression

MATCHING

Match each item with the correct statement below.

a. deflation
b. Frances Perkins
c. John Maynard Keynes
d. 21st Amendment
e. Wagner Act

f. Huey Long
g. bank holiday
h. devalue
i. CCC

1. As Secretary of Labor, she was the first woman appointed to the Cabinet.
2. English economist who favored increased federal spending to stimulate the economy.
3. Louisiana governor and advocate of "Share the Wealth" program, who attacked FDR's New Deal.
4. Viewed as "Labor's Magna Carta," it gave workers the right to join a union and to bargain.
5. Falling prices and wages.
6. Provided for the repeal of Prohibition.
7. This program put young men to work on conservation projects.
8. The closing of the nation's banks until they were found to be financially sound.
9. Reduce the worth of the dollar.

1. ANS: B   DIF: Easy   REF: 622   OBJ: 24.0
   TOP: FDR's Presidency
2. ANS: C   DIF: Easy   REF: 626   OBJ: 24.0
   TOP: Economics
3. ANS: F   DIF: Easy   REF: 632   OBJ: 24.0
   TOP: FDR's New Deal / Critics
4. ANS: E   DIF: Easy   REF: 634   OBJ: 24.0
   TOP: Labor Unions
5. ANS: A   DIF: Easy   REF: 624   OBJ: 24.0
   TOP: Economics
6. ANS: D   DIF: Easy   REF: 626   OBJ: 24.0
   TOP: Constitution
7. ANS: I   DIF: Easy   REF: 626   OBJ: 24.0
   TOP: FDR's New Deal
8. ANS: G   DIF: Easy   REF: 623–624   OBJ: 24.0
   TOP: FDR's Presidency
9. ANS: H   DIF: Easy   REF: 624   OBJ: 24.0
   TOP: Economics

MULTIPLE CHOICE

1. The "hundred days" was the time period
   a. between FDR's election and the first inauguration.
   b. immediately following FDR's first inauguration.
   c. concluding FDR's first term.
   d. immediately following FDR's second inauguration.

   ANS: B   DIF: Medium   REF: 622   OBJ: 24.1
   TOP: FDR's Presidency

2. The four-month period between election and inauguration of a new President was eliminated by
   a. order of the Supreme Court.
   b. ratification of the Twentieth Amendment.
   c. ratification of the Twenty-first Amendment.
   d. order of the Federal Election Commission.

   ANS: B   DIF: Medium   REF: 622–623   OBJ: 24.1
   TOP: Constitution

3. Raising the real income of farmers to parity was the purpose of the
   a. Civilian Conservation Corps.   c. Farm Credit Act.
   b. Agricultural Adjustment Act.   d. Tennessee Valley Authority.

   ANS: B   DIF: Medium   REF: 628   OBJ: 24.1
   TOP: FDR's New Deal / Farm Policy

4. The Glass-Steagall Act reformed the
   a. banking system.   c. election system.
   b. tax system.   d. securities system.

   ANS: A   DIF: Medium   REF: 624   OBJ: 24.1
   TOP: FDIC

5. The Twenty-first Amendment ended
   a. stock speculation.   c. thc four-month "lame-duck" period.
   b. Prohibition.   d. the gold standard.

   ANS: B   DIF: Medium   REF: 626   OBJ: 24.1
   TOP: Constitution

6. In "Schechter v. United States," the Supreme Court declared that the
   a. NRA was unconstitutional.
   b. Social Security Act was unconstitutional.
   c. AAA was unconstitutional.
   d. SEC was constitutional.

   ANS: A   DIF: Medium   REF: 632   OBJ: 24.2
   TOP: Supreme Court

7. Putting farm products in storage in years of surplus and then releasing them in years of scarcity was known as
   a. soil conservation.
   b. an ever-normal granary.
   c. federal crop insurance.
   d. parity.

   ANS: B   DIF: Medium   REF: 638   OBJ: 24.3
   TOP: Farming

8. In 1938, Roosevelt resumed large-scale spending to counter the
   a. Congressional purge.
   b. Roosevelt recession.
   c. expansion of Italy, Germany, and Japan.
   d. actions of the Supreme Court.

   ANS: B   DIF: Medium   REF: 638   OBJ: 24.3
   TOP: FDR's Presidency / Economics

9. Establishment of a minimum wage of 25 cents an hour was set by the
   a. Department of Labor.
   b. Wagner Act.
   c. Fair Labor Standards Act.
   d. Supreme Court.

   ANS: A   DIF: Medium   REF: 634–635   OBJ: 24.3
   TOP: Minimum Wage

10. Roosevelt's first cabinet was made up of
    a. loyal Democrats.
    b. professors and scholars.
    c. a mixture of politicians, leaders, and friends.
    d. former cabinet members.

    ANS: C   DIF: Medium   REF: 622   OBJ: 24.1
    TOP: FDR's Presidency

11. Roosevelt's first actions as President included all of the following EXCEPT
    a. promising he would follow Hoover's program.
    b. calling for a special session of Congress.
    c. declaring a bank holiday.
    d. presenting an emergency banking bill.

    ANS: A   DIF: Medium   REF: 623   OBJ: 24.1
    TOP: FDR's Presidency

12. FDR's "pump priming" required
    a. balancing the federal budget.
    b. running up a federal deficit.
    c. limiting production.
    d. repealing Prohibition.

    ANS: B   DIF: Medium   REF: 626   OBJ: 24.1
    TOP: FDR's New Deal

13. The first Agricultural Adjustment Act (AAA)
    a. paid farmers not to grow crops.
    b. was declared unconstitutional by the Supreme Court.
    c. was unsuccessful in raising farm prices.
    d. paid farmers not to grow crops AND was declared unconstitutional by the Supreme Court.

    ANS: D   DIF: Medium   REF: 628, 634   OBJ: 24.1
    TOP: The Great Depression / Farm Policy

14. FDR intended the National Industrial Recovery Act to help industry recover through
    a. government takeovers of basic industries.
    b. financial sacrifice by owners of businesses.
    c. a partnership between government and business.
    d. a partnership between government and labor.

    ANS: C   DIF: Medium   REF: 628   OBJ: 24.1
    TOP: FDR's New Deal

15. To regulate the stock market and to prevent abuses by sellers of stocks and bonds, Congress in 1934 set up the
    a. Federal Deposit Insurance Corporation.
    b. Reconstruction Finance Corporation.
    c. Securities and Exchange Commission.
    d. NLRB.

    ANS: C   DIF: Medium   REF: 625   OBJ: 24.1
    TOP: Stock Market

16. The purpose of the WPA was to
    a. help business.
    b. reestablish confidence in the banking system.
    c. provide immediate financial aid to farmers.
    d. provide work for the able-bodied unemployed.

    ANS: D   DIF: Medium   REF: 631   OBJ: 24.2
    TOP: The Great Depression

17. In 1934, right-wing opponents of the New Deal, including both Democrats and Republicans, formed the
    a. "Share the Wealth" League.   c. American Liberty League.
    b. Bull Moose party.   d. Chamber of Commerce.

    ANS: C   DIF: Medium   REF: 631   OBJ: 24.2
    TOP: FDR's New Deal / Critics

18. The Social Security Act provided all of the following EXCEPT
    a.   income to the elderly.
    b.   public assistance to certain needy persons.
    c.   low-income housing.
    d.   unemployment insurance.

    ANS: C   DIF: Medium   REF: 633   OBJ: 24.2
    TOP: Social Security

19. The TVA was criticized at the outset because
    a.   it was unfair competition for private industry.
    b.   it helped a prosperous region.
    c.   it benefited only the wealthy.
    d.   it damaged the environment.

    ANS: A   DIF: Medium   REF: 626–627   OBJ: 24.2
    TOP: FDR's New Deal

20. The WPA provided
    a.   jobs only for young men between ages 18 and 25.
    b.   jobs for many unemployed people including writers and artists.
    c.   a series of dams on the Tennessee River.
    d.   loans to homeowners.

    ANS: B   DIF: Medium   REF: 631   OBJ: 24.2
    TOP: The Great Depression

21. The Democratic platform of the 1936 election was based on the idea that the duty of government
    was to
    a.   protect the family and home.
    b.   establish a democracy of opportunity for all.
    c.   aid those overtaken by disaster.
    d.   all of the above

    ANS: D   DIF: Medium   REF: 636   OBJ: 24.2
    TOP: Presidential Elections

22. The term "Forgotten Man" refers to those
    a.   who had not voted in 1936.
    b.   who had voted against FDR in 1936.
    c.   who were neither rich nor successful.
    d.   whom the New Deal had not been able to help.

    ANS: C   DIF: Medium   REF: 637   OBJ: 24.2
    TOP: FDR's New Deal

23. The Social Security Act provided for
    a.   old-age insurance.   c.   unemployment insurance.
    b.   public assistance.   d.   all of the above

    ANS: D   DIF: Medium   REF: 633   OBJ: 24.2
    TOP: Social Security

24. Which of the following is an accomplishment of the New Deal?
    a. minimun wage laws
    b. balanced federal budget
    c. enlargement of the Supreme Court
    d. reduced government control over public utilities

    ANS: A   DIF: Medium   REF: 640   OBJ: 24.3
    TOP: FDR's New Deal / Minimum Wage

25. The New Deal came to an end in 1938 because
    a. the Supreme Court ruled most New Deal programs unconstitutional.
    b. FDR was stricken with polio.
    c. national concern shifted to overseas aggression.
    d. FDR was defeated in his bid for reelection.

    ANS: C   DIF: Medium   REF: 639   OBJ: 24.3
    TOP: FDR's New Deal

26. The course of business recovery from 1933 to 1939
    a. was steadily upward.
    b. was up one year and down the next.
    c. peaked in 1935.
    d. was upward until hit by a recession in 1937–1938.

    ANS: D   DIF: Medium   REF: 638   OBJ: 24.3
    TOP: U.S. Business

27. Roosevelt's plan of February 1937—to organize the federal courts—was undertaken
    a. with the approval of his cabinet.
    b. without consulting his cabinet.
    c. without consulting Democratic party leaders.
    d. without consulting his cabinet or Democratic party leaders.

    ANS: D   DIF: Medium   REF: 637–638   OBJ: 24.3
    TOP: FDR's Presidency

28. FDR's New Deal programs resulted in all of the following EXCEPT
    a. reduction in taxes.   c. giant increases in the national debt.
    b. alienation of business leaders.   d. a rise in the national income.

    ANS: A   DIF: Medium   REF: 630, 638   OBJ: 24.3
    TOP: FDR's New Deal

29. Which of the following was a result of the other three?
    a. Congress passes a law allowing federal judges to retire at age 70.
    b. The Supreme Court strikes down the AAA.
    c. The NRA is declared unconstitutional.
    d. Roosevelt attempts to pack the Court.

    ANS: A   DIF: Medium   REF: 632, 634, 638
    OBJ: 24.3   TOP: Supreme Court

30. The "Roosevelt Recession" demonstrated that
    a. the New Deal was over.
    b. Roosevelt had underestimated the economy's dependence on government spending.
    c. the business community hated Roosevelt.
    d. the depression was over.

    ANS: B   DIF: Medium   REF: 638   OBJ: 24.3
    TOP: FDR's Presidency / Economics

31. Most New Deal programs
    a. were continuations of earlier programs.
    b. were aimed at trust-busting.
    c. were aimed at helping farmers.
    d. greatly expanded the role of government.

    ANS: D   DIF: Medium   REF: 624–638   OBJ: 24.3
    TOP: FDR's New Deal

32. FDR's relations with Congress were soured early in his second term by
    a. his sudden stoppage of large-scale government spending.
    b. his attempt to reform the Supreme Court.
    c. the increase in unemployment.
    d. the passage of the Fair Labor Standards Act.

    ANS: B   DIF: Medium   REF: 637–638   OBJ: 24.3
    TOP: FDR's Presidency

33. President Roosevelt permitted the federal deficit to rise because
    a. federal deficits didn't bother him.
    b. he felt it was necessary to restore the economy.
    c. he was opposed to higher income taxes.
    d. spending money made him popular with the American people.

    ANS: B   DIF: Medium   REF: 626   OBJ: 24.1
    TOP: FDR's Presidency / Economics

34. Which of the following would be consistent with Keynesian economics?
    a. a Constitutional amendment mandating a balanced federal budget
    b. a free market with little or no government involvement
    c. a tax decrease during a recession
    d. "Reaganomics"

    ANS: C   DIF: Medium   REF: 626   OBJ: 24.1
    TOP: Economics

35. A newspaper headline proclaiming "A Switch in Time Saves Nine" probably referred to
    a. the treaty observing the Open Door Policy toward China.
    b. the beginning of Social Security payments to millions of Americans.
    c. the election of Democratic governors in Southern states.
    d. a Supreme Court decision upholding a state minimum-wage law.

    ANS: D   DIF: Medium   REF: 637–638   OBJ: 24.3
    TOP: Supreme Court

36. The outcome of President Roosevelt's attempted "purge" of conservative Democrats in 1938 showed that
    a. he was extremely popular with the American people.
    b. the President must assert himself as the head of his political party.
    c. the American people objected to Roosevelt's interference in local elections.
    d. the Solid South was no longer solidly behind the Democratic party.

    ANS: C   DIF: Medium   REF: 639   OBJ: 24.3
    TOP: FDR's Presidency

37. In his attempt to pack the Court and purge his party, President Roosevelt showed that he could be
    a. compassionate.   c. forgiving.
    b. ruthless.   d. tolerant.

    ANS: B   DIF: Medium   REF: 638   OBJ: 24.3
    TOP: Franklin Roosevelt

SHORT ANSWER

In one or two sentences, define and distinguish between the terms given below.

1. the "hundred days"

    ANS:
    The Hundred Days refers to the first 100 days of FDR's first term when he pushed a barrage of programs through Congress aimed at getting the economy moving.

    DIF: Hard   REF: 622–623   OBJ: 24.0   TOP: FDR's Presidency

2. modified gold standard

    ANS:
    When FDR put the nation on a modified gold standard, every dollar still had to be secured by some gold. People had to turn their gold coins and certificates over to the Federal Reserve banks. From then on, debtors could use any form of coin or currency.

    DIF: Hard   REF: 624–625   OBJ: 24.0   TOP: Money

3. AAA

    ANS:
    The Agricultural Adjustment Acts aimed at raising farm prices by limiting production and controlling farm surpluses.

    DIF: Hard   REF: 628   OBJ: 24.0   TOP: Farming

4. court packing

ANS:
Court packing refers to FDR's attempt to increase the number of Supreme Court justices from 9 to 15 if the justices refused to retire at the age of 70. His aim was to make the Supreme Court approve New Deal programs.

DIF: Hard   REF: 638   OBJ: 24.0   TOP: Supreme Court

ESSAY

1. Which of the following statements is an example of comparison reasoning? Write your answer on a separate sheet of paper and support your answer with a paragraph explaining why you chose it.
    A. The National Recovery Administration represented the thinking of business groups like the Chamber of Commerce and the leading trade groups.
    B. President Roosevelt put the country on a modified gold standard in order to make prices and wages rise.
    C. The Wagner Act guaranteed the right of workers to join unions and to bargain collectively.
    D. Roosevelt's margin of victory in the 1936 election was larger than his margin in 1932.

    ANS:
    answer D Students' paragraphs should support their answer.

    DIF: Hard   REF: 613–614, 635–637   OBJ: 24.0
    TOP: Presidential Elections

2. In his New Deal, FDR did not aim to "change the rules of the American game." Rather, "he tried to use the government to deal out the cards so that everybody would have a better chance to win a good life." Use this claim as the conclusion of an essay in which you supply evidence supporting it.

    ANS:
    FDR tried to keep the old rules by attempting to balance the federal budget. He tried to give everyone a fair chance by including as many people as possible in the works programs of the New Deal, and by helping homeowners refinance through the Home Owners Loan Corporation. NRA codes aimed to keep up prices and wages, set maximum hours and minimum wages, and gave workers the right to organize into unions. The AAA was an attempt to help the farmers and the CCC was a program to help the younger generation. The Securities and Exchange Commission brought assurances of a safer, saner market. The second Hundred Days aimed not so much at recovery as at reform. Reforms were seen in the new Social Security program, disability and unemployment insurances, "soak the rich " taxes, the dissolution of unfair public utilities holding companies, and the Wagner Act with its National Labor Relations Board.

    DIF: Hard   REF: 623–640   OBJ: 24.0   TOP: FDR's New Deal

3. Describe the New Deal proposals that were designed primarily to help the economy recover from the depression.

ANS:
Answers will vary but could include the following ideas: The major New Deal proposals that were designed primarily to help the economy recover from the depression included the National Industrial Recovery Act, the Agricultural Adjustment Act, the Farm Credit Act, the bank holiday, the Emergency Banking Act, the Glass-Steagall Act, the Gold Reserve Act, the Public Works Administration, and the Home Owners Loan Corporation.

DIF: Hard   REF: 623–630   OBJ: 24.1   TOP: FDR's New Deal

4. Is it accurate to describe Franklin Roosevelt as a believer in Keynesian economics? Explain your answer.

ANS:
Answers will vary but could include the following ideas: Franklin Roosevelt was not a strict believer in Keynesian economics. He was not guided by any single economic philosophy. Moreover, he was very uncomfortable with continuing high deficits. He viewed deficit spending as an emergency tactic for coping with a crisis. When, in 1937, he thought the crisis had passed, he cut federal spending significantly in order to get back to a balanced budget. The "Roosevelt Recession" ensued, and he resumed large-scale spending once again out of necessity rather than conviction.

DIF: Hard   REF: 626   OBJ: 24.1
TOP: FDR's Presidency / Economics

5. Describe the New Deal proposals that were designed primarily to provide relief to victims of the depression.

ANS:
Answers will vary but could include the following ideas: The New Deal proposal designed primarily to provide relief to victims of the depression included the Civilian Conservation Corps, the Resettlement Administration, the Federal Emergency Relief Act, the Civil Works Administration, the Works Progress Administration, the National Youth Administration, and the Social Security Act. Student answers should reflect understanding of relief—efforts taken to help individuals.

DIF: Hard   REF: 626–630   OBJ: 24.2   TOP: FDR's New Deal

6. Describe how the Roosevelt administration shifted its emphasis from recovery to reform after the 1934 congressional elections.

ANS:
Answers could include the following: Bolstered by the Democratic majorities in Congress following the 1934 elections and angered by the Supreme Court's striking down of the NRA, Roosevelt launched the "second 100 days" of the New Deal in 1935. Unlike the first, which concentrated on proposals to provide recovery from the depression, the second aimed at altering the relationship of the government to the people. The package included protection against financial hardship brought on by unemployment, old age, and certain other causes; guarantees for unionized workers to bargain collectively and be protected from unfair practices by employers; higher taxes for the rich; a corporate income tax; and action against monopolistic utility companies. Never before had the federal government attempted to provide a safety net under American citizens or to patrol the internal workings of the private sector.

DIF: Hard   REF: 631–640   OBJ: 24.2   TOP: FDR's New Deal

7. What group of Americans remained largely "forgotten" by the New Deal, and what possible reason could explain their being neglected?

ANS:
Answers will vary but could include the following ideas: African-Americans remained largely "forgotten" by the New Deal. Although needy African-Americans benefited from relief and employment programs, discrimination in the distribution of benefits was common, especially in the administration of agricultural programs in the South and housing programs in the cities. Possible reasons include Franklin Roosevelt's unwillingness to jeopardize Southern political support by adopting a pro-African-American stance, the nation's long history of relegating African-Americans to second-class citizenship, and the historical ties binding African-Americans to the Republican party, ties that gave them little voice in a Democratic administration.

DIF: Hard   OBJ: 24.2   TOP: FDR's New Deal

8. Did Roosevelt's plan to change the Supreme Court succeed or fail? Explain your answer.

ANS:
Answers could include the following: Succeed—Although Roosevelt never won approval for packing the Court, he succeeded in stopping the assault on New Deal legislation. Congress passed legislation allowing federal judges to retire at age 70 with full pay, and soon Roosevelt was appointing justices who were more philosophically aligned with him. In the long run, his plan to change the Court succeeded. Fail—Roosevelt badly misgauged public sentiment. The people saw through his argument that he merely wanted to reorganize the courts for greater efficiency. The packing scheme was seen as an underhanded way of altering the Court for political purposes. While Roosevelt eventually was able to shape the Court to his liking, his attempt to pack the Court tarnished his administration and gave ammunition to critics who accused him of being a dictator.

DIF: Hard   REF: 637–639   OBJ: 24.3   TOP: Supreme Court

9. What permanent effects did the New Deal have on life in the United States?

ANS:
Answers will vary but could include the following ideas: The New Deal left the legacy of a large government that assumed responsibility for the economic health of the nation. Since the 1930s, Democratic administrations have sought to enlarge upon the New Deal with programs that patch up holes in the public assistance fabric. Republican administrations, while criticizing the administrative bureaucracy of large government, have neither fundamentally dismantled the most important programs nor challenged the social contract that Franklin Roosevelt made with the American people more than 50 years ago.

DIF: Hard   OBJ: 24.3   TOP: FDR's New Deal

MATCHING

Match each item with the correct statement below.
a. Sidney Hillman
b. Mary (Molly) Dewson
c. John L. Lewis
d. W.E.B. Du Bois
e. Eleanor Roosevelt
f. John Bankhead
g. John Steinbeck
h. Langston Hughes
i. Frances Perkins

1. His novel immortalized the Okies who left the Dust Bowl in the 1930s to go west.
2. Headed the Niagara Movement; urged equality for African-Americans; renounced citizenship.
3. He brought his Amalgamated Clothing Workers into the CIO.
4. Democratic director of women's work and influential in getting women New Deal positions.
5. Became "the conscience of the New Deal and the eyes of the President."
6. A poet who helped spark the "Black Renaissance."
7. A sponsor of the Farm Tenant Act of 1937 that provided loans to help tenants buy farms.
8. The United Mine Workers president who founded the CIO in 1935.

1. ANS: G   DIF: Easy   REF: 643   OBJ: 25.0
   TOP: The Great Depression
2. ANS: D   DIF: Easy   REF: 648   OBJ: 25.0
   TOP: American History / Equal Rights
3. ANS: A   DIF: Easy   REF: 652–653   OBJ: 25.0
   TOP: Labor Unions
4. ANS: B   DIF: Easy   REF: 651   OBJ: 25.0
   TOP: Women's Rights
5. ANS: E   DIF: Easy   REF: 650   OBJ: 25.0
   TOP: Eleanor Roosevelt
6. ANS: H   DIF: Easy   REF: 649   OBJ: 25.0
   TOP: Black Renaissance
7. ANS: F   DIF: Easy   REF: 645   OBJ: 25.0
   TOP: FDR's New Deal / Farming
8. ANS: C   DIF: Easy   REF: 652–653   OBJ: 25.0
   TOP: Labor Unions

MULTIPLE CHOICE

1. Which of the following practices did NOT help farmers in the Dust Bowl to conserve soil?
   a. shelterbelts
   b. terrace gardening
   c. contour plowing
   d. sharecropping

   ANS: D   DIF: Medium   REF: 643   OBJ: 25.1
   TOP: The Great Depression / Farming

2. Farmers who tilled the land in exchange for a percentage of the crops were called
   a. sharecroppers.
   b. Okies.
   c. Arkies.
   d. migrants.

   ANS: A   DIF: Medium   REF: 644   OBJ: 25.1
   TOP: Sharecropping

3. Which of the following programs instituted during the New Deal remains in effect today?
   a. AAA
   b. TVA
   c. PWA
   d. CCC

   ANS: B   DIF: Medium   REF: 644   OBJ: 25.1
   TOP: FDR's New Deal

4. He organized the Niagara Movement and demanded immediate equality for African-Americans. He was
   a. Langston Hughes.
   b. Denmark Vesey.
   c. W. E. B. Du Bois.
   d. Frederick Douglass.

   ANS: C   DIF: Medium   REF: 648   OBJ: 25.2
   TOP: African-American History / Equal Rights

5. Which of the following groups were prevented from voting under the "grandfather clauses"?
   a. African-Americans
   b. women
   c. people over age 65
   d. union members

   ANS: A   DIF: Medium   REF: 646   OBJ: 25.2
   TOP: Voting Rights

6. The flowering of African-American culture and pride in the 1930s was known by all of the following names EXCEPT the
   a. Harlem Renaissance.
   b. Niagara Movement.
   c. New Negro Movement.
   d. Black Renaissance.

   ANS: B   DIF: Medium   REF: 649   OBJ: 25.2
   TOP: Harlem Renaissance

7. Women gained a greater voice in shaping the policies of the Democratic party largely through the work of
   a. Mary Dewson.
   b. Florence Allen.
   c. Florence Kahn.
   d. Dorothea Lange.

   ANS: A   DIF: Medium   REF: 650–651   OBJ: 25.3
   TOP: Women's Rights

8. Which of the following categories of workers would have been LEAST likely to join the AF of L in the 1930s?
   a. carpenters
   b. steelworkers
   c. bricklayers
   d. plumbers

   ANS: B   DIF: Medium   REF: 652   OBJ: 25.4
   TOP: Labor Unions

9. The union practice in which employees refused to leave their place of work was known as
   a. collective bargaining.
   c. strike-breaking.
   b. the sit-down strike.
   d. picketing.

   ANS: B   DIF: Medium   REF: 653   OBJ: 25.4
   TOP: Labor Unions

10. A labor organization that admitted many members of minority groups in the 1930s was the
    a. Carpenters' Union.
    b. AF of L.
    c. United Mine Workers.
    d. International Ladies Garment Workers Union.

    ANS: D   DIF: Medium   REF: 654   OBJ: 25.4
    TOP: Labor Unions

11. Which of the following did NOT contribute to the formation of the Dust Bowl?
    a. a long drought
    c. crop rotation
    b. years of intensive farming
    d. lack of trees

    ANS: C   DIF: Medium   REF: 643   OBJ: 25.1
    TOP: The Great Depression / Farming

12. Which of these was NOT a Dust Bowl state in the 1930s?
    a. California
    c. Oklahoma
    b. Arkansas
    d. Nebraska

    ANS: A   DIF: Medium   REF: 643   OBJ: 25.1
    TOP: The Great Depression / Farming

13. The sharecropping system developed because of the
    a. lack of unskilled farm workers in the United States.
    b. loss of good farm land in the Dust Bowl.
    c. large-scale arrival of immigrants from southern and eastern Europe.
    d. end of slavery in the United States.

    ANS: D   DIF: Medium   REF: 644   OBJ: 25.1
    TOP: Sharecropping

14. A primary goal of the Soil Conservation Act of 1936 was the
    a. reduction of rural unemployment.
    b. decrease of farm surpluses.
    c. provision of clean camps for migrant workers.
    d. end of the crop-lien system.

    ANS: B   DIF: Medium   REF: 643–644   OBJ: 25.1
    TOP: FDR's New Deal / Farming

15. The most serious weakness of the first Agricultural Act was that it
    a. caused serious crop shortages.
    c. did little to help tenant farmers.
    b. increased the price of farm goods.
    d. reduced the number of shelterbelts.

    ANS: C   DIF: Medium   REF: 644   OBJ: 25.1
    TOP: FDR's New Deal / Farming

16. The Rural Electrification Administration helped bring electric power to rural areas
   a. by setting up a giant utility company.
   b. by lending money at low interest to farmers' cooperatives and others.
   c. by making grants to big utility companies to build rural lines.
   d. by setting the rates utility companies could charge rural customers.

   ANS: B   DIF: Medium   REF: 645–646   OBJ: 25.1
   TOP: FDR's New Deal / Farming

17. If you read newspaper articles about the Bonus Army, listened to radio reports about the CIO, and worked for the Soil Erosion Service, you were probably living during the years
   a. 1931–1933.   c. 1935–1937.
   b. 1933–1935.   d. 1937–1939.

   ANS: B   DIF: Medium   REF: 643–652   OBJ: 25.1
   TOP: The Great Depression

18. By the end of the 1930s, the New Deal had accomplished all of the following to help the farmer EXCEPT
   a. tree planting on the Great Plains.
   b. elimination of the sharecropper system.
   c. getting electricity to the majority of farm homes.
   d. training in soil conservation.

   ANS: B   DIF: Medium   REF: 643–646   OBJ: 25.1
   TOP: FDR's New Deal / Farming

19. Which of these statements about the advancement of African-Americans up to 1940 is NOT true?
   a. "Grandfather clauses" limiting African-American suffrage had been struck down by the Supreme Court.
   b. Other voting restrictions were trivial and kept few African-Americans from voting.
   c. African-Americans had an effective national organization to represent them in major court cases and to publicize their cause.
   d. Some African-Americans served as close advisers to President Roosevelt.

   ANS: B   DIF: Medium   REF: 646–649   OBJ: 25.2
   TOP: African-American History / Equal Rights

20. Which of the following is NOT correctly paired?
   a. W.E.B. Du Bois—"The Crisis"
   b. Langston Hughes—Black Brain Trust
   c. Countee Cullen—The Harlem Renaissance
   d. Moorfield Storey—NAACP

   ANS: B   DIF: Medium   REF: 648–649   OBJ: 25.2
   TOP: African-American History

21. Which of the following statements was the result of the other three?
    a. During the depression, African-Americans won a greater number of jobs at the federal level.
    b. President Roosevelt spoke out publicly against lynchings, calling them acts of "collective murder."
    c. In the 1930s, many African-Americans switched their allegiance from the Republican party to the Democratic party.
    d. African-Americans played a prominent role in the Roosevelt administration.

    ANS: C   DIF: Medium   REF: 648–649   OBJ: 25.2
    TOP: The Great Depression / African-Americans

22. FDR refused to support an anti-lynching bill because
    a. he believed strongly in states' rights.
    b. he knew the Supreme Court would declare the law unconstitutional.
    c. he feared loss of Southern support in Congress.
    d. he believed strongly in states' rights AND he knew the Supreme Court would declare the law unconstitutional.

    ANS: C   DIF: Medium   REF: 649   OBJ: 25.2
    TOP: FDR's Presidency / Domestic Policy

23. Which of the following discriminatory practices against African-Americans was NOT ended or eased during the years 1915–1939?
    a. use of the poll tax
    b. segregation of government employees by race
    c. grandfather clauses
    d. union restrictions against African-American workers

    ANS: A   DIF: Medium   REF: 646–649, 654
    OBJ: 25.2   TOP: Voting Rights

24. Most African-Americans supported the New Deal because New Deal programs generally
    a. ended white control of the South.
    b. extended equal opportunity to African-Americans.
    c. paid African-Americans the same salaries as whites.
    d. involved more African-Americans in government than ever before.

    ANS: D   DIF: Medium   REF: 648–649   OBJ: 25.2
    TOP: FDR's New Deal / African-Americans

25. Women during the 1930s made the greatest gains by
    a. securing higher wages than men.
    b. becoming an independent voting force.
    c. winning jobs in the federal government.
    d. competing for leadership positions in business.

    ANS: C   DIF: Medium   REF: 650–651   OBJ: 25.3
    TOP: Women's Rights

26. Most Americans in the 1930s believed women should
    a. have equality with men.
    b. enter the mainstream of political and economic life.
    c. take jobs away from the traditional "breadwinners."
    d. support their families as wives and mothers.

    ANS: D   DIF: Medium REF: 649   OBJ: 25.3
    TOP: Women's Rights

27. What union practice did the Supreme Court ban in 1939?
    a. picketing   c. collective bargaining
    b. strike-breaking   d. sit-down striking

    ANS: D   DIF: Medium REF: 653   OBJ: 25.4
    TOP: Labor Unions / Supreme Court

28. The CIO differed from the AF of L in its emphasis on
    a. peaceful tactics.   c. exclusion of immigrants.
    b. organization of skilled workers. d. organization of heavy industry.

    ANS: D   DIF: Medium REF: 652   OBJ: 25.4
    TOP: Labor Unions

29. The organizing principle of the Congress of Industrial Organizations was
    a. to have one union for each giant industry enrolling skilled and unskilled workers.
    b. to have one union for skilled workers and another for unskilled workers in each major industry.
    c. to have one big national union like the old Knights of Labor.
    d. to set up separate unions for women workers.

    ANS: A   DIF: Medium REF: 652   OBJ: 25.4
    TOP: Labor Unions

30. In its first five years (1935–1940) the CIO failed
    a. to get labor contracts in the coal, steel, rubber, and textile industries.
    b. to get an increase in total union membership in the United States.
    c. to win acceptance for industrial unions by the AF of L.
    d. to get more union members among women and African-American workers.

    ANS: C   DIF: Medium REF: 652–654 OBJ: 25.4
    TOP: Labor Unions

31. Which of the following events took place first?
    a. The CIO starts over 4,000 strikes.
    b. The AF of L expels the CIO.
    c. The Supreme Court bans the use of the sit-down strike.
    d. Craft unions begin to recover from the Great Crash.

    ANS: D   DIF: Medium REF: 652–654 OBJ: 25.4
    TOP: Labor Unions

32. Which of the following statements is an OPINION rather than a fact?
    a. Lack of capital tied sharecroppers to the land with bonds of debt.
    b. In the mid-1930s, only one farm family in ten had electricity.
    c. Farmers during the depression suffered more than any other group among the American population.
    d. In the 1930s, a third of a million people escaped the Dust Bowl to become migrant workers.

    ANS: C   DIF: Medium   OBJ: 25.1
    TOP: The Great Depression / Farming

33. Most of the economic problems faced by farmers during the depression years can probably be attributed to
    a. falling demand and rising supply.   c. falling demand and falling supply.
    b. rising demand and falling supply.   d. rising demand and rising supply.

    ANS: A   DIF: Medium   REF: 628   OBJ: 25.1
    TOP: The Great Depression / Farming

34. The practice in the 1930s that MOST clearly violated the spirit of the Fifteenth Amendment was the use of
    a. literacy tests.   c. sit-down strikes.
    b. immigration quotas.   d. crop liens.

    ANS: A   DIF: Medium   REF: 646–647   OBJ: 25.2
    TOP: Voting Rights

35. Which of the following would have been the LEAST satisfied with the accomplishments of the New Deal?
    a. John L. Lewis   c. Frances Perkins
    b. W. E. B. Du Bois   d. John Bankhead

    ANS: B   DIF: Medium   REF: 649   OBJ: 25.2
    TOP: FDR's New Deal / Critics

36. In 1931 three out of four school boards responding to a survey said that they would not hire married women as teachers if their husbands worked. From 1932 to 1937, federal law forbade more than one family member working in the civil service. Which of the following do you think is the MOST likely outcome of an opinion poll conducted among Americans living in 1936?
    a. 82 percent thought wives whose husbands work should not hold jobs.
    b. 80 percent backed equal pay for women.
    c. 76 percent favored better job opportunities for women.
    d. 72 percent thought that there should be more two-income families.

    ANS: A   DIF: Medium   OBJ: 25.3   TOP: Women's Rights

37. The New Deal agency that probably did the MOST to advance the cause of organized labor in the 1930s was the
    a. TVA.   c. REA.
    b. NLRB.   d. AAA.

    ANS: B   DIF: Medium   OBJ: 25.4   TOP: FDR's New Deal

SHORT ANSWER

In one or two sentences, define and distinguish between the terms given below.

1. Federal Emergency Relief Act

   ANS:
   The Federal Emergency Relief Act (FERA) of 1933 loaned money to poor sharecroppers and other tenants.

   DIF: Hard   REF: 644–645   OBJ: 25.0
   TOP: FDR's New Deal / Farming

2. poll tax

   ANS:
   A poll tax was a tax everyone had to pay before going to the polls to vote in some southern states. This was one method used to keep African-Americans from voting.

   DIF: Hard   REF: 647   OBJ: 25.0   TOP: Voting Rights

3. literacy test

   ANS:
   Literacy tests were supposed to limit the vote to people who could read. Often the tests for African-Americans were more difficult than those for whites.

   DIF: Hard   REF: 646–647   OBJ: 25.0   TOP: Voting Rights

ESSAY

1. Which of the following statements is an example of cause-and-effect reasoning? Write your answer on a separate sheet of paper and support your answer with a paragraph explaining why you chose it.
   A. The precious soil of the Great Plains blew all the way to the East Coast and out into the Atlantic Ocean.
   B. John Steinbeck wrote about the hard journeys and frustrated lives of the Okies in his novel, The Grapes of Wrath.
   C. The AAA made the lives of sharecroppers worse by paying landowners to take some land out of production. The land they took out of production was often the land the sharecroppers farmed.
   D. Some unions leaders were not happy with the craft approach. They felt that the age of crafts had gone out with the horse and buggy. John L. Lewis believed that the industrial world needed a new kind of labor organization.

   ANS:
   answer C Students' paragraphs should support their answer.

   DIF: Hard   REF: 644–645   OBJ: 25.0   TOP: Sharecropping

2. Who were the "forgotten" Americans whom Eleanor Roosevelt championed and how did their lives change?

ANS:
Student answers will vary but could include these ideas: In her frequent travels around the United States during the Depression, Eleanor Roosevelt learned about groups of "forgotten Americans." She became the champion of women, African-Americans, immigrants, the poor. These groups saw changes achieved with her help and New Deal legislation. Women gained political influence and power. They worked in Washington, on the Democratic Party's Platform Committee, in the Civil Works Administration, in the court system, and as ambassadors and government officers. African-Americans, immigrants, and the poor were helped by laws such as the Wagner Act, which provided opportunities for union membership. African-Americans especially were encouraged by Mrs. Roosevelt. She made them feel that the government cared about them, and was a good friend of African-American leader Mary McCleod Bethune. A group of African-Americans came to be close advisors to the President.

DIF: Hard REF: 642, 649–651 OBJ: 25.0
TOP: FDR's New Deal / Eleanor Roosevelt

3. Briefly explain how the sharecropper class developed, how they earned their living, and what particular problems they faced during the 1930s.

ANS:
Answers will vary but could include the following ideas: The sharecropper class grew up during the Reconstruction period. With the end of slavery, newly freed African-Americans and poor whites tilled the land in exchange for a percentage, or share, of the crops. They did not own the land on which they lived, and they were not paid wages. Since they had no capital with which to work, they pledged their share of the crops in advance to secure seed, clothing, and other necessities of life. As a result, they remained constantly in debt and tied to the land. During the 1930s, the sharecroppers' lives worsened when the government paid farmers to take land out of production. Usually this land was the marginal plots farmed by the sharecroppers.

DIF: Hard REF: 644–645 OBJ: 25.1 TOP: Sharecropping

4. Evaluate the effectiveness of New Deal programs designed to ease the hardships of farmers. Explain your answer and cite specific examples.

ANS:
Answers will vary but could include the following ideas: Some of the programs designed to help farmers were the CCC, the TVA, the first AAA, the Federal Emergency Relief Act, the Bankhead-Jones Tenant Farmers Act, and the REA. Taken as a whole, these programs helped ease the plight of the farmers. For example, the CCC taught farmers how to plant shelterbelts, practice terracing and contour plowing, and rotate crops. Other programs set up dams, reforested the land, and controlled grazing. Yet others tried to resettle farmers, electrify farm households, and provide clean camps for migrant workers. Even so, the problems of the farmers were not to be solved in a few years, nor by a single farm program out of Washington.

DIF: Hard REF: 643–646 OBJ: 25.2
TOP: FDR's New Deal / Farming

5. The Roosevelt administration made efforts to bring African-Americans full equality as citizens. What were some of those efforts? Why were they limited in scope?

ANS:
Answers will vary but could include the following ideas: The Roosevelt administration tried to involve more African-Americans in government through use of the "Black Cabinet" and through the appointment of African-Americans to federal office. However, the success of such measures was limited. There was still southern opposition to the anti-lynching bill and continued inequity in federal programs. African-Americans were not allowed to live in the model towns built with government money in the Tennessee Valley. Moreover, when the NRA codes went into effect, the codes allowed African-Americans to be paid less than whites.

DIF: Hard   REF: 648–649   OBJ: 25.2   TOP: Civil Rights

6. Assess the gains and losses of the women's rights movement during the 1930s. Which, if any, of the losses have been turned into victories during the past 50 or 60 years? Explain.

ANS:
Answers will vary but could include the following ideas: Eleanor Roosevelt, Francis Perkins, and Mary Dewson were women who made gains in government. Such gains, however, were offset by the continued economic and social inequality of women. Women in the 1930s still held traditional jobs in professional areas considered to consist of "women's work." They earned less than men, and they failed to secure supervisory positions. Since the end of the depression, and especially in recent years, a higher percentage of women work, and these women hold a greater variety of jobs than did their predecessors. However, as in the past, women usually earn less than their male counterparts.

DIF: Hard   REF: 650–651   OBJ: 25.2   TOP: Women's Rights

7. Despite the crippling economic depression of the 1930s, organized labor made great strides forward. Speculate on why this may have happened.

ANS:
Answers will vary but could include the following ideas: Labor advanced its cause with the help of government support of unions. Examples of this government support include the National Recovery Act and the National Labor Relations Board. The NLRB was set up by the Wagner Act. In addition, the depression placed economic curbs on the power of big business, thus protecting labor and opening the door to unions.

DIF: Hard   REF: 652–654   OBJ: 25.4   TOP: Labor Unions

8. How did the AF of L and the CIO differ in their approaches to organizing labor? Could either organization have achieved success without the other? Explain your answer.

ANS:
Answers will vary but could include the following ideas: The AF of L tried to organize workers by craft (or trade), while the CIO tried to organize workers by industry. Either organization could have achieved success without the other. However, the AF of L helped pave the way for the CIO. Then, as the CIO grew in strength, it too set precedents that benefited the AF of L. Together the two unions helped make organized labor a force that business and political leaders could not ignore.

DIF: Hard   REF: 652–654   OBJ: 25.4   TOP: Labor Unions

9. "By focusing on the 'forgotten Americans,' the New Deal updated and carried on the progressive tradition in American politics." Assess the validity of this generalization as it applies to economic, social, and political policies of the New Deal and of the Progressive years.

ANS:
Answers will vary but could include the following ideas: The New Deal emphasis upon reform, regulation of big business, and protection of public health and safety, built upon the reform measures of the Progressives. In other ways, the New Deal departed from progressive traditions by attempting new experiments in the areas of social, political, and economic policy, such as the Social Security Act (from Chapter 24) and government labor codes.

DIF: Hard   REF: 643–654   OBJ: 25.4   TOP: FDR's New Deal

(page intentionally left blank)

MATCHING

Match each item with the correct statement below.

a. Lend-Lease
b. Atlantic Charter
c. "Panay"
d. scapegoating
e. anti-Semitism
f. Munich pact
g. nonaggression pact
h. "Mein Kampf"
i. Good Neighbor
j. isolationism

1. United States gunboat sunk by Japan in China in 1937, for which Japan apologized.
2. FDR's program to provide Britain all aid short of war without requiring Britain to make payment.
3. Agreement in which Daladier and Chamberlain tried to appease Hitler.
4. Blaming a country's problems on a particular group.
5. 1939 agreement between Germany and the USSR not to fight and to share control of Poland.
6. Opposition to overseas involvement.
7. The book Hitler wrote while in prison that became the Nazi Bible.
8. Name given FDR's policy toward Latin America.
9. Statement of postwar aims issued by Churchill and FDR in 1941.
10. Hatred of Jews.

1. ANS: C DIF: Easy REF: 659 OBJ: 26.0
   TOP: U.S. / Japanese Relations
2. ANS: A DIF: Easy REF: 669 OBJ: 26.0
   TOP: FDR's Presidency / Foreign Policy
3. ANS: F DIF: Easy REF: 662 OBJ: 26.0
   TOP: Munich Pact
4. ANS: D DIF: Easy REF: 657 OBJ: 26.0
   TOP: Scapegoating
5. ANS: G DIF: Easy REF: 663 OBJ: 26.0
   TOP: WWII-Germany / Russia
6. ANS: J DIF: Easy REF: 660 OBJ: 26.0
   TOP: Isolationism
7. ANS: H DIF: Easy REF: 657 OBJ: 26.0
   TOP: Hitler
8. ANS: I DIF: Easy REF: 659 OBJ: 26.0
   TOP: FDR's Presidency / Foreign Policy
9. ANS: B DIF: Easy REF: 669–670 OBJ: 26.0
   TOP: Postwar
10. ANS: E DIF: Easy REF: 657 OBJ: 26.0
    TOP: Anti-Semitism

MULTIPLE CHOICE

1. A political organization that many Germans, unhappy with conditions in their nation after World War I, joined was Hitler's
   a. Communist party.
   b. Fascist party.
   c. National Socialist party.
   d. German Christian party.

   ANS: C   DIF: Medium   REF: 657   OBJ: 26.1
   TOP: Nazi Party

2. The agreement to dismember Czechoslovakia was made in the
   a. Munich Pact.
   b. Neutrality Act of 1937.
   c. Platt Amendment.
   d. Versailles Peace Treaty.

   ANS: A   DIF: Medium   REF: 662   OBJ: 26.1
   TOP: Munich Pact

3. A British Prime Minister who favored a policy of appeasement was
   a. Winston Churchill.
   b. Cordell Hull.
   c. Neville Chamberlain.
   d. Henry Stimson.

   ANS: C   DIF: Medium   REF: 662   OBJ: 26.1
   TOP: British History

4. The term that became a label for President Roosevelt's dealings with Latin America was the
   a. "Good Neighbor policy."
   b. "Platt Amendment."
   c. "Atlantic Charter."
   d. "phony war."

   ANS: A   DIF: Medium   REF: 659   OBJ: 26.1
   TOP: FDR's Presidency / Foreign Policy

5. A measure by which the United States made plans for Philippine independence was the
   a. "Good Neighbor policy."
   b. Neutrality Act of 1939.
   c. Tydings-McDuffie Act.
   d. Japanese-American Commercial Treaty.

   ANS: C   DIF: Medium   REF: 660   OBJ: 26.1
   TOP: U.S. / Foreign Policy

6. The first head of the U.S. Navy's Bureau of Aeronautics was
   a. Billy Mitchell.
   b. William A. Moffett.
   c. Thomas E. Dewey.
   d. Cordell Hull.

   ANS: B   DIF: Medium   REF: 667   OBJ: 26.2
   TOP: U.S. Naval History

7. The system of French defenses erected after World War I was known as the
   a. Ultra defense.
   b. Maginot line.
   c. Sea Lion plan.
   d. Buffer zone.

   ANS: B   DIF: Medium   REF: 664   OBJ: 26.2
   TOP: French History

8. The measure by which President Roosevelt could give aid to countries whose defense he considered vital to the defense of the United States was the
   a. Tydings-McDuffie Act.   c. Cash-and-Carry Act.
   b. Neutrality Act of 1939.   d. Lend-Lease plan.

   ANS: D   DIF: Medium   REF: 669   OBJ: 26.2
   TOP: FDR's Presidency / Foreign Policy

9. The British leader who inspired his people during the Battle of Britain was
   a. Winston Churchill.   c. Neville Chamberlain.
   b. Cordell Hull.   d. Henry Stimson.

   ANS: A   DIF: Medium   REF: 667   OBJ: 26.2
   TOP: British Leaders

10. The Japanese plan to extend its domination of neighboring countries was called the
    a. Greater East Asia Co-Prosperity Sphere.
    b. Good Neighbor policy.
    c. Ultra Secret.
    d. Quarantine policy.

    ANS: A   DIF: Medium   REF: 670   OBJ: 26.3
    TOP: Japan / WWII

11. The head of a warlike government that came into power in October 1941 was
    a. Benito Mussolini.   c. Chiang Kai-shek.
    b. Francisco Franco.   d. Hideki Tojo.

    ANS: D   DIF: Medium   REF: 671   OBJ: 26.3
    TOP: Japan / WWII

12. The statement "no state has the right to intervene in the internal or external affairs of another" comes from the
    a. Pan-American declaration of 1933.   c. Atlantic Charter of 1941.
    b. Munich Pact of 1938.   d. Four Freedoms speech of 1941.

    ANS: A   DIF: Medium   REF: 659   OBJ: 26.1
    TOP: Pan-American Declaration

13. An institution invented by the Nazis to hold and dispose of Jews and political opponents was a (an)
    a. concentration camp.   c. quarantine camp.
    b. German district.   d. isolation district.

    ANS: A   DIF: Medium   REF: 658   OBJ: 26.1
    TOP: Holocaust

14. According to Senator Nye, the U.S. risked being drawn into war by
    a. bankers and arms manufacturers.   c. pacifists.
    b. isolationists.   d. immigrants from Germany.

    ANS: A   DIF: Medium   REF: 660   OBJ: 26.1
    TOP: WWII / Economics

15. President Roosevelt's policies toward Latin America were aimed at
    a. encouraging United States investment there.
    b. being a friendly and helpful neighbor.
    c. maintaining United States isolation.
    d. "speaking softly and carrying a big stick."

    ANS: B   DIF: Medium   REF: 659   OBJ: 26.1
    TOP: FDR's Presidency / Foreign Policy

16. The event that started World War II in Europe was Germany's invasion of
    a. Poland.   c. France.
    b. the Soviet Union.   d. Belgium.

    ANS: A   DIF: Medium   REF: 663   OBJ: 26.1
    TOP: WWII

17. The Platt Amendment gave the United States the right to
    a. close the Panama Canal to enemy shipping.
    b. block European attempts to set up colonies or bases in the Americas.
    c. collect debts owed to European nations by Latin American nations.
    d. intervene in the internal affairs of Cuba.

    ANS: D   DIF: Medium   REF: 659   OBJ: 26.1
    TOP: U.S. / Foreign Policy

18. All of the following were examples of aggression by the Axis prior to 1939 EXCEPT
    a. the Italian invasion af Ethiopia.
    b. German arms shipments to Franco in Spain.
    c. the German occupation of the Rhineland.
    d. the Japanese seizure of Manchuria.

    ANS: B   DIF: Medium   REF: 658–659   OBJ: 26.1
    TOP: WWII

19. From 1933 to 1939 Congress responded to war and threats of war in the world by
    a. ordering the arming of American merchant vessels.
    b. insisting on freedom of the seas.
    c. putting limits on the sale of arms to belligerents.
    d. stopping manufacture of armaments.

    ANS: C   DIF: Medium   REF: 660   OBJ: 26.1
    TOP: WWII / U.S. Response

20. Which of the following most reflected the desire of the United States for neutrality prior to
    1941?
    a. "destroyers-for-bases" deal   c. convoying of British ships
    b. Lend-Lease Act   d. passage of Tydings-McDuffie Act

    ANS: D   DIF: Medium   REF: 660   OBJ: 26.1
    TOP: WWII - U.S. Sentiment

21. General Billy Mitchell tried to convince military leaders that
    a. air power was vital to the defense of the nation.
    b. submarines could choke off United States contact with Europe.
    c. tank divisions would be the key to success in future wars.
    d. research into chemical warfare was desperately needed.

    ANS: A   DIF: Medium   REF: 665–666   OBJ: 26.2
    TOP: WWII / Air Force

22. When did France surrender to Germany?
    a.   April 1940   c.   June 1940
    b.   May 1940   d.   July 1940

    ANS: C   DIF: Medium   REF: 665   OBJ: 26.2
    TOP: WWII

23. The co-signers of the Atlantic Charter were
    a.   Churchill and Roosevelt.   c.   Stalin and Hitler.
    b.   Mussolini and Hitler.   d.   Chamberlain and Roosevelt.

    ANS: A   DIF: Medium   REF: 669–670   OBJ: 26.2
    TOP: WWII-U.S. / British Relations

24. In November 1939, which country was the victim of invasion by a more powerful neighbor?
    a.   China   c.   Finland
    b.   Denmark   d.   Albania

    ANS: C   DIF: Medium   REF: 663   OBJ: 26.2
    TOP: WWII-Soviet Union / Finland

25. In the "destroyer deal" with Great Britain the United States
    a. agreed to manufacture warships for Britain.
    b. agreed to sell Britain 50 new battleships.
    c. vowed to destroy the Nazi aggressors.
    d. traded 5O old destroyers in exchange for the use of 8 British naval bases.

    ANS: D   DIF: Medium   REF: 669   OBJ: 26.2
    TOP: WWI- U.S. / British Relations

26. The Battle of Britain took place in the
    a.   fall of 1940.   c.   fall of 1941.
    b.   spring of 1941.   d.   spring of 1942.

    ANS: A   DIF: Medium   REF: 667   OBJ: 26.2
    TOP: WWII Battles

27. As a result of Japanese aggression in Southeast Asia in 1941, the United States
    a. seized all Japanese ships in U.S. ports.
    b. placed an embargo on all trade with Japan.
    c. requested that Japan be dismissed from the League of Nations.
    d. seized all Japanese ships in U.S. ports and placed an embargo on all trade with Japan.

    ANS: B   DIF: Medium   REF: 670–671   OBJ: 26.3
    TOP: WWII-U.S. / Japanese Relations

28. In the 1940 election, both Roosevelt and Wilkie supported all of the following EXCEPT
   a. helping Great Britain.
   c. the TVA.
   b. conscription.
   d. building up United States arms.

   ANS: C   DIF: Medium   REF: 669   OBJ: 26.2
   TOP: Presidential Elections

29. The most effective factor in slowing the Nazi drive into the Soviet Union in 1941 was
   a. the Soviet air force.
   c. the breaking of Nazi codes.
   b. United States aid to the Soviets.
   d. winter weather.

   ANS: D   DIF: Medium   REF: 670   OBJ: 26.3
   TOP: WWII-Nazi / Soviet Union

30. What areas did United States troops occupy in 1941?
   a. Manchuria and the Philippines
   c. Mexico and Cuba
   b. British Guyana and Mexico
   d. Greenland and Iceland

   ANS: D   DIF: Medium   REF: 670   OBJ: 26.3
   TOP: WWII

31. The "Day of Infamy" refers to the
   a. German bombing of Conventry.
   b. Japanese surprise attack on Pearl Harbor.
   c. signing of the Munish Pact.
   d. German seizure of Czechoslovakia.

   ANS: B   DIF: Medium   REF: 672   OBJ: 26.3
   TOP: WWII

32. According to many historians, Hitler's greatest military blunder was
   a. abandoning operation "Sea Lion."
   c. condemning FDR before the Reichstag.
   b. attacking the USSR.
   d. invading France.

   ANS: B   DIF: Medium   REF: 670   OBJ: 26.3
   TOP: WWII-Nazi / Soviet Union

33. What was the major Allied supply route to China?
   a. the Burma Road
   c. the South China Sea
   b. the Yangtze River
   d. the Trans-Siberian Railroad

   ANS: A   DIF: Medium   REF: 670   OBJ: 26.3
   TOP: WWII / Supply Routes

34. In late 1941, the Japanese government demanded that the United States
   a. withdraw from the Philippines.
   b. cut off aid to Chiang Kai-shek.
   c. restore earlier trade agreements.
   d. close one of its military bases in China.

   ANS: B   DIF: Medium   REF: 670–671   OBJ: 26.3
   TOP: WWII-U.S. / Japanese Relations

© Prentice-Hall, Inc.

35. What evidence best illustrates that the mood of the American public was strongly isolationist before 1939?
    a. reaction to the "Panay" incident
    b. the Good Neighbor policy
    c. passage of a conscription act
    d. a 1937 public opinion poll on a proposed constitutional amendment

    ANS: D   DIF: Medium   REF: 661   OBJ: 26.1
    TOP: WWII-U.S. Sentiment

36. Which of the following events preceded the Japanese attack on Pearl Harbor?
    a. a United States embargo on goods to Japan
    b. a United States cutoff of aid to China
    c. United States attacks on Japanese bases in French Indochina
    d. internment of Japanese in the United States

    ANS: A   DIF: Medium   REF: 670–671   OBJ: 26.3
    TOP: Pearl Harbor

37. One consequence of the end of the Japanese-American Commercial Treaty of 1911 was
    a. Japan's invasion of Mongolia to find new resources.
    b. the bombing of United States shipping in China.
    c. the temporary hindering of Japanese aggression toward its neighbors.
    d. the bombing of the "Panay."

    ANS: C   DIF: Medium   OBJ: 26.1
    TOP: U.S. / Japanese Relations

38. The person MOST likely to have predicted an event like the destruction of Conventry was
    a. Wendell L. Wilkie.   c. Billy Mitchell.
    b. Neville Chamberlain.   d. Lazaro Cardenas.

    ANS: C   DIF: Medium   REF: 665–667   OBJ: 26.2
    TOP: WWII / Air Force

39. "War is not inevitable for this country. Such a claim is defeatism in the true sense." Who was MOST likely to have delivered this statement in an April 1941 speech?
    a. Franklin Roosevelt   c. Frank Knox
    b. Billy Mitchell   d. Wendell Wilkie

    ANS: D   DIF: Medium   REF: 668–669   OBJ: 26.2
    TOP: WWII / U.S. Sentiment

40. The alliance between the United States and the Soviet Union was formed after the Nazis invaded
    a. France.   c. Poland.
    b. Turkey.   d. Russia.

    ANS: D   DIF: Medium   OBJ: 26.3   TOP: WWII-U.S. / Soviet

41. In the opinion of many historians, Hitler's greatest military error was
    a. abandoning operation "Sea Lion."   c. sinking American convoy escorts.
    b. attacking the Soviet Union.   d. invading France.

    ANS: B   DIF: Medium   REF: 670   OBJ: 26.3
    TOP: WWII / Nazi / Soviet

42. "I believe that I interpret the will of the Congress and of the people when I assert that we will . . . make it very certain that this form of treachery shall never again endanger us." The MOST likely date on which President Roosevelt spoke these words is
    a. December 12, 1937.   c. May 7, 1941.
    b. September 21, 1939.   d. December 8, 1941.

    ANS: D   DIF: Medium   REF: 671–672   OBJ: 26.3
    TOP: Pearl Harbor

43. All of the following occurred before the Japanese attack on China in 1937 EXCEPT the
    a. Japanese withdrawal from the League of Nations.
    b. Japanese invasion of Manchuria.
    c. promise of independence to the Philippines by the Tydings-McDuffie Act.
    d. Japanese occupation of bases in northern Indochina.

    ANS: D   DIF: Medium   REF: 670   OBJ: 26.3
    TOP: WWII-Japan / China

44. Which of the following pairs of names does NOT belong with the others?
    a. Franklin Roosevelt and Winston   c. Joseph Stalin and Adolf Hitler
       Churchill
    b. Chiang Kai-shek and Hideki Tojo   d. Benito Mussolini and Adolf Hitler

    ANS: B   DIF: Medium   REF: 671   OBJ: 26.3
    TOP: WWII-World Leaders

ESSAY

1. What is the main point of the following argument? Write your answer on a separate sheet of paper and support your answer with a paragraph explaining why you chose it.
     The Germans made Hitler their God. When they geeted each other, they no longer said, "Gruss Gott" (God be with you!) but "Heil Hitler!" And anyone who used the old greeting was suspected of treason. They set up their German Christian church to make Christianity serve the Master Race.
   A. The Germans made Hitler the god of their culture and changed their church to reflect his ideas.
   B. The term "Heil Hitler" became the fashionable way to greet others.
   C. The Germans were suspicious and judged others by the greeting they used.
   D. The Germans considered themselves to be the Master Race.

   ANS:
   answer A Students' paragraphs should support their answer.

   DIF: Hard   REF: 657–658   OBJ: 26.0   TOP: Hitler / Nazi Party

2. Explain the point of view of those who demanded that the United States remain neutral in the 1930s, and describe four ways in which FDR was able to circumvent those demands after World War II began in September 1939.

ANS:
Americans remembered the senseless slaughter of WWI. Some became pacifists, refusing to consider war for any reason. Some became isolationists, hoping to fence off our country from the rest of the world. A few historians agreed, arguing that the world would have been better off had the U.S. not entered WWI. Congressional hearings seemed to show that arms makers and bankers had led us into WWI for profit. After September 1939, the President achieved the passage of a new Neutrality Act in 1939, which repealed the embargo on selling or shipping arms to the belligerents. Roosevelt approved selling American military equipment to private companies that were buying for the British, but England was running out of money. The destroyers-for-bases deal traded 50 old U.S. destroyers for the use of eight British naval bases. The Lend-Lease plan gave the British war materials without immediate payment.

DIF: Hard   OBJ: 26.0   TOP: FDR's Presidency / Foreign Relations

3. Based on what you have read in the chapter, identify and explain the factors that lead to Adolph Hitler's rise to power.

ANS:
Answers will vary but could include the following ideas: World War I had completely unsettled the German nation. Its political system had changed and its economy was in turmoil, with millions unemployed. Political parties could not unite to deliver firm guidance. Hitler, with his plan for a Third Reich, offered a clear and simple picture of the future to many Germans. He was a master at using radio to spread his message effectively. With his anti-Semitism he also provided Germans with a scapegoat—the Jews—to bear the blame for postwar distress.

DIF: Hard   OBJ: 26.1   TOP: Hitler's Rise to Power

4. How did Hitler use his theory of a Master Race to entrench himself in power? To what ends did Hitler's theory of a Master Race and his anti-semitism ultimately lead? Give specific examples.

ANS:
Answers will vary but could include the following ideas: Hitler told the Germans that the Jews and other people who were not part of the "Master Race" were to blame for Germany's problems. He set up concentration camps where millions of Jews and other scapegoats were systematically tortured and killed. Hitler controlled the media, set up a new German Christian Church, and silenced any opposition to his plans. He built up Germany's military and then invaded other countries in the hopes that one day the Third Reich would rule the world.

DIF: Hard   OBJ: 26.1   TOP: Hitler's Rise to Power

5. In your opinion, what effect did the policy of appeasement have on the eventual outbreak of World War II?

ANS:
Answers will vary but could include the following ideas: Germany was determined to gain control of Europe. To avoid conflict, Britain and France attempted to appease Hitler, allowing him to seize Austria and to gain control of the Sudetenland. The invasion of the rest of Czechoslovakia in March 1939 showed appeasement to be a failure. When Germany invaded Poland, England and France declared war on Germany.

DIF: Hard   OBJ: 26.1   TOP: Hitler's Rise to Power

6. Summarize the steps Roosevelt took to prepare the United States for war in 1940 and 1941.

ANS:
Answers will vary but could include the following ideas: FDR called for the nation to rearm. He wanted factories to turn out 50,000 planes a year. He also wanted to build a two-ocean navy. The United States also bought time by sending vital war supplies to its allies. A new draft law went into effect late in 1940 to build up the size of the army. Roosevelt also approved the arming of merchant ships.

DIF: Hard   OBJ: 26.2   TOP: FDR's Presidency

7. Describe four ways in which President Roosevelt was able to assist the Allied nations in their war against the Axis powers without involving the United States in open conflict.

ANS:
Answers will vary but could include the following ideas: FDR convinced Congress to lift the arms embargo. He also allowed American military equipment to be sold to private companies that were buying for the British. The "Destroyers for Bases" deal allowed the United States to exchange 50 old U.S. destroyers for the use of eight British naval bases. When the British ran low on cash, FDR persuaded Congress to pass the "Lend-Lease" plan permitting the United States to lend or lease military supplies to the Allies.

DIF: Hard   OBJ: 26.2   TOP: FDR's Presidency / Foreign Policy

8. Describe Japan's plans for Asia and how they led to the attack on Pearl Harbor.

ANS:
Answers will vary but could include the following ideas: The Japanese wanted to achieve domination of the Far East. They seized Manchuria in 1931 and attacked China itself in 1937. They also seized bases in French Indochina. The United States opposed Japanese expansion. In 1941, the United States placed an embargo on Japan, which hurt Japan's economy. When the United States demanded that Japan withdraw from China, Japan decided to go to war with the United States.

DIF: Hard   OBJ: 26.3   TOP: U.S. / Japanese Relations

9. "World War II was not an inevitable war." Explain what actions various heads of state might have taken that could have prevented the conflict.

ANS:
Answers will vary but could include the following ideas: If members of the League of Nations had imposed stronger sanctions against Italy and Japan for their early aggression, those nations might not have continued on their expansionist ways. In similar fashion, there were several opportunities to check Hitler. Quick responses in the Rhineland and in Austria might have slowed Hitler. If Britain and France had resisted his movements in Czechoslovakia, German generals might have acted to oust Hitler.

DIF: Hard   OBJ: 26.3   TOP: WWII / Possible Prevention

10. "By 1933, whatever faint chances had once existed for a cooperative international response to the depression disappeared, and each major power looked to its own resources for a solution." Expand on this statement to show how the Great Depression played a part in the movement toward World War II.

ANS:
Answers will vary but could include the following ideas: In the United States the Great Depression helped the nation to continue to focus on its own problems. This may have bolstered the isolationist mood that had been strong in the country since the end of World War I. On the international scene, the unwillingness or inability of nations to cooperate on economic matters lessened the chances of cooperation in other areas, for example in cooperating to stop the aggressive expansion of Germany, Italy, or Japan.

DIF: Hard   OBJ: 26.3   TOP: WWII / Great Depression

(page intentionally left blank)

MATCHING

Match each item with the correct statement below.

a. Manhattan Project
b. Normandy
c. James B. Doolittle
d. Leningrad
e. rationing

f. Erwin Rommel
g. internment
h. A. Philip Randolph
i. Douglas MacArthur
j. Charles Drew

1. Developed the blood bank for storing blood plasma.
2. Site of D-Day invasion in June 1944.
3. Secret program to develop the atomic bomb.
4. Confinement of Japanese-Americans on the West Coast in camps from 1942 to 1944.
5. System of limiting distribution of products that are in short supply.
6. Led American bombing raids on Tokyo in 1942.
7. He led the "Afrika Korps."
8. Leader of American army in the Pacific.

1. ANS: J   DIF: Easy   REF: 676   OBJ: 27.0
    TOP: WWII / African-Americans
2. ANS: B   DIF: Easy   REF: 688   OBJ: 27.0
    TOP: WWII Battles
3. ANS: A   DIF: Easy   REF: 698   OBJ: 27.0
    TOP: WWII / Atomic Weapons
4. ANS: G   DIF: Easy   REF: 677   OBJ: 27.0
    TOP: WWII / Japanese-American Internment
5. ANS: E   DIF: Easy   REF: 675   OBJ: 27.0
    TOP: Rationing
6. ANS: C   DIF: Easy   REF: 683   OBJ: 27.0
    TOP: WWII / U.S. Military Leaders
7. ANS: F   DIF: Easy   REF: 680–681   OBJ: 27.0
    TOP: WWII / German Military Leaders
8. ANS: I   DIF: Easy   REF: 695   OBJ: 27.0
    TOP: WWII / U.S. Military Leaders

MULTIPLE CHOICE

1. The heroism of Dorie Miller helped clear the way for African-Americans to serve actively in the
    a. Air Force.
    b. Army.
    c. Navy.
    d. Marines.

    ANS: C   DIF: Medium   REF: 676   OBJ: 27.1
    TOP: WWII / African-Americans

2. African-American engineers in the army helped offset Japanese advances in Asia by building the
   a. Burma Road.
   b. Ledo Road.
   c. "defensive perimeter."
   d. Siegfried Line.

   ANS: B   DIF: Medium   REF: 676   OBJ: 27.1
   TOP: WWII / African-Americans

3. Which pair of countries was Nazi Germany unable to conquer?
   a. Poland and France
   b. France and England
   c. Russia and France
   d. Russia and England

   ANS: D   DIF: Medium   OBJ: 27.2   TOP: WWII

4. Because of his shrewdness and daring as a general, he earned the nickname the "Desert Fox."
   He was
   a. George Patton.
   b. Bernard Montgomery.
   c. Erwin Rommel.
   d. Jurgen von Arnim.

   ANS: C   DIF: Medium   REF: 680   OBJ: 27.2
   TOP: WWII / German Military Leaders

5. In January 1943, Franklin Roosevelt and Winston Churchill charted the future course of war at a
   meeting held in
   a. Yalta.
   b. Potsdam.
   c. Casablanca.
   d. London.

   ANS: C   DIF: Medium   REF: 684–685   OBJ: 27.2
   TOP: WWII

6. The critical D-Day invasion was directed by the Supreme Commander of Allied Forces, General
   a. George Patton.
   b. Courtney Hodges.
   c. A. M. Patch.
   d. Dwight D. Eisenhower.

   ANS: D   DIF: Medium   REF: 688   OBJ: 27.3
   TOP: WWII Battles

7. The agreements reached at Yalta opened the way for Russia to make all of the following
   "satellites" EXCEPT
   a. Poland.
   b. Hungary.
   c. Austria.
   d. Bulgaria.

   ANS: C   DIF: Medium   REF: 691–692   OBJ: 27.3
   TOP: WWII

8. In an effort to retake the Pacific, the Allies fought the greatest sea battle of all time, the Battle of
   a. Leyte Gulf.
   b. Luzon.
   c. Manila Bay.
   d. Coral Sea.

   ANS: A   DIF: Medium   REF: 696   OBJ: 27.4
   TOP: WWII Battles

9. In 1942 he left the Philippines promising, "I shall return!" In October 1944, he fulfilled that promise. He was
   a. George McDuffie.
   b. Chester A. Nimitz.
   c. A. C. McAuliffe.
   d. Douglas MacArthur.

   ANS: D   DIF: Medium   REF: 696   OBJ: 27.4
   TOP: WWII / U.S. Military Leaders

10. The first inhabited city to experience the horrors of atomic destruction was
   a. Hiroshima.
   b. Alamogordo.
   c. Tokyo.
   d. Nagasaki.

   ANS: A   DIF: Medium   REF: 699   OBJ: 27.4
   TOP: Atomic Weapons

11. Upon United States entry into the war in 1942, the Axis powers possessed all of the following advantages over the Allies EXCEPT
   a. shorter supply routes.
   b. control of long battlefronts.
   c. seasoned military troops.
   d. greater industrial outputs.

   ANS: D   DIF: Medium   REF: 675   OBJ: 27.1
   TOP: WWII

12. The United States government tried all of the following measures to control inflation during the war EXCEPT
   a. rationing of goods.
   b. levying high income taxes.
   c. balancing the federal budget.
   d. instituting wage and price controls.

   ANS: C   DIF: Medium   REF: 675, 679   OBJ: 27.1
   TOP: U.S. Economy / WWII

13. A. Philip Randolph did all of the following EXCEPT
   a. protest the discrimination in wartime industries.
   b. create the Brotherhood of Sleeping Car Porters.
   c. oppose American involvement in World War II.
   d. win greater rights for African-American railroad workers.

   ANS: C   DIF: Medium   REF: 677   OBJ: 27.1
   TOP: WWII / Civil Rights

14. Which of the following gains did African-Americans and/or women NOT make during World War ll?
   a. less discrimination in hiring on the home front
   b. an end to social and political discrimination
   c. expanded roles in the military
   d. the desegregation of the armed forces

   ANS: B   DIF: Medium   REF: 676–678   OBJ: 27.1
   TOP: WWII / Discrimination

15. Which of fhe following was one of FDR's major reasons for holding Japanese-Americans in camps during the war?
    a. Most refused to take loyalty oaths to the United States.
    b. Most belonged to anti-American organizations.
    c. The government had also interned people of German and Italian ancestry.
    d. Fear of a Japanese invasion on the West Coast.

    ANS: D   DIF: Medium   REF: 677   OBJ: 27.1
    TOP: WWII / Japanese-American Internment

16. The United States used all of the following methods to raise funds for the war effort EXCEPT
    a. raising income taxes.
    b. borrowing from corporations.
    c. borrowing from individuals.
    d. enacting a national wartime sales tax.

    ANS: D   DIF: Medium   REF: 679   OBJ: 27.1
    TOP: WWII / U.S. Economics

17. During World War II, the number of women workers in the American labor force increased by
    a. 2 million.   c. 6 million.
    b. 4 million.   d. 8 million.

    ANS: C   DIF: Medium   REF: 678   OBJ: 27.1
    TOP: Women's Roles in WWII

18. World War II had all of the following effects on the "home front" EXCEPT
    a. full employment.   c. increased taxes.
    b. deflation.   d. rationing of scarce goods.

    ANS: B   DIF: Medium   REF: 675–679   OBJ: 27.1
    TOP: WWII / U.S. Economics

19. Soon after Pearl Harbor the Allies agreed that the first goal was to defeat Germany because
    a. if the Germans won in Europe, the United States would have to face the aggressor nations alone.
    b. the United States had more territorial interests in Europe.
    c. our Pacific fleet had been wiped out at Pearl Harbor.
    d. Churchill and Roosevelt believed that Japan would give up if Germany surrendered.

    ANS: A   DIF: Medium   REF: 679   OBJ: 27.2
    TOP: WWII

20. Probably the MOST serious threat to Allied success in 1942 was
    a. Japanese assaults on the Philippines.   c. Japanese control of the Pacific.
    b. German assaults on Russia.   d. German control of the Atlantic.

    ANS: D   DIF: Medium   REF: 680   OBJ: 27.2
    TOP: WWII

21. Which of the following did most Latin American countries do during World War II?
    a.   broke diplomatic relations with the Axis
    b.   provided war materials to the Allies
    c.   declared war on the Axis
    d.   all of the above

    ANS: D   DIF: Medium   REF: 682   OBJ: 27.2
    TOP: WWII / Latin America

22. In heated hand-to-hand combat on this island, the Allies finally turned back the Japanese advance through the Pacific. The island was
    a.   Iwo Jima.   c.   Wake.
    b.   Midway.   d.   Guadalcanal.

    ANS: D   DIF: Medium   REF: 684   OBJ: 27.2
    TOP: WWII Battles

23. The Battle of the Coral Sea was significant to naval history because
    a.   both sides suffered unusually heavy losses.
    b.   opposing commanders made serious "tactical" errors.
    c.   both sides claimed "strategical" victories.
    d.   opposing ships never encountered each other.

    ANS: D   DIF: Medium   REF: 683   OBJ: 27.2
    TOP: WWII Battles

24. The battles of the Coral Sea and Midway were important to the history of World War II because the United States
    a.   regained Allied control of Burma.
    b.   opened the way for an air raid on Tokyo.
    c.   upset the naval balance in the Pacific.
    d.   saved the Philippines from Japanese invasion.

    ANS: C   DIF: Medium   REF: 683–684   OBJ: 27.2
    TOP: WWII Battles

25. Increased used of the airplane in World War II
    a.   made air battles more important than those on land and sea.
    b.   led to more widespread destruction of lives and property.
    c.   resulted in fewer civilian deaths than in past wars.
    d.   restricted the mobility and range of warfare.

    ANS: B   DIF: Medium   REF: 686–688   OBJ: 27.3
    TOP: WWII / Air Warfare

26. Which of the following events occurred BEFORE the D-Day invasion?
    a.   Roosevelt's reelection to a fourth term
    b.   the Allied entry into Rome
    c.   the Battle of the Bulge
    d.   the Yalta Conference

    ANS: B   DIF: Medium   OBJ: 27.3   TOP: WWII

27. The British RAF relentlessly pounded German cities and industrial centers using a military tactic known as
   a. "channel-hopping."
   c. "saturation" bombing.
   b. "pinpoint" attack.
   d. "leap-frogging."

   ANS: C   DIF: Medium   REF: 687   OBJ: 27.3
   TOP: WWII

28. The D-Day invasion was designed to drive the
   a. Japanese out of the Philippines.
   c. Germans out of France.
   b. Italians out of North Africa.
   d. Russians out of Poland.

   ANS: C   DIF: Medium   REF: 688   OBJ: 27.3
   TOP: WWII Battles

29. Roosevelt swept to reelection in 1944 because he had
   a. the united support of farmers and laborers.
   b. already broken the two-term tradition.
   c. a weak Republican opponent.
   d. a war yet to win.

   ANS: D   DIF: Medium   REF: 691   OBJ: 27.3
   TOP: Presidential Elections

30. At Yalta, Josef Stalin made all of the following promises EXCEPT to
   a. give up claims to German reparations.
   b. allow Eastern European countries their choice of governments.
   c. support the United States against Japan.
   d. allow free elections in Poland.

   ANS: A   DIF: Medium   REF: 691   OBJ: 27.3
   TOP: WWII

31. When Churchill said "shake hands with Russia as far east as possible," he was concerned with
   a. Russian dominance of eastern Europe.
   b. establishing good relations with the Soviets after the war.
   c. forcing the unconditional surrender of Germany.
   d. Eisenhower's refusal to cooperate with the Russians.

   ANS: A   DIF: Medium   OBJ: 27.3
   TOP: Russian / European Relations

32. Truman's major justification for using the atomic bomb against Japan was that
   a. it would keep Russia from taking Japan.
   b. it would avenge Japanese atrocities.
   c. it would save American lives.
   d. it would save the taxpayers a lot of money.

   ANS: C   DIF: Medium   REF: 699   OBJ: 27.4
   TOP: Truman's Presidency / Nuclear Weapons

33. The deliberate and planned destruction of European Jews by the Nazis was known as
    a. concentration.
    c. internment.
    b. the Holocaust.
    d. fascism.

    ANS: B   DIF: Medium   REF: 700   OBJ: 27.4
    TOP: The Holocaust

34. Which of the following groups of Americans would have identified with the statement, "A Jim Crow army cannot fight for a free world"?
    a. women
    c. Japanese-Americans
    b. African-Americans
    d. rank-and-file soldiers

    ANS: B   DIF: Medium   REF: 676–677   OBJ: 27.1
    TOP: Civil Rights

35. During the war years, the cost of living in the United States went up by 29%, while wages rose by 50%. Based on your knowledge of economics, which of the following actions by the federal government would have been the MOST likely to curb this inflationary situation?
    a. an increase in national spending
    c. an increase in interest rates
    b. a reduction in federal income taxes
    d. a reduction in social security taxes

    ANS: C   DIF: Medium   OBJ: 27.1
    TOP: WWII / U.S. Economics

36. Which of the following is INCORRECTLY paired?
    a. Dwight D. Eisenhower—D-Day
    b. A. C. McAuliffe—Battle of the Bulge
    c. James B. Doolittle—Battle of Midway
    d. Douglas MacArthur—Battle of Manila

    ANS: C   DIF: Medium   REF: 688, 691, 696
    OBJ: 27.2   TOP: U.S. Leaders / WWII

37. World War II differed from World War I in all of the following ways EXCEPT that
    a. air power proved decisive.
    b. destruction was confined to the battlefields.
    c. sonar helped neutralize the use of submarines.
    d. amphibious landings were more common.

    ANS: B   DIF: Medium   OBJ: 27.2   TOP: WWII

38. If you read newspaper headlines about a meeting of the "Big Three" at Yalta, grieved over President Roosevelt's death, and rejoiced at the announcement of V-E Day, you were probably living in the year
    a. 1943.
    c. 1945.
    b. 1944.
    d. 1946.

    ANS: C   DIF: Medium   REF: 691   OBJ: 27.3
    TOP: WWII

39. "The victory is but half won. The West is free but the East is still in bondage." When President Truman made this remark,
    a. Germany had surrendered; Japan had not.
    b. Japan had surrendered; Germany had not.
    c. Germany, Italy, and Japan had surrendered.
    d. eastern Europe remained in German control.

ANS: A   DIF: Medium   REF: 695   OBJ: 27.4
TOP: WWII / Germany's Surrender

ESSAY

1. What point of view do the following statements express about women's efforts during World War II? Write your answer on a separate sheet of paper and support your answer with a paragraph explaining why you chose it.

   Women took on a wide variety of jobs and surprised the men who had said they were too weak and delicate to be lumberjacks, blast furnace operators, stevedores, or blacksmiths. They handled complex machinery in shipyards and airplane factories. Many showed their talents as doctors, dentists, chemists, and lawyers.
   A. favorable
   B. unfavorable
   C. very favorable
   D. unbiased

   ANS:
   answer A Students' paragraphs should support their answer.

   DIF: Hard   OBJ: 27.0   TOP: Women's Roles in WWII

2. Choose one of the topics below for your essay.
   A. Write an essay to supply evidence to support the following claim: "The cost of World War II for the United States was small compared to that for the rest of the world."
   B. Write an essay providing the background and interpretation for the following claim: "The secret message that the 'Italian navigator' and his crew had landed 'safe and happy' in the 'New World' remains one of history's most ironic statements." (To point out the irony, you will have to show that the "safe and happy" landing had unexpected unhappy consequences.)

   ANS:
   Part A: The United States did not enter WWII until well after Germany had taken France, bombed England, and seized much Russian territory. No major part of United States territory had been touched by the war. The losses incurred by the United States due to WWII were staggering—almost 300,000 casualties. But Russia lost as many as 18 million; Germany, 4 million; Japan, 2 million; and China, possibly 22 million. Europe as a whole lost about 6 million Jews to German death camps, as well as millions of others.
   Part B: This statement is ironic because it can be seen in two opposite ways. In one sense it was literally true: The scientists who conducted the test were "safe" because no mishaps occurred and because it had been a success they were "happy." But in light of the problems and challenges that the advent of nuclear weapons has brought to the world, the "safe and happy" phrase seems false.

   DIF: Hard   OBJ: 27.0   TOP: WWII Losses / Nuclear Weapons

3. Compare the war aims of the United States in World War I with American war aims in World War II. Which President do you think had the easiest time mobilizing the American people to fight for these aims—President Wilson or President Roosevelt? Explain.

    ANS:
    Answers will vary but could include the following ideas: The United States attempted to stop aggressors from overrunning the world in both World War I and World War II. However, the United States had more idealistic aims in World War I than it had in World War II. President Wilson tried to rally Americans by calling on them to "make the world safe for democracy." President Roosevelt, on the other hand, overcame resistance to American war efforts as a result of the Japanese attack on Pearl Harbor. Because of this overt act against the United States, Roosevelt had an easier time mobilizing Americans for war.

    DIF: Hard   OBJ: 27.1   TOP: WWI / WWII

4. What were the effects on American society of mobilization for World War II?

    ANS:
    Answers will vary but could include the following ideas: There were increased opportunities for women and minorities. Mobilization also brought an end to the Great Depression and increased the authority of government in light of the new national emergency.

    DIF: Hard   REF: 675–679   OBJ: 27.1
    TOP: WWII / Effects on U.S. Society

5. In observing the American home front during the war, the famous American anthropologist Margaret Mead remarked, "This generation will have to make new patterns. . . . [T]he men who left this country in 1941–42 will come back to a new generation of girls." What events might have prompted Mead to predict the emergence of a "new generation of girls"? What "new patterns" do you think she was referring to?

    ANS:
    Answers will vary but could include the following ideas: A growing number of women took a wide variety of jobs as millions of men left for battlefronts in Europe and the Pacific. Many women also volunteered for the armed services, taking a more active part in the military than they had in the past. Because of these new roles, women began to question their former status as wives and mothers, thus laying open the way for "new patterns" in American society.

    DIF: Hard   REF: 676–678   OBJ: 27.1
    TOP: Women's Roles in WWII

6. What events in 1942 finally turned the course of the war against the Axis powers?

    ANS:
    Answers will vary but could include the following ideas: Allied victories in the battle for the Atlantic, Allied inroads in Africa, the Russian victory at Stalingrad, and United States successes in turning back the Japanese advance in the Pacific were turning points in the war with the Axis powers.

    DIF: Hard   REF: 684–685   OBJ: 27.2
    TOP: WWII / Allied Victories

7. Compare the conduct of war in Europe and the Pacific. What types of strategies and weapons were essential to Allied victory in both theaters? What tactics were unique to the Pacific?

ANS:
Answers will vary but could include the following ideas: Allied victories on both fronts depended upon attacks on enemy home territories. This meant disrupting supply lines and retaking conquered lands. Many battles in Europe and the Pacific also depended upon the element of surprise. Because of the heavy use of such new weapons as the airplane, the enemy was often not seen and large numbers of civilians suffered casualties. The war in the Pacific differed from the war in Europe because of the "island-hopping" campaign of the United States. In addition, the United States marines played a more prominent role in the Pacific than they had in Europe. The use of naval aircraft carriers similarly introduced a new type of naval warfare to the Pacific, one in which warring ships remained out of sight of each other.

DIF: Hard   REF: 679–700   OBJ: 27.3
TOP: WWII / European & Pacific Theaters

8. What did President Roosevelt hope to achieve at the 1945 meeting at Yalta? Why do some historians today question the deal that Roosevelt negotiated with Stalin? What factors or events at the time of the conference help explain why Roosevelt may have struck such a deal? Given this historic frame of reference, do you think Roosevelt had any other option(s) open to him? Why or why not?

ANS:
Answers could include the following: Roosevelt hoped to set the terms for Nazi surrender at Yalta. He also wanted to enlist Soviet support in the war against Japan. Some historians have questioned the deal Roosevelt negotiated with Stalin because Stalin provided no guarantees that he would keep his word. Stalin, who had broken his word in the past, used Yalta to win concessions that set the stage for Soviet domination of eastern Europe. Because Soviet armies had unrivaled power in eastern Europe, Roosevelt believed he had no choice but to meet Soviet terms. Some may point out that the United States did not yet have the atomic bomb and consequently relied heavily on Soviet forces in planning the defeat of Japan. Others may take Churchill's position that, once the deals were struck, Eisenhower should have pushed American forces as far east as possible to ensure Soviet compliance with the agreements reached at Yalta.

DIF: Hard   REF: 691–692   OBJ: 27.3
TOP: Russian / U.S. Relations in WWII

9. What arguments did President Truman consider when he weighed the decision to drop the atomic bomb on Japan? Using your knowledge of world affairs today, how did Truman's decision help change the course of history?

ANS:
Answers will vary but could include the following ideas: The Japanese refusal to surrender and the potential loss of enormous numbers of American lives were Truman's most powerful arguments. Truman's decision to drop the bomb launched the United States and the world into a new age of warfare. The potential for destruction had been raised, along with new fears for the future.

DIF: Hard   REF: 698–699   OBJ: 27.4
TOP: Truman's Presidency / Atomic Weapons

10. "World War II tested—and proved—the effectiveness of democracy as a system of government."
Assess the validity of this generalization, using evidence from Chapter 27.

ANS:
Answers will vary but could include the following ideas: The United States government rallied the support of Americans behind the war without suppression of dissenters or the use of martial law. The one notable exception was the internment of Japanese-Americans.

DIF: Hard   OBJ: 27.4   TOP: WWII

(page intentionally left blank)

MATCHING

Match each item with the correct statement below.

a. Alger Hiss
b. Dean Acheson
c. Bernard Baruch
d. George Marshall
e. Mao Zedong

f. Trygve Lie
g. Robert Taft
h. Dwight Eisenhower
i. Strom Thurmond
j. Thomas Dewey

1. Led Communist takeover of mainland China.
2. First Secretary General of the United Nations.
3. First Commander of NATO.
4. Under Secretary of State, believed the Communists intended to take over the world.
5. "Dixiecrat" candidate for President in 1948.
6. Viewed by pollsters and papers as the most likely man to be elected President in 1948.
7. Developed a plan providing billions in aid to Western Europe.
8. "Mr. Republican" in the 80th Congress who wanted to limit U.S. commitments abroad.
9. Proposed a world agency with control over atomic energy.
10. Government official accused of providing classified documents to the Soviets.

1. ANS: E   DIF: Easy   REF: 722   OBJ: 28.0
   TOP: Communist Leaders
2. ANS: F   DIF: Easy   REF: 708   OBJ: 28.0
   TOP: United Nations
3. ANS: H   DIF: Easy   REF: 718   OBJ: 28.0
   TOP: NATO
4. ANS: B   DIF: Easy   REF: 709   OBJ: 28.0
   TOP: Communism / U.S. Response
5. ANS: I   DIF: Easy   REF: 719   OBJ: 28.0
   TOP: Presidential Elections
6. ANS: J   DIF: Easy   REF: 719   OBJ: 28.0
   TOP: Presidential Elections
7. ANS: D   DIF: Easy   REF: 710   OBJ: 28.0
   TOP: Marshall Plan
8. ANS: G   DIF: Easy   REF: 714   OBJ: 28.0
   TOP: 80th Congress
9. ANS: C   DIF: Easy   REF: 708   OBJ: 28.0
   TOP: Atomic Energy
10. ANS: A   DIF: Easy   REF: 721   OBJ: 28.0
    TOP: U.S. Espionage

MULTIPLE CHOICE

1. The economic plan started in 1948 to help European nations recover from the effects of World War II was called the
   a. Truman Plan.
   b. Eisenhower Plan.
   c. Kennan Plan.
   d. Marshall Plan.

   ANS: D   DIF: Medium   REF: 710–711   OBJ: 28.1
   TOP: Marshall Plan

2. The policy of containment was designed to
   a. control the spread of atomic secrets.
   b. stop the spread of communism.
   c. limit the spread of closed shops.
   d. help the spread of civil rights laws.

   ANS: B   DIF: Medium   REF: 709   OBJ: 28.1
   TOP: Communism

3. According to Churchill, an "iron curtain" separated the
   a. Soviet Union and China.
   b. Soviet Union and the United States.
   c. United States and Western Europe.
   d. nations of Eastern Europe and Western Europe.

   ANS: D   DIF: Medium   REF: 708–709   OBJ: 28.1
   TOP: Soviet Union / European Relations

4. Marshall Tito was a Communist leader in
   a. Greece.
   b. Yugoslavia.
   c. Turkey.
   d. the United States.

   ANS: B   DIF: Medium   REF: 709   OBJ: 28.1
   TOP: Communist Leaders

5. In 1949 the United States, Canada, and ten Western European countries formed an alliance that became known as
   a. SEATO.
   b. NATO.
   c. HVAC.
   d. ANZUS.

   ANS: B   DIF: Medium   REF: 717   OBJ: 28.2
   TOP: Communist Leaders

6. The Twenty-second Amendment
   a. limited any President after Harry S Truman to two terms.
   b. repealed the Eighteenth Amendment.
   c. gave 18-year-olds the right to vote.
   d. enabled the United States to join the United Nations.

   ANS: A   DIF: Medium   REF: 715   OBJ: 28.2
   TOP: Constitution

7. The act that set up the Central Intelligence Agency and placed military leadership in the Joint Chiefs of Staff is the
   a. Taft-Hartley Act.
   b. Presidential Succession Act.
   c. Employment Act.
   d. National Security Act.

   ANS: D   DIF: Medium   REF: 715   OBJ: 28.2
   TOP: CIA

8. I claimed that the State Department was infested with Communist agents. I am
   a. Joseph McCarthy.
   b. Harry Truman.
   c. Julius Rosenberg.
   d. Alger Hiss.

   ANS: A   DIF: Medium   REF: 723   OBJ: 28.3
   TOP: Communism / McCarthy

9. All of the following were convicted in the 1950s of espionage EXCEPT
   a. Morton Sobell.
   b. Nicola Sacco.
   c. Klaus Fuchs.
   d. Julius Rosenberg.

   ANS: B   DIF: Medium   REF: 723   OBJ: 28.3
   TOP: U.S. Espionage

10. The ANZUS pact was a mutual defense treaty between
    a. the United States and the Philippines.
    b. a group of nations including the United States, Japan, and Taiwan.
    c. the United States and South Korea.
    d. a group of nations that included the United States, Australia, and New Zealand.

    ANS: D   DIF: Medium   REF: 726   OBJ: 28.3
    TOP: U.S. / Foreign Treaties

11. Which of the following is NOT one of the five permanent members of the United Nations Security Council?
    a. France
    b. Japan
    c. Britain
    d. China

    ANS: B   DIF: Medium   REF: 707   OBJ: 28.1
    TOP: United Nations

12. Both the Marshall Plan and the Point Four Program
    a. provided billions of dollars in aid to Asia.
    b. were applauded by the Soviets.
    c. aimed at fighting communism by promoting economic growth.
    d. are still being used today.

    ANS: C   DIF: Medium   REF: 710–711   OBJ: 28.1
    TOP: Communism

13. What is the CORRECT chronological order of the following events related to the growing conflict between the Soviet Union and the West? I. The Marshall Plan begins. II. Churchill gives his "iron curtain" speech. III. The United States announces the Truman Doctrine. IV. The Greek Civil War erupts.
    a. I, II, III, IV
    b. II, III, IV, I
    c. II, IV, III, I
    d. IV, III, II, I

    ANS: C   DIF: Medium   REF: 708–710   OBJ: 28.1
    TOP: Soviet Union / Western Conflicts

14. The Truman Doctrine stated that it would be the policy of the United States to
    a. help strong countries to take over weak countries.
    b. remain neutral in global affairs.
    c. only help Greece and Turkey.
    d. support free people who were resisting takeovers by armed minorities.

    ANS: D   DIF: Medium   REF: 709   OBJ: 28.1
    TOP: Truman's Presidency / Foreign Policy

15. Truman called the 80th Congress a "Do-Nothing Congress" because
    a. its members were seldom present for votes on major bills.
    b. it did nothing to help American workers.
    c. it refused to support his Fair Deal with legislation.
    d. it overrode most of his vetoes.

    ANS: C   DIF: Medium   REF: 715   OBJ: 28.2
    TOP: Truman's Presidency / Domestic Policy

16. The United States economy faced all of the following problems after World War II EXCEPT
    a. a severe depression.
    b. inflation.
    c. strikes.
    d. shortages of consumer goods.

    ANS: A   DIF: Medium   REF: 713   OBJ: 28.2
    TOP: Post WWII Economy

17. President Truman took all of the following steps to improve civil rights EXCEPT
    a. desegregating of the armed forces.
    b. appointing the first African-American judge to the federal courts.
    c. asking for anti-lynching laws.
    d. trying to integrate public schools in the South.

    ANS: D   DIF: Medium   REF: 715   OBJ: 28.2
    TOP: Civil Rights

18. The main purpose of the Taft-Hartley Act was to
    a. curb union power.
    b. help settle disputes between management and unions.
    c. assure workers of a minimum wage.
    d. fight union corruption.

    ANS: A   DIF: Medium   REF: 714   OBJ: 28.2
    TOP: Labor Unions

19. According to the Presidential Succession Act of 1947, who follows the Vice-President in line for the Presidency?
    a. Secretary of State
    b. Speaker of the House
    c. presiding officer of the Senate
    d. Secretary of Defense

    ANS: B   DIF: Medium   REF: 715   OBJ: 28.2
    TOP: U.S. Government / Executive Branch

20. Which nation was NOT an original member of NATO in 1949?
    a. West Germany
    b. Great Britain
    c. Canada
    d. Norway

    ANS: A   DIF: Medium   REF: 717–718   OBJ: 28.2
    TOP: NATO

21. The Taft-Hartley Act
    a. was supported by Truman.
    b. resulted in a decline in union members.
    c. outlawed the closed shop.
    d. strengthened union power.

    ANS: C   DIF: Medium   REF: 714   OBJ: 28.2
    TOP: Labor Unions

22. The Atomic Energy Act of 1946 put control of "fissionable materials" in the hands of
    a. a federal agency.
    b. private industry.
    c. the United Nations.
    d. state government.

    ANS: A   DIF: Medium   REF: 712–713   OBJ: 28.2
    TOP: Atomic Weapons

23. "Demobilization" refers to the
    a. government's top secret plan to produce fissionable materials.
    b. Republican party's campaign slogan in 1946.
    c. reaction of labor leaders to the Taft-Hartley Act.
    d. process of bringing American soldiers home after World War II.

    ANS: D   DIF: Medium   REF: 711–712   OBJ: 28.2
    TOP: WWII

24. Nazi leaders were tried and convicted for their war crimes at hearings held in
    a. Potsdam.
    b. Yalta.
    c. Berlin.
    d. Nuremberg.

    ANS: D   DIF: Medium   REF: 716   OBJ: 28.2
    TOP: Nazis

25. A major reason that Truman fired MacArthur was
    a. his limited success in pushing North Korea back across the 38th parallel.
    b. the high number of combat deaths.
    c. Truman's jealousy of MacArthur's popularity.
    d. his speaking out against Truman's policy of a limited war.

    ANS: D   DIF: Medium   REF: 725–726   OBJ: 28.3
    TOP: Korean War

26. Which event started the Korean War?
    a. The UN sent troops to liberate North Korea.
    b. Communist China invaded Korea.
    c. North Korea attacked South Korea.
    d. Truman sent U.S. troops to liberate Korea from the Communists.

    ANS: C   DIF: Medium   REF: 724   OBJ: 28.3
    TOP: Korean War

27. Which of the following was NOT a goal of the Fair Deal?
    a. raising the minimum wage   c. passing the Taft-Hartley Act
    b. extending Social Security benefits d. building more public housing

    ANS: C   DIF: Medium   REF: 721   OBJ: 28.3
    TOP: Truman's Presidency / Domestic Policy

28. Which of the following statements about the Korean War is NOT accurate?
    a. UN soldiers participated in the Korean War.
    b. American soldiers participated in the Korean War.
    c. Russian soldiers participated in the Korean War.
    d. Chinese soldiers participated in the Korean War.

    ANS: C   DIF: Medium   REF: 724   OBJ: 28.3
    TOP: Korean War

29. The 38th parallel divided
    a. China and the Soviet Union.   c. North and South Korea.
    b. China and Taiwan.   d. Japan and the Soviet Union.

    ANS: C   DIF: Medium   REF: 723   OBJ: 28.3
    TOP: Korean War

30. Which of the following events did NOT play a role in the rise of Senator McCarthy?
    a. the Atomic Energy Act   c. the fall of China to the Communists
    b. the Alger Hiss case   d. the confessions of Klaus Fuchs

    ANS: A   DIF: Medium   REF: 721–723   OBJ: 28.3
    TOP: Communism / McCarthy

31. The Red Scare of the late 1940s and the early 1950s resulted in all of the following EXCEPT
    a. requiring government workers to take loyalty oaths.
    b. banning of the Communist party in the United States.
    c. deportation of Communist party members.
    d. blacklisting of people who worked in the media.

    ANS: B   DIF: Medium   REF: 721, 723   OBJ: 28.3
    TOP: Communism

32. Which one of the following pairs is INCORRECTLY matched?
    a. Chiang Kai-shek—Taiwan   c. Mao Zedong—China
    b. Stalin—Japan   d. Syngman Rhee—South Korea

    ANS: B   DIF: Medium   REF: 722, 724   OBJ: 28.3
    TOP: Asian Leaders

33. "Soviet pressure against the free institutions of the western world is something that can be contained by the adroit and vigilant application of counter-force at a series of constantly shifting geographical and political points, corresponding to the shifts and maneuvers of Soviet policy." Which of the following is evidence that the United States followed the advice given in the above statement?
    a. The Soviet Union gets veto power as a member of the Security Council.
    b. Truman sponsors the GI Bill of Rights.
    c. Congress passes the Marshall Plan.
    d. Truman proposes his Fair Deal.

    ANS: C   DIF: Medium   REF: 710–711   OBJ: 28.1
    TOP: Marshall Plan

34. If you read newspaper editorials about the Taft-Hartley Act, listened to radio reports about the Berlin Airlift, and voted in the Truman-Dewey election, you were probably living during the years
    a. 1941–1945.   c. 1951–1955.
    b. 1946–1950.   d. 1956–1960.

    ANS: B   DIF: Medium   REF: 714, 717, 719
    OBJ: 28.2   TOP: U.S. History / 1946–1950

35. Which one of the following statements is a FACT rather than an opinion?
    a. The Taft-Hartley Act was a slave labor law.
    b. The 80th Congress was a Do-Nothing Congress.
    c. Members of the Mississippi and Alabama delegations walked out of the 1948 Democratic convention in protest of the party's civil rights plank.
    d. Dewey would have made a better President than Truman.

    ANS: C   DIF: Medium   REF: 719   OBJ: 28.2
    TOP: Presidential Elections

36. Which of the following was a consequence of the Berlin blockade?
    a. Germany played a minor role in the recovery of Europe.
    b. West Berlin became a part of East Germany.
    c. Stalin lifted the blockade, thus ending the cold war.
    d. The western powers formed the North Atlantic Treaty Organization.

    ANS: D   DIF: Medium   REF: 717   OBJ: 28.2
    TOP: NATO

37. All of the following led many Americans to say that the Democrats were "soft on Communism" EXCEPT
    a. Truman's statement that the Hiss case was a "red herring."
    b. Truman's response to the Berlin Blockade.
    c. the victory of Mao Zedong in mainland China.
    d. the fall of Czechoslovakia, Poland, and other Eastern European nations to the Communists.

    ANS: B   DIF: Medium   REF: 708–709, 721–722
    OBJ: 28.3   TOP: Communism / U.S. Response

SHORT ANSWER

In one or two sentences, define and distinguish between the terms given below.

1. Cold War

    ANS:
    The Cold War refers to the verbal combat and strained relations between the U.S. and the USSR after World War II. Despite the strained relations, no open fighting took place.

    DIF: Hard   OBJ: 28.0   TOP: U.S. / Soviet Relations

2. iron curtain

    ANS:
    The "iron curtain" was Churchill's term for the invisible line that separates the free world from the Communist world.

    DIF: Hard   REF: 708   OBJ: 28.0   TOP: Communism

3. containment

    ANS:
    Containment is an element of U.S. foreign policy that aims to prevent communism from spreading beyond where it exists.

    DIF: Hard   REF: 709   OBJ: 28.0
    TOP: Communism / U.S. Foreign Policy

ESSAY

1. Which of the following is the strongest example of comparison reasoning? Write your answer on a separate sheet of paper and support your answer with a paragraph explaining why you chose it.
   a. The Korean War was like World War II - we had to stop the Communist expansion.
   b. Anzus was like a NATO for the Pacific - both were alliances led by the United States.
   c. Truman winning the 1948 election was like an old pitcher, past his prime, hurling three consecutive no-hitters.
   d. The Truman doctrine was like a modern-day Monroe Doctrine.

   ANS:
   answer B Students' paragraphs should support their answer.

   DIF: Hard   REF: 717–718, 726   OBJ: 28.0
   TOP: U.S. / Foreign Treaties

2. Choose one of the topics below for your essay.
   A. What were the causes of the "cold war" that followed World War II? Include in your analysis five specific areas of distrust or disagreement.
   B. Explain how the United States came to be involved in the Korean War.

   ANS:
   Part A: The fear that Soviet influence would increase underlay much of the American response to world events after 1945. Specific causes of the Cold War included the lack of the promised free elections in Poland and the setting up of a Soviet puppet government there, as well as continued Soviet control over the Baltic republics and Eastern Europe. Russia failed to remove its troops from Iran, and pressured Turkey for military bases and control of the straits from the Black Sea to the Mediterranean. In Greece, pro-Soviet regimes in the Balkans supported the civil war. Part B: The United States was part of the Allied occupation force in Korea. Russian troops had occupied the land north of that line. When the U.S. removed its troops, both North and South threatened war. In early 1950, the South mobilized, but the North struck first. The U.S. furnished military support to the South, and then the UN sent forces into battle against the North Koreans.

   DIF: Hard   REF: 708–711, 721–726   OBJ: 28.0
   TOP: U.S. / Soviet Relations / Korean War

3. Who was primarily responsible for starting the Cold War—the United States or the Soviet Union? Explain your answer.

   ANS:
   Answers will vary but could include the following ideas: The Soviet Union was responsible for starting the Cold War: Stalin broke the Yalta agreements by refusing to hold free elections in Poland. The Soviets also supported Communist forces in Hungary, Bulgaria, and Romania. The United States was responsible for starting the Cold War: Truman refused to give up America's atomic monopoly, while he also used the Truman Doctrine and the Marshall Plan to extend American power around the Soviet Union.

   DIF: Hard   REF: 708–711   OBJ: 28.1
   TOP: U.S. / Soviet Relations

4. How is the United Nations organized?

ANS:
Answers will vary but could include the following ideas: The UN General Assembly includes delegates from every member nation. The Assembly fixes the UN budget, admits new members, and elects member nations to UN agencies. The Security Council includes 15 members. Of these, the Big Five have permanent seats and the right to vote. The Security Council has the power to look into disputes and to act against any nation that threatens the peace. The Secretariat, headed by a Secretary-General, handles the UN's day-to-day affairs.

DIF: Hard   REF: 707–708   OBJ: 28.1   TOP: United Nations

5. What were the causes and consequences of the Truman Doctrine?

ANS:
Answers will vary but could include the following ideas: By early 1947, many American leaders were alarmed by what they saw as a Soviet threat to the Free World. For example, the Greek government was under attack by Communist insurgents supported from neighboring Communist countries. The Truman Doctrine declared America's determination to lead and defend the Free World. In the short run, the Truman Doctrine led to the passage of the Greek-Turkish Aid bill. In the long run, the Truman Doctrine committed the United States to a global policy of containing Communist expansion.

DIF: Hard   REF: 709–710   OBJ: 28.1
TOP: Truman's Presidency / Foreign Policy

6. What were the causes and consequences of the Berlin blockade?

ANS:
Answers will vary but could include the following ideas: Stalin imposed the Berlin blockade in an attempt to prevent the Western powers from setting up a separate West German government and to keep Germany from helping European recovery. As a result of the blockade's failure, the Western powers approved the Basic Law for the German Federated Republic. In addition, the Berlin blockade helped to accelerate the formation of NATO.

DIF: Hard   REF: 717–718   OBJ: 28.2   TOP: NATO

7. Most political experts agreed that Truman would lose the 1948 presidential election. What were the major reasons for his winning?

ANS:
Answers will vary but could include the following ideas: Truman skillfully convinced people that the 80th Congress had done nothing but serve the powerful corporations. He successfully appealed to African-Americans by calling for civil rights laws. And finally, his whirlwind whistle-stop train tour showed that he was a spunky fighter who never gave up. In contrast, Dewey appeared too reserved and overconfident.

DIF: Hard   REF: 719–720   OBJ: 28.3   TOP: Presidential Elections

8. What events caused the second "red scare" in the United States?

    ANS:
    Answers will vary but could include the following ideas: The combined stresses of the cold war with Russia, the Alger Hiss case, the "fall" of China, the Soviet atomic bomb, and the atomic spy cases frightened the country. On very little evidence, many Americans began to suspect that there was a strong Communist conspiracy to take over the United States.

    DIF: Hard   REF: 721–723   OBJ: 28.3   TOP: Communism

9. Do you believe that Truman was justified in ordering American troops into battle in Korea without asking for Congressional approval? Why or why not?

    ANS:
    Answers will vary but could include the following ideas: Agree with Truman's decision—As Commander-in-Chief, under the Constitution he could order U.S. troops into battle in Korea. Disagree with Truman's decision—Under the Constitution, only Congress has the right to declare war. Truman's action therefore created a dangerous precedent for the future.

    DIF: Hard   REF: 723–726   OBJ: 28.3   TOP: Korean War

10. Why did President Truman fire General MacArthur? What Constitutional provisions gave Truman this authority?

    ANS:
    Answers will vary but could include the following ideas: Truman fired MacArthur because he could not tolerate the general's open challenge to his order to keep the war inside Korea. His authority to do this came from the constitutional provision that the President is Commander-in-Chief of all U.S. armed forces.

    DIF: Hard   REF: 725–726   OBJ: 28.3
    TOP: Korean War and Constitution

(page intentionally left blank)

MATCHING

Match each item with the correct statement below.

a. Rosa Parks
b. John Foster Dulles
c. the Middle East
d. "Brown v. Topeka Board of Education"
e. Korea

f. Nikita Khrushchev
g. Little Rock, Ark.
h. Fidel Castro
i. Adlai Stevenson
j. "Plessy v. Ferguson"

1. The Eisenhower Doctrine aimed at helping any country in _____ to resist Communist aggression.
2. In 1957 President Eisenhower sent paratroopers to _____ to enforce school integration.
3. When _____ replaced Stalin in 1953, he called for "peaceful coexistence" with the U.S.
4. When _____ refused to give up her bus seat, a new era in civil rights was launched in the South.
5. The Democratic presidential candidate defeated by Eisenhower in 1952 and 1956 was _____.
6. Eisenhower went to _____ soon after his inauguration to seek a way to end the war there.
7. Secretary of State _____ threatened "massive retaliation" against the USSR.
8. The Supreme Court decision in _____ struck down the "separate but equal" doctrine.
9. In 1959 _____ took over as Cuba's leader in what became a Communist revolution.

1. ANS: C   DIF: Easy   REF: 745   OBJ: 29.0
   TOP: Communism / U.S. Policy
2. ANS: G   DIF: Easy   REF: 739–740   OBJ: 29.0
   TOP: Civil Rights Movement
3. ANS: F   DIF: Easy   REF: 733   OBJ: 29.0
   TOP: U.S. / Soviet Relations
4. ANS: A   DIF: Easy   REF: 740   OBJ: 29.0
   TOP: Civil Rights
5. ANS: I   DIF: Easy   REF: 730, 737   OBJ: 29.0
   TOP: Presidential Elections
6. ANS: E   DIF: Easy   REF: 731   OBJ: 29.0
   TOP: Korean War
7. ANS: B   DIF: Easy   REF: 731   OBJ: 29.0
   TOP: U.S. / Soviet Relations
8. ANS: D   DIF: Easy   REF: 738–739   OBJ: 29.0
   TOP: Supreme Court
9. ANS: H   DIF: Easy   REF: 748   OBJ: 29.0
   TOP: Cuban History

MULTIPLE CHOICE

1. What name was given to John Foster Dulles' strategy for fighting Communism?
   a. blitzkrieg
   b. brinkmanship
   c. containment
   d. imperialism

   ANS: B   DIF: Medium   REF: 731   OBJ: 29.1
   TOP: Communism

2. On September 8, 1954, the United States, Australia, Great Britain, France, New Zealand, Pakistan, the Philippines, and Thailand formed an alliance that became known as
   a. SEATO.
   b. METO.
   c. the Paris Pact.
   d. the Dulles Pact.

   ANS: A   DIF: Medium   REF: 732   OBJ: 29.1
   TOP: Communism / SEATO

3. He was a Vietnamese Communist who led the Viet Minh troops to victory. He was
   a. Ho Chi Minh.
   b. Bao-Dai.
   c. Mao Zedong.
   d. Mossadegh.

   ANS: A   DIF: Medium   REF: 731   OBJ: 29.1
   TOP: Communism

4. During President Eisenhower's first term,
   a. Khrushchev visited the United States.
   b. Congress adopted the Eisenhower Doctrine.
   c. the Korean War ended.
   d. the Soviets launched "Sputnik."

   ANS: C   DIF: Medium   REF: 731   OBJ: 29.1
   TOP: Korean War

5. "Parity" is best defined as
   a. the ratio of Democrats to Republicans in the Senate.
   b. the word that McCarthy used to describe the actions of Brigadier General Ralph Zwicker.
   c. the relation of farm prices to nonfarm prices during the period from 1910 to 1914.
   d. the word that Eisenhower used to describe his plan to reduce the activities of the federal government.

   ANS: C   DIF: Medium   REF: 735   OBJ: 29.2
   TOP: Farming

6. In "Brown v. Board of Education," the Supreme Court held that
   a. the states, not the federal government, have to deal with civil rights.
   b. racially separate facilities do not violate the Fourteenth Amendment.
   c. racial segregation in public schools is unconstitutional.
   d. racial separate facilities damage the education of white children.

   ANS: C   DIF: Medium   REF: 738–739   OBJ: 29.3
   TOP: Supreme Court

7. Over 100 southern members of Congress signed the "Southern Manifesto" in reaction to
   a. the Supreme Court decision in "Brown v. Board of Education."
   b. the Montgomery bus boycott.
   c. the crisis in Little Rock.
   d. the Supreme Court decision in "Plessy v. Ferguson."

   ANS: A   DIF: Medium   REF: 739   OBJ: 29.3
   TOP: Supreme Court

8. Which one of the following tactics did Martin Luther King, Jr., urge his followers to practice?
   a. collective bargaining
   c. massive retaliation
   b. nonviolent demonstration
   d. peaceful coexistence

   ANS: B   DIF: Medium   REF: 740   OBJ: 29.3
   TOP: Civil Rights

9. The lawyer who became the first African-American to sit on the Supreme Court was
   a. Thurgood Marshall.
   c. Lyndon Johnson.
   b. Earl Warren.
   d. Martin Luther King.

   ANS: A   DIF: Medium   REF: 738–739   OBJ: 29.3
   TOP: Supreme Court

10. Palestinians are
    a. Hungarian refugees who fled to the United States.
    b. Cuban refugees who fled to the United States.`
    c. Egyptian refugees who fled to Israel.
    d. Arab refugees who fled to the West Bank.

    ANS: D   DIF: Medium   REF: 742–743   OBJ: 29.4
    TOP: Mid–East Conflicts

11. The Eisenhower Doctrine stated that the
    a. United States would help any Middle Eastern country that requested aid to resist military
       aggression from any Communist-backed nation.
    b. United States would strive to be first in space.
    c. Truman Doctrine would no longer apply to Europe.
    d. United States would help the Western powers run the Suez Canal.

    ANS: A   DIF: Medium   REF: 745   OBJ: 29.4
    TOP: Eisenhower's Presidency / Foreign Policy

12. The young lawyer who overthrew Batista and took control of Cuba was
    a. Fidel Castro.
    c. Gamal Nasser.
    b. Anastas Mikoyan.
    d. King Hussein.

    ANS: A   DIF: Medium   REF: 748   OBJ: 29.4
    TOP: Cuban History

13. The U-2 was a
    a. high-flying American spy plane.
    b. German rocket that preceded the V-2.
    c. British satellite.
    d. liquid-fuel rocket that could travel 1,000 miles per hour.

    ANS: A   DIF: Medium   REF: 734   OBJ: 29.4
    TOP: U.S. / Soviet Relations

14. The armistice that ended the Korean War resulted in
    a. all of Korea becoming Communist.
    b. Korea being divided near the 38th parallel.
    c. all of Korea becoming democratic.
    d. the Chinese gaining control of Korea.

    ANS: B   DIF: Medium   REF: 731   OBJ: 29.1
    TOP: Korean War

15. As a result of their defeat in the battle of Dienbienphu, the
    a. Russians withdrew from Austria.   c. French withdrew from Vietnam.
    b. United States withdrew from Egypt.   d. Japanese withdrew from Taiwan.

    ANS: C   DIF: Medium   REF: 732   OBJ: 29.1
    TOP: Vietnamese History

16. In regard to Vietnam in the 1950s, the United States
    a. supported the existing government.
    b. declared its neutrality.
    c. sent millions of dollars to aid France.
    d. sent American forces to put down guerrilla fighting.

    ANS: C   DIF: Medium   REF: 732   OBJ: 29.0
    TOP: Vietnamese History

17. As a result of the Soviet launching of Sputnik, the federal government
    a. passed the National Defense Education Act to produce more scientists and science teachers.
    b. appointed Robert Goddard to head the United States space program.
    c. created NASA to coordinate United States space efforts.
    d. passed the National Defense Education Act to produce more scientists and science teachers AND created NASA to coordinate United States space efforts.

    ANS: D   DIF: Medium   REF: 745   OBJ: 29.0
    TOP: Space Exploration

18. Upon taking office, Eisenhower's goals as President included
    a. reducing the size of the government.
    b. encouraging private business interests.
    c. increasing defense spending and the size of the armed forces.
    d. reducing the size of the government AND encouraging private business interests.

    ANS: D   DIF: Medium   REF: 734   OBJ: 29.0
    TOP: Eisenhower's Presidency

19. As a result of the 1954 Geneva Conference, Vietnam was
    a. returned to French control.
    b. divided into a northern Communist section and a southern "free" section.
    c. turned over to the control of Ho Chi Minh.
    d. occupied by a United Nations peacekeeping force.

    ANS: B   DIF: Medium   REF: 732   OBJ: 29.1
    TOP: Vietnamese History

© Prentice-Hall, Inc.

20. Which one of the following ideas is NOT associated with Eisenhower's foreign policy?
    a. massive retaliation
    c. brinkmanship
    b. flexible response
    d. the "New Look"

    ANS: B   DIF: Medium   REF: 731   OBJ: 29.1
    TOP: Eisenhower's Presidency / Foreign Policy

21. During the Eisenhower years, the major farm issue in the United States was
    a. public versus private power.
    b. rising prices.
    c. the need to check "security risks" among small farmers.
    d. overproduction.

    ANS: D   DIF: Medium   REF: 735   OBJ: 29.2
    TOP: Farming

22. Which of the following statements about Senator McCarthy's fall from power is MOST accurate?
    a. President Eisenhower exposed and defeated McCarthy.
    b. Television exposed and defeated McCarthy.
    c. Radio exposed and defeated McCarthy.
    d. Adlai Stevenson exposed and defeated McCarthy.

    ANS: B   DIF: Medium   REF: 736–737   OBJ: 29.2
    TOP: Communism / McCarthy

23. All of the following were examples of how the Eisenhower administration helped extend the thinking of the New Deal EXCEPT
    a. increasing Social Security benefits.
    b. increasing minimum wage.
    c. amending the Atomic Energy Act to give private companies a larger role in atomic research.
    d. creating new programs for urban slum clearance and for public housing.

    ANS: C   DIF: Medium   REF: 736   OBJ: 29.2
    TOP: Eisenhower's Presidency / Federal Programs

24. He was Chief Justice of the Supreme Court from 1953 to 1969. Under his leadership, the court reached a landmark decision in the case of "Brown v. Board of Education." He was
    a. John Marshall.
    c. Thurgood Marshall.
    b. Albert Gore.
    d. Earl Warren.

    ANS: D   DIF: Medium   REF: 738   OBJ: 29.3
    TOP: Supreme Court

• 25. Martin Luther King, Jr., was a leader in which one of the following events?
    a. the Little Rock school crisis
    c. the Montgomery bus boycott
    b. "Brown v. Board of Education"
    d. the lunch counter sit-ins

    ANS: C   DIF: Medium   REF: 740–741   OBJ: 29.3
    TOP: Civil Rights Movement

26. Which of the following key events in the civil rights movement occurred LAST?
    a. The Civil Rights Act of 1960 becomes a law.
    b. Eisenhower orders troops into Little Rock.
    c. The Montgomery bus boycott begins.
    d. The Supreme Court reaches a decision in "Brown v. Board of Education."

    ANS: A   DIF: Medium   REF: 741   OBJ: 29.3
    TOP: Civil Rights Movement

27. The Civil Rights Acts of 1957 and 1960 aimed at helping African-Americans
    a. acquire full voting rights.
    b. acquire additional job opportunities.
    c. attend integrated schools.
    d. take legal action against the "Southern Manifesto."

    ANS: A   DIF: Medium   REF: 741   OBJ: 29.3
    TOP: Civil Rights Movement

28. Operation Paperclip succeeded in
    a. bringing German rocket engineers to the United States.
    b. toppling the Iranian government of Mossadegh.
    c. deposing the corrupt King Farouk of Egypt.
    d. helping the government of Chiang Kai-shek to escape to Taiwan.

    ANS: A   DIF: Medium   REF: 744   OBJ: 29.4
    TOP: Space Exploration

29. As President, Eisenhower sent American forces to all of the following places EXCEPT
    a. the Straits of Formosa.   c. Little Rock.
    b. Lebanon.   d. Egypt.

    ANS: D   DIF: Medium   REF: 739–740, 746
    OBJ: 29.4   TOP: Eisenhower's Presidency / Foreign Policy

30. During the 1950s, the United States and the Soviet Union demanded a cease-fire and troop withdrawal from
    a. Hungary.   c. East Berlin.
    b. the Suez Canal.   d. the Formosa Strait.

    ANS: B   DIF: Medium   REF: 743   OBJ: 29.4
    TOP: Suez Canal

31. The Suez crisis in 1956 was finally settled by
    a. the Soviet Union and the United States acting through the United Nations.
    b. Israel's surrender.
    c. the sending of American troops to oversee troop withdrawal from the area.
    d. French and British occupation of Egypt.

    ANS: A   DIF: Medium   REF: 743   OBJ: 29.4
    TOP: Suez Canal

32. Which of the following events of the 1950s ended a period of reduced tensions between the United States and the Soviet Union?
    a. the launch of "Sputnik"
    b. Soviet capture of a U.S. spy plane
    c. Khrushchev's call for "peaceful coexistence"
    d. the 1955 summit conference in Geneva

    ANS: B   DIF: Medium   REF: 747   OBJ: 29.4
    TOP: Soviet / U.S. Relations

33. As a result of the U-2 incident,
    a. Eisenhower apologized to Khrushchev.
    b. Eisenhower did not visit the Soviet Union.
    c. the summit meeting between the United States and the U.S.S.R. took place as scheduled.
    d. Fidel Castro rose to power in Cuba.

    ANS: B   DIF: Medium   REF: 747   OBJ: 29.4
    TOP: Soviet / U.S. Relations

34. Which one of the following countries did NOT attack Egypt in 1956?
    a. Israel   c. Russia
    b. Great Britain   d. France

    ANS: C   DIF: Medium   REF: 743   OBJ: 29.4
    TOP: Egyptian History

35. Quemoy and Matsu were
    a. the names given to Russia's first two satellites.
    b. the first Chinese ambassadors to the United States.
    c. the cities from which the Germans launched their V-2 rockets.
    d. the names of two islands controlled by the Nationalist Chinese.

    ANS: D   DIF: Medium   REF: 746   OBJ: 29.4
    TOP: Communism / China

36. In his farewell address, Eisenhower warned of dangers posed by the
    a. new Democratic administration.   c. misuse of the Eisenhower Doctrine.
    b. Castro regime in Cuba.   d. military industrial complex.

    ANS: D   DIF: Medium   REF: 748   OBJ: 29.4
    TOP: Eisenhower's Presidency

37. Which of the following statements is a FACT rather than an opinion?
    a. Khrushchev should have accepted Eisenhower's "open skies" proposal.
    b. Brinkmanship is a dangerous and immoral foreign policy.
    c. The "New Look" would strengthen America's overall defense position.
    d. The Viet Minh defeated the French at Dienbienphu.

    ANS: D   DIF: Medium   REF: 732   OBJ: 29.1
    TOP: Vietnamese History

38. Eisenhower said, "The government has to be liberal when it is talking about the relationship between government and the individual, and conservative when talking about the national economy and the individual's pocket book." Which of the following developments is evidence that Eisenhower followed his own advice?
    a. increasing Social Security benefits
    b. increasing income tax
    c. the enactment of Benson's Agricultural Act
    d. increasing Social Security benefits and trying to lower the income tax

    ANS: D   DIF: Medium   REF: 736   OBJ: 29.2
    TOP: Eisenhower's Presidency / Domestic Policy

39. Which of the following events helped cause McCarthy's fall from power?
    a. the Army-McCarthy hearings
    b. Eisenhower's farewell address
    c. "Life" magazine's "Crisis In America" issue
    d. the Supreme Court decision in "Brown v. Board of Education"

    ANS: A   DIF: Medium   REF: 736–737   OBJ: 29.2
    TOP: Communism / McCarthy

40. "Mob rule cannot be allowed to override the decisions of our courts." When President Eisenhower made this statement, he was most likely referring to the
    a. crisis at Central High School in Little Rock.
    b. Army-McCarthy hearings.
    c. Supreme Court ruling in "Plessy v. Ferguson."
    d. decision by Rosa Parks to refuse to give up her bus seat.

    ANS: A   DIF: Medium   REF: 739–740   OBJ: 29.3
    TOP: Civil Rights Movement

41. If you watched Khrushchev's visit to the United States on television, read newspaper articles about the Little Rock crisis, and wrote a letter to the editor to complain about "Sputnik," you were probably living during the years
    a. 1950–1953.   c. 1957–1959.
    b. 1954–1956.   d. 1960–1963.

    ANS: C   DIF: Medium   REF: 739, 744, 747
    OBJ: 29.4   TOP: Eisenhower's Presidency

42. "It's time to lose our carnival. To revitalize America's educational dream we must stop kowtowing to the mediocre." The author of this passage would have been MOST likely to
    a. support the Soil Bank.
    b. oppose the sale of TVA.
    c. sign the "Southern Manifesto."
    d. support the National Defense Education Act.

    ANS: D   DIF: Medium   REF: 745   OBJ: 29.4
    TOP: Education

ESSAY

1. What is the main point of this paragraph? Write your answer on a separate sheet of paper and support your answer with a paragraph explaining why you chose it.

    The Civil Rights Act of 1957 was followed by another in 1960, again passed with bi-partisan support. When the Republicans and Democrats met in their conventions to draw up platforms, both supported desegregation. At last the nation was turning back to the unsolved problems of the Civil War. Americans were addressing their racial problems and African-Americans themselves were in the vanguard of bringing about that change.
    A. Two civil rights acts have been passed in recent history.
    B. Both the Republican and Democratic parties support segregatin.
    C. The nation is finally solving its racial problems.
    D. African-Americans are solving the nation's racial problems.

    ANS:
    answer C Students' paragraphs should support their answer.

    DIF: Hard   REF: 738–742   OBJ: 29.0
    TOP: Civil Rights Movement

2. Choose five or six events of the 1950s that you feel best characterize the Eisenhower years. Present and defend your choice in an essay. Add a concluding generalization about the period. (This concluding statement should point out one or two main tendencies of the Eisenhower Presidency. For example, was it characterized by radical reform? By extreme partisanship? By adventurism in foreign affairs?)

    ANS:
    The first successful hydrogen bomb in 1952; John Foster Dulles' policy of brinkmanship and massive retaliation; the establishment of SEATO and METO; aid to the French in Indochina and the resultant escalation of the Vietnam conflict; the Marines sent to Lebanon and the Navy to the Formosa Strait; Krushchev's visit to the U.S.; the Summits; Castro's takeover in Cuba; the creation of HEW; a weak response to McCarthy; the appointment of Earl Warren to the Supreme Court; the Brown decision; paratroopers to Little Rock; the two Civil Rights bills; "Sputnik" and the Defence Education Act in response; and the Eisenhower Doctrine for the Middle East. The Eisenhower years were a period of much activity in foreign affairs and important changes in domestic affairs. Overseas, our nation tried on a new "peace-keeper" mantle in an age of nuclear weapons.

    DIF: Hard   REF: 729–748   OBJ: 29.0
    TOP: Eisenhower's Presidency

3. What issues did Dwight Eisenhower successfully use to defeat Adlai Stevenson in the 1952 presidential election?

    ANS:
    Answers will vary but could include the following ideas: Eisenhower successfully used these pledges—to end the Korean War, to roll back the Iron Curtain, to balance the budget, to lower the national debt, and to "return honesty to government"—in order to defeat Stevenson in the 1952 presidential election.

    DIF: Hard   REF: 729–730   OBJ: 29.1   TOP: Presidential Elections

4. How did John Foster Dulles plan to change U.S. foreign policy?

ANS:
Answers will vary but could include the following ideas: Secretary of State Dulles threatened "massive retaliation" against the Soviet Union or against Communist China if they attacked any country. He further pledged to go "to the brink of war" to preserve the peace of the world. Finally, Dulles vowed to turn back the Communist tide in Asia and to free the "captive peoples" under Soviet rule in Eastern Europe.

DIF: Hard   REF: 731   OBJ: 29.1
TOP: Communism / U.S. Foreign Policy

5. In what ways was President Eisenhower liberal and in what ways was he conservative?

ANS:
Answers will vary but could include the following ideas: President Eisenhower said that he wanted his administration to be "liberal when it was talking about the relationship between government and the individual. . . ." For example, Ike approved an increase in Social Security benefits and in the minimum wage. President Eisenhower said that he wanted his administration to be "conservative when talking about the national economy and the individual's pocket book." For example, he ended the wage-and-price controls imposed during the Korean War and attempted to reduce the activities of the federal government.

DIF: Hard   REF: 729–748   OBJ: 29.2
TOP: Eisenhower's Presidency

6. What factors helped to bring about the collapse of Senator McCarthy's power?

ANS:
Answers will vary but could include the following ideas: The Army-McCarthy hearings through television gave a national audience the opportunity to watch McCarthy's tactics. The Senator treated witnesses rudely and showed himself an unscrupulous bully. A few months later, the Senate condemned McCarthy for conduct "contrary to senatorial traditions."

DIF: Hard   REF: 736–737   OBJ: 29.2
TOP: Communism / McCarthy

7. Why were nonviolent demonstrations an effective way for African-Americans to achieve progress in claiming their rights in the 1950s?

ANS:
Answers will vary but could include the following ideas: Nonviolent demonstrations helped to mobilize what Dr. King later called a national "coalition of conscience" to fight segregation. Dr. King felt that all people need to be educated in the ways of peace and decency. He said, if you fight your enemies with violence, you will be using their weapons and brutalizing yourself. But, he felt, if you are peaceful and simply do not go along with them, you will eventually prevail.

DIF: Hard   REF: 738–742   OBJ: 29.3
TOP: Civil Rights Movement

8. Describe one piece of legislation and one judicial decision made during the Eisenhower administration that extended civil rights.

ANS:
Answers will vary but could include the following ideas: The Civil Rights Acts of 1957 and 1960 began the process of protecting African-American voting rights. The Supreme Court's decision in "Brown v. Board of Education" began the process of ending segregation in the nation's public schools.

DIF: Hard   REF: 738–742   OBJ: 29.3
TOP: Civil Rights Movement

9. Khrushchev demanded that Eisenhower apologize for ordering U-2 flights over Russia. When Eisenhower refused, the summit meeting collapsed. Do you agree or disagree with Eisenhower's refusal to apologize? Explain your answer.

ANS:
Answers will vary but could include the following ideas: Students who agree with Ike's decision can argue that the United States had a right to defend itself by collecting information about Soviet military capabilities. In addition, an apology would have humiliated both Eisenhower and the American people. Those who feel it was an unwise decision can argue that Eisenhower had an overriding responsibility to work for a relaxation of world tensions. The United States had no right to send a spy plane over Soviet territory. Eisenhower had an obligation to apologize and to prevent the summit from collapsing.

DIF: Hard   REF: 747–748   OBJ: 29.4   TOP: U.S. / Soviet Relations

(page intentionally left blank)

MATCHING

Match each item with the correct statement below.

a. demography
b. xerography
c. John Dewey
d. megalopolis
e. California

f. Early Bird
g. General Motors
h. gross national product (GNP)
i. GI Bill
j. Catch 22

1. The study of population and population changes.
2. Educational philosopher who favored "learning by doing."
3. The most populous state since 1964.
4. A copying process.
5. The total value of goods and services produced in a country each year.
6. Title of a Joseph Heller novel—today it refers to any no-win situation
7. Auto manufacturer that started the idea of annual model changes in design.
8. Name of sprawling giant cities.
9. First American communications satellite.
10. Paid the costs of higher education for veterans.

1. ANS: A   DIF: Easy   REF: 751   OBJ: 30.0
   TOP: Demography
2. ANS: C   DIF: Easy   REF: 764   OBJ: 30.0
   TOP: Education
3. ANS: E   DIF: Easy   REF: 751–752   OBJ: 30.0
   TOP: Demography
4. ANS: B   DIF: Easy   REF: 761   OBJ: 30.0
   TOP: U.S. Inventions
5. ANS: H   DIF: Easy   REF: 757   OBJ: 30.0
   TOP: Gross National Product
6. ANS: J   DIF: Easy   REF: 767   OBJ: 30.0
   TOP: U.S. Writers
7. ANS: G   DIF: Easy   REF: 762   OBJ: 30.0
   TOP: Automobile Era
8. ANS: D   DIF: Easy   REF: 755   OBJ: 30.0
   TOP: Suburban Sprawl
9. ANS: F   DIF: Easy   REF: 760   OBJ: 30.0
   TOP: Space Exploration
10. ANS: I   DIF: Easy   REF: 764   OBJ: 30.0
    TOP: Education

MULTIPLE CHOICE

1. An SMSA is a
   a. rural population surrounding a small farming community.
   b. dense population surrounding a central city.
   c. suburban population surrounding a farming community.
   d. rural population surrounding a suburban community.

   ANS: B   DIF: Medium   REF: 754   OBJ: 30.1
   TOP: Suburban Sprawl

2. The Constitution requires a federal census in order to
   a. count the population every ten years.
   b. set up a commission to study housing needs.
   c. regulate prices and wages according to population distribution.
   d. remove disreputable books from public libraries.

   ANS: A   DIF: Medium   REF: 751   OBJ: 30.1
   TOP: Constitution / Census

3. The Sunbelt states are located in the
   a. North and Northeast.   c. South and Southwest.
   b. West and Southwest.   d. East and Southeast.

   ANS: C   DIF: Medium   REF: 752   OBJ: 30.1
   TOP: Geography

4. When a machine automatically performs a manufacturing process, it is called
   a. automation.   c. microprocessing.
   b. xerography.   d. electronics.

   ANS: A   DIF: Medium   REF: 761   OBJ: 30.2
   TOP: U.S. Inventions

5. John Dewey's beliefs about education centered around learning
   a. the basics—English, math, and social studies.
   b. science and math.
   c. by doing.
   d. by reading.

   ANS: C   DIF: Medium   REF: 764   OBJ: 30.3
   TOP: Education

6. Which one of the following men is INCORRECTLY paired with the book he authored?
   a. James Bryant Conant—"The American High School Today"
   b. Fulton J. Sheen—"Peace of Soul"
   c. Norman Vincent Peale—"The Power of Positive Thinking"
   d. Sigmund Freud—"Peace of Mind"

   ANS: D   DIF: Medium   REF: 764   OBJ: 30.3
   TOP: U.S. Writers

7. I was one of the most persuasive preachers of the 1950s. My revival meetings drew hundreds of thousands to make "decisions for Christ." I am
   a. Jackson Pollack.
   b. John Dewey.
   c. Billy Graham.
   d. Joshua Loth Lieberman.

   ANS: C   DIF: Medium   REF: 764–765   OBJ: 30.3
   TOP: Religion

8. A member of the Moral Majority would probably be a
   a. Hindu.
   b. Zen Buddhist.
   c. nihilist.
   d. Fundamentalist Protestant.

   ANS: D   DIF: Medium   REF: 765   OBJ: 30.3
   TOP: Religion

9. The first great popular Rock 'n Roll star or group was
   a. Andy Warhol.
   b. the Beatles.
   c. Elvis Presley.
   d. J. D. Salinger.

   ANS: C   DIF: Medium   REF: 767   OBJ: 30.4
   TOP: Music

10. Abstract painters strive to
    a. make their work as realistic as possible.
    b. use only oil paints on their canvases.
    c. express their own private visions in their works.
    d. use traditional methods to create art.

    ANS: C   DIF: Medium   REF: 766   OBJ: 30.4
    TOP: Abstract Artists

11. Which of the following probably occurred as a result of Americans moving to the suburbs?
    a. Immigration began to decline.
    b. Government regulations became stricter.
    c. Automobile ownership increased.
    d. Per capita income declined.

    ANS: C   DIF: Medium   REF: 758   OBJ: 30.1
    TOP: Automobile Era

12. Americans in the 1970s had a greater life expectancy because of
    a. improved diet.
    b. medical advances.
    c. "miracle drugs."
    d. all of the above

    ANS: D   DIF: Medium   REF: 756   OBJ: 30.0
    TOP: Demography / Aging

13. All of the following are by-products of the automobile EXCEPT
    a. computers.
    b. credit cards.
    c. parking garages.
    d. shopping centers.

    ANS: A   DIF: Medium   REF: 757   OBJ: 30.0
    TOP: Automobile Era

14. Which of the following men is NOT correctly paired with the product or process he helped develop?
    a. John von Neumann—computer
    b. Robert Hutchins—television
    c. Edwin Land—instant photography
    d. Chester Carlson—xerography

    ANS: B   DIF: Medium   REF: 761   OBJ: 30.0
    TOP: Inventions

15. All of the following were true of the majority of Americans by 1970 EXCEPT that they
    a. were high school graduates.
    b. believed in God.
    c. owned television sets.
    d. were unskilled laborers.

    ANS: D   DIF: Medium   OBJ: 30.0   TOP: Demography

16. All of the following were abstract expressionist painters of the 1950s and 1960s EXCEPT
    a. Robert Motherwell.
    b. Willem de Kooning.
    c. Helen Frankenthaler.
    d. Katherine Anne Porter.

    ANS: D   DIF: Medium   REF: 766   OBJ: 30.0
    TOP: Abstract Artists

17. All of the following were novelists of the 1950s and 1960s EXCEPT
    a. Rube Goldberg.
    b. Saul Bellow.
    c. Ralph Ellison.
    d. Eudora Welty.

    ANS: A   DIF: Medium   REF: 767–768   OBJ: 30.0
    TOP: U.S. Writers

18. The area of the United States called the Sunbelt experienced
    a. the slowest growth of population after World War II.
    b. the fastest growth of population after World War II.
    c. no growth in population after World War II.
    d. no growth in population after World War I.

    ANS: B   DIF: Medium   REF: 752   OBJ: 30.1
    TOP: Demography

19. By 1970 the majority of African-Americans
    a. lived in urban areas.
    b. who were eligible, voted.
    c. lived in the South.
    d. lived in urban areas AND who were eligible, voted.

    ANS: A   DIF: Medium   REF: 755   OBJ: 30.1
    TOP: Demography

20. All of the following describe U.S. population trends since World War II EXCEPT
    a. growth of suburbs.
    b. more and smaller farms.
    c. migration of people west.
    d. increasing mobility.

    ANS: B   DIF: Medium   REF: 751–756   OBJ: 30.1
    TOP: Demography / Population Trends

21. "One of the greatest changes I've noticed in my lifetime is the erasing of distinctions between rural and city people. Now you can't tell the difference." Which of the following probably contributed most to the change noted in the statement?
    a. abstract art
    b. religion
    c. television
    d. free public schools

    ANS: C   DIF: Medium   OBJ: 30.2   TOP: Television

22. The first credit cards were offered by
    a. suburban shopping centers.
    b. large gasoline companies.
    c. television stores.
    d. downtown department stores.

    ANS: B   DIF: Medium   REF: 758   OBJ: 30.2
    TOP: Credit

23. Which of the following products probably had the greatest effect on American life?
    a. synthetic textiles like nylon and Dacron
    b. automobiles
    c. electric typewriters
    d. dishwashers

    ANS: B   DIF: Medium   REF: 758–759   OBJ: 30.2
    TOP: Automobile Era

24. Regarding the plan to build an interstate highway system, President Eisenhower
    a. vetoed the program.
    b. supported the program on condition that the states pay for 90% of the construction costs.
    c. supported the program.
    d. supported the program but was unable to persuade Congress to pass the bill.

    ANS: C   DIF: Medium   REF: 757   OBJ: 30.2
    TOP: Eisenhower's Domestic Programs

25. Which one of the following new inventions was NOT created in a research laboratory?
    a. microprocessor
    b. laser
    c. credit card
    d. photovoltaic cell

    ANS: C   DIF: Medium   REF: 763   OBJ: 30.2
    TOP: U.S. Inventions

26. Which one of the following statements about television is NOT true?
    a. By 1970, over 90% of all American homes had at least one television set.
    b. By the 1970s, satellites brought events from all over the world into the nation's homes.
    c. By the 1960s, instant replay enabled television viewers to see events played again and again.
    d. By the mid-1960s, over half of all American homes had VCRs attached to their television sets.

    ANS: D   DIF: Medium   REF: 760   OBJ: 30.2
    TOP: Television

27. Trends between 1950 and 1970 included which of the following?
   a. a decline in farm productivity
   b. people became increasingly mobile
   c. per capita income increased
   d. a decline in farm productivity AND people became increasingly mobile

   ANS: D   DIF: Medium   REF: 752–756   OBJ: 30.2
   TOP: Demography / Trends

28. Between 1930 and 1970, college enrollment
   a. increased.
   b. decreased.
   c. stayed the same.
   d. increased until about 1950 and then decreased rapidly.

   ANS: A   DIF: Medium   REF: 764   OBJ: 30.3
   TOP: Education

29. Which of the following are reasons for education becoming increasingly important after World War II?
   a. need to increase the number of farm workers
   b. concern that the Soviet Union's school system was superior
   c. fewer jobs for unskilled people due to automation
   d. concern that the Soviet Union's school system was superior AND fewer jobs for unskilled people due to automation

   ANS: D   DIF: Medium   REF: 764   OBJ: 30.3
   TOP: Education

30. Which one of the following statements about high school enrollment in the United States is CORRECT?
   a. By 1970, 90 percent of all Americans aged 14 to 17 were in high school.
   b. In 1910 less than 1 percent of all Americans aged 14 to 17 were in high school.
   c. In 1930 about 10 percent of all Americans aged 14 to 17 were in high school.
   d. In 1950 about 50 percent of all Americans aged 14 to 17 were in high school.

   ANS: A   DIF: Medium   REF: 764   OBJ: 30.3
   TOP: Education

31. Which one of the following statements about religion in the United States is NOT true?
   a. Attendance at churches began to decline by the end of the 1950s.
   b. The 1960s were a relatively trouble-free time for churches in America.
   c. During the 1960s some people turned away from traditional Western religion and sought answers in Hinduism and Zen Buddhism.
   d. About a third of all Protestants in the 1980s were Fundamentalists.

   ANS: B   DIF: Medium   REF: 765   OBJ: 30.3
   TOP: Religion

32. "Nihilism" is the
    a. total rejection of law and institutions.
    b. strong belief in life after death.
    c. belief in the Christian church.
    d. philosophy of education supported by James Bryant Conant.

    ANS: A   DIF: Medium   REF: 765   OBJ: 30.3
    TOP: Philosophy

33. Which one of the following statements about American writers is NOT true?
    a. Several American novelists have won the Nobel Prize for Literature.
    b. After World War II, American writers ceased to use the South as a setting for their stories.
    c. Ralph Ellison's novel, "Invisible Man," discusses the conditions of African-Americans in America.
    d. J. D. Salinger's novel, "Catcher in the Rye," is the story of an adolescent trying to escape hypocrisy.

    ANS: B   DIF: Medium   REF: 767   OBJ: 30.4
    TOP: U.S. Writers

34. Which one of the following was a consequence of advances in surgery and the invention of "miracle drugs"?
    a. a growing economy   c. an aging population
    b. the move to the suburbs   d. the move to the West

    ANS: C   DIF: Medium   REF: 756   OBJ: 30.1
    TOP: Demography / Aging

35. Which one of the following was NOT a cause of the economic boom after World War II?
    a. Wartime savings gave a big boost to sales.
    b. Rising oil prices stimulated industrial growth.
    c. Government spending kept the economy booming.
    d. America's export trade flourished.

    ANS: B   DIF: Medium   OBJ: 30.2   TOP: Post WWII Economy

36. Marlon Brando played a tough motorcycle gang leader in the film "The Wild One." When Brando was asked, "What are you rebelling against?" he replied, "What d'ya got?" Brando's reply is an example of
    a. Hinduism.   c. Fundamentalism.
    b. Zen Buddhism.   d. nihilism.

    ANS: D   DIF: Medium   REF: 765   OBJ: 30.3
    TOP: Philosophy

37. If you purchased a number one hit by Elvis Presley, looked at a new exhibit by Jackson Pollack, and became the first person on your block to own a television set, you were probably living during the years
    a. 1950–1959.
    b. 1960–1969.
    c. 1970–1979.
    d. 1980–1989.

    ANS: A   DIF: Medium   REF: 760, 766–767
    OBJ: 30.4   TOP: Culture in 1950s

38. Which of the following does NOT belong with the other three?
    a. Eudora Welty
    b. Katherine Anne Porter
    c. Helen Frankenthaler
    d. Carson McCullers

    ANS: C   DIF: Medium   REF: 766–767   OBJ: 30.4
    TOP: U.S. Writers

SHORT ANSWER

In one or two sentences, define and distinguish between the terms given below.

1. minimal art

   ANS:
   Minimal art, also called "pop art," was a popular art of the 1960s that saw simple objects as art. Andy Warhol and Claes Oldenburg were artists of this school.

   DIF: Hard   REF: 766   OBJ: 30.0   TOP: Minimal Art

2. interstate highways

   ANS:
   Interstate highways are a network of superhighways across the U.S. originally funded by Congress during the Eisenhower administration.

   DIF: Hard   REF: 757   OBJ: 30.0   TOP: Automobile Era

3. baby boom

   ANS:
   The baby boom refers to the huge increase in birth-rate, or "population explosion," that followed World War II and lasted throughout the 1950s.

   DIF: Hard   REF: 751   OBJ: 30.0   TOP: Demography

ESSAY

1. What point of view do the following statements express about automobiles? Write your answer on a separate sheet of paper and support your answer with a paragraph explaining why you chose it. As automobile traffic increased, poor pedestrians had to risk their lives when they crossed the street. Millons of automobiles polluted the atmosphere with carbon monoxide and hydrocarbons. It was hard to live without automobiles, but could Americans learn to live with them?
   A. favorable
   B. extremely favorable
   C. unfavorable
   D. unbiased

   ANS:
   answer c Students' paragraphs should support their answer.

   DIF: Hard   REF: 758   OBJ: 30.0   TOP: Automobile Era

2. The forces of demography and "magic machines" transformed the American way of life during the post–World War II years. Present six specific examples of such forces and their impact. (Discuss demography trends in one paragraph and "magic machines" in another.)

   ANS:
   Demographic changes and new machines transformed the American way of life during the post-WWII years. The high birth rate and large influx of immigrants after the war forced improvements in public services. Even though the " baby boom" was slowing by the 1960s, there was population growth in the west, south, and north as large numbers of people moved. Many left the farms to live in the cities, and many in the cities moved out to the suburbs. The population began to get older, with advances in medical care and diet. "Magic machines" affected the American economy and way of life. The automobile allowed the greater mobility mentioned above, and fostered both "the new model" buying habit and credit card. New metal and plastic technologies developednew items and packaging became an industry in itself. Xerography brought convenience and computers offered automation. and fantastic speed. Television became a "great leveler" for the culture.

   DIF: Hard   REF: 751–763   OBJ: 30.0
   TOP: Demography / Inventions

3. In what ways does the federal census influence American life?

   ANS:
   Answers will vary but could include the following ideas: The federal census has become an important influence upon American life. For example, cities use census information to plan for their water supply, their roads, and their schools. Businesses use census data to help predict the size of the market for their product.

   DIF: Hard   REF: 751   OBJ: 30.1   TOP: Demography

4. How did farm life change after World War II?

ANS:
Answers will vary but could include the following ideas: During the years after World War II, the number of farms fell from a peak of 6.8 million in 1935 to under 3 million in 1970. At the same time, the farms that remained grew much larger in size and became far more productive. In 1950 one farm worker could feed 15 people. Twenty years later the same farm worker could produce enough for 45. For those who remained on the farm, the spread of telephones and automobiles meant that they became less isolated during the postwar years.

DIF: Hard   REF: 752–753   OBJ: 30.1   TOP: Post WWII / Farming

5. Based on what you have read in the chapter, summarize the causes and consequences of suburban growth after World War II.

ANS:
Answers will vary but could include the following ideas: The automobile and rising prosperity made suburban growth possible. As the suburbs grew, the nation's cities lost population. By the 1980s, three-fourths of the American people lived in cities or their surrounding suburbs, with the larger part in the suburbs.

DIF: Hard   REF: 753–756   OBJ: 30.1   TOP: American Mobility

6. In what ways did the automobile change American life after World War II? Support your answers with specifics.

ANS:
Answers will vary but could include the following ideas: The automobile helped cause the growth of the suburbs and the decline of the railroads. Automobile sales were a major cause of the postwar boom. The nation's increasing use of automobiles also stimulated the construction of the interstate highway system.

DIF: Hard   REF: 757–760   OBJ: 30.2   TOP: Automobile Era

7. Evaluate the economic advantages and disadvantages of automation.

ANS:
Answers will vary but could include the following ideas: Automation has increased the quantity and efficiency with which goods are produced. Automation created a demand for experts and specially trained technicians, while reducing the need for work-skilled labor. For example, in the late 1970s, untrained teenagers suffered twice the rate of unemployment of the older, skilled workers.

DIF: Hard   OBJ: 30.2   TOP: Automation

8. Historians have called the years between 1945 and 1960 the "Age of Affluence" and the "Age of Anxiety." Which do you think is a better label for this period? Can you think of a better label? Explain your answer.

ANS:
Answers will vary but could include the following ideas: Those who feel that the years between 1945 and 1960 were an Age of Affluence can point to the nation's rising prosperity and low rates of unemployment and inflation. Those who feel that the years between 1945 and 1960 were an Age of Anxiety can point to the nation's fear of Communist subversion and to the rise of McCarthyism. Labels for the period will differ.

DIF: Hard   OBJ: 30.3   TOP: Post WWII in U.S.

9. What did books written between the end of World War II and 1970 show about American life?

ANS:
Answers will vary but could include the following ideas: Many of the postwar writers dealt with the impact of rapid change on American life. For example, J. D. Salinger's "Catcher in the Rye" was a story of an adolescent trying to escape hypocrisy. In "Invisible Man," Ralph Ellison's black hero gradually saw that he was powerless and that the world was out of his reach. William Faulkner wrote about how the South (and America) lost the ideals of its farming past.

DIF: Hard   REF: 767–768   OBJ: 30.4   TOP: U.S. Writers

10. The artist Andy Warhol once predicted that, "The day will come when everyone will be famous for fifteen minutes." What new machines have made it possible for previously unknown people to become instant celebrities?

ANS:
Answers will vary but could include the following ideas: The television, communications satellite, pocket radio, and instant camera have played important roles in creating a communications revolution. As a result, events can now be recorded and transmitted around the world. For the first time in history, the world is a global village in which any citizen can suddenly be seen and heard by people in every country.

DIF: Hard   REF: 760–761   OBJ: 30.4   TOP: Inventions

(page intentionally left blank)

MATCHING

Match each item with the correct statement below.

a. Bay of Pigs
b. poll tax
c. Minutemen
d. Peace Corps
e. Laos

f. Richard Nixon
g. East Berlin
h. China
i. Alliance for Progress
j. Attorney General

1. Site of an unsuccessful attempt to invade Cuba and overthrow Castro.
2. Kennedy's "Marshall Plan" for Latin America.
3. The 24th Amendment banned this method of preventing African-Americans from voting.
4. Program for sending volunteers overseas to help people in underdeveloped nations.
5. Nation in which Great Britain, the U.S., and the U.S.S.R. established a coalition government.
6. This nation called the Soviet Union a "paper tiger" after the Cuban missile crisis.
7. Missiles developed in the 1960s and housed in underground concrete silos.
8. The Soviets built a wall in 1961 to prevent escapes from here.
9. Republican presidential candidate defeated by John F. Kennedy in 1960.
10. Cabinet post that John F. Kennedy gave to his brother Robert.

1. ANS: A DIF: Easy REF: 780 OBJ: 31.0
   TOP: Cuba / Bay of Pigs
2. ANS: I DIF: Easy REF: 782 OBJ: 31.0
   TOP: Kennedy's Presidency / Foreign Policy
3. ANS: B DIF: Easy REF: 788 OBJ: 31.0
   TOP: Constitution
4. ANS: D DIF: Easy REF: 782 OBJ: 31.0
   TOP: Kennedy's Presidency / Foreign Program's
5. ANS: E DIF: Easy REF: 779 OBJ: 31.0
   TOP: Laos
6. ANS: H DIF: Easy REF: 786 OBJ: 31.0
   TOP: Cuban Missile Crisis
7. ANS: C DIF: Easy REF: 784 OBJ: 31.0
   TOP: Nuclear Weapons
8. ANS: G DIF: Easy REF: 781 OBJ: 31.0
   TOP: Communism / Berlin Crisis
9. ANS: F DIF: Easy REF: 776 OBJ: 31.0
   TOP: Presidential Elections
10. ANS: J DIF: Easy REF: 778 OBJ: 31.0
    TOP: Kennedy's Presidency

MULTIPLE CHOICE

1. Kennedy appointed as his Secretary of State
   a. C. Douglas Dillon.
   b. Robert S. McNamara.
   c. Dean Rusk.
   d. Adlai Stevenson.

   ANS: C   DIF: Medium   REF: 777   OBJ: 31.1
   TOP: Kennedy's Presidency

2. The program that sent American volunteers to help underdeveloped nations was the
   a. Peace Corps.
   b. Alliance for Progress.
   c. New Frontier.
   d. Marshall Plan.

   ANS: A   DIF: Medium   REF: 782   OBJ: 31.1
   TOP: Kennedy's Presidency / Foreign Programs

3. Kennedy's policy of meeting Soviet aggression without necessarily threatening nuclear attack was called
   a. summit meetings.
   b. ncutralization.
   c. wars of national liberation.
   d. flexible response.

   ANS: D   DIF: Medium   REF: 782   OBJ: 31.2
   TOP: Kennedy's Presidency / Foreign Policy

4. The leader of South Vietnam who was overthrown in 1963 was
   a. Sekou Toure.
   b. Mao Tse-tung.
   c. Viet Minh.
   d. Ngo Dinh Diem.

   ANS: D   DIF: Medium   REF: 787   OBJ: 31.3
   TOP: Vietnam War

5. Kennedy's "Grand Design" was a plan for
   a. massive economic aid to Latin America.
   b. landing an American on the moon before 1970.
   c. joining the European Common Market in lowering tariffs.
   d. helping Communist satellites to win independence from the Soviet Union.

   ANS: C   DIF: Medium   REF: 786   OBJ: 31.3
   TOP: Kennedy's Presidency / Foreign Trade

6. In 1963 when John F. Kennedy said, "I am a Berliner," he was referring to
   a. his pledge that the United States would not allow free people to be strangled.
   b. his decision to tear down the Berlin Wall.
   c. his support for the unification of East and West Berlin.
   d. his apology for withdrawing U.S. troops from West Germany.

   ANS: A   DIF: Medium   REF: 782   OBJ: 31.0
   TOP: Kennedy's Presidency / Foreign Policy

7. Kennedy lived to witness which of the following events?
   a. landing of a man on the moon
   b. United States withdrawal from Vietnam
   c. United States superiority over the Soviets in nuclear weapons
   d. an end to the violence of the civil rights movement

   ANS: C   DIF: Medium   REF: 793   OBJ: 31.0
   TOP: Kennedy's Presidency

8. John F. Kennedy's New Frontier program received the most Congressional support in the area of
   a. federal aid to education.   c. urban renewal.
   b. medical care for the aged.   d. tax cuts.

   ANS: C   DIF: Medium   REF: 788   OBJ: 31.0
   TOP: Kennedy's Presidency / Domestic Policy

9. The biggest question mark in Kennedy's chances for election in 1960 was
   a. his religion.   c. his choice of a running mate.
   b. his performance in the debates.   d. his competition from Hubert Humphrey.

   ANS: A   DIF: Medium   REF: 775   OBJ: 31.0
   TOP: Presidential Elections

10. Kennedy put his policy of "flexible response" into practice by
    a. approving support of the Bay of Pigs invasion.
    b. ordering a naval "quarantine" around Cuba.
    c. supporting progressive governments in the new nations of Africa.
    d. ordering a naval "quarantine" around Cuba AND supporting progressive governments in the new nations of Africa.

    ANS: D   DIF: Medium   REF: 785   OBJ: 31.0
    TOP: Kennedy's Presidency / Foreign Policy

11. Kennedy's leading opponent in NATO was
    a. Konrad Adenauer.   c. Charles De Gaulle.
    b. Harold Macmillan.   d. Richard Nixon.

    ANS: C   DIF: Medium   REF: 786   OBJ: 31.3
    TOP: Kennedy's Presidency / Foreign Policy

12. Under Kennedy, the United States adopted the policy of deterring a Soviet nuclear attack with the threat of
    a. a first strike.   c. flexible response.
    b. a missile gap.   d. mutual assured destruction.

    ANS: D   DIF: Medium   REF: 783–784   OBJ: 31.3
    TOP: Kennedy's Presidency / Soviet Union

13. Michael Harrington's book, "The Other America," spoke about
    a. poverty in America.   c. the Peace Corps.
    b. communism in America.   d. women in America.

    ANS: A   DIF: Medium   REF: 790   OBJ: 31.4
    TOP: U.S. Poverty

14. Kennedy's domestic programs faced opposition from all of the following organizations EXCEPT the

a. Roman Catholic Church. c. Council of Economic Advisers.
b. American Medical Association. d. Republican party.

ANS: C   DIF: Medium   REF: 788–790   OBJ: 31.4
TOP: Kennedy's Presidency / Domestic Programs

15. The drive to end segregation in Birmingham, Alabama, was led by

a. Medgar Evers. c. A. Philip Randolph.
b. Martin Luther King, Jr. d. Mahalia Jackson.

ANS: B   DIF: Medium   REF: 790   OBJ: 31.4
TOP: Civil Rights Movement

16. Kennedy's assassination was investigated by the

a. Southern Christian Leadership Conference.
b. Warren Commission.
c. RAND Corporation.
d. Joint Chiefs of Staff.

ANS: B   DIF: Medium   REF: 792   OBJ: 31.5
TOP: Kennedy's Assassination

17. Which of the following individuals was NOT involved in the events surrounding Kennedy's assassination?

a. John B. Connally c. Lyndon B. Johnson
b. Lee Harvey Oswald d. Michael Harrington

ANS: D   DIF: Medium   REF: 792   OBJ: 31.5
TOP: Kennedy's Assassination

18. Which of the following was NOT a feature of the 1960 election?

a. The popular vote was very close.
b. Television played a major role in the campaign.
c. Kennedy was the youngest major party candidate in history.
d. Nixon challenged the results of the voting.

ANS: D   DIF: Medium   REF: 775–776   OBJ: 31.1
TOP: Presidential Elections

19. Hubert Humphrey was eliminated as a contender for the Democratic nomination after Kennedy's primary victory in

a. West Virginia. c. Vermont.
b. Texas. d. Alabama.

ANS: A   DIF: Medium   REF: 775   OBJ: 31.1
TOP: Presidential Elections

20. During the Berlin crisis, Khrushchev did all of the following EXCEPT
    a. build a wall separating East and West Berlin.
    b. call for the evacuation of West Berlin by the United States, Britain, and France.
    c. threaten to sign a peace treaty with East Germany.
    d. cut off all access by land to West Berlin.

    ANS: D   DIF: Medium   REF: 780–781   OBJ: 31.2
    TOP: Communism / Berlin Crisis

21. Under Kennedy the central focus of American foreign policy remained the intention of
    a. abolishing dictatorships everywhere.
    b. stopping the expansion of communism.
    c. dismantling nuclear weapons.
    d. overthrowing communism in the Soviet Union.

    ANS: B   DIF: Medium   REF: 779–781   OBJ: 31.2
    TOP: Kennedy's Presidency / Foreign Policy

22. The Bay of Pigs invasion was defeated mainly because
    a. there was no popular uprising against Castro.
    b. the Soviet Union threatened nuclear retaliation.
    c. Kennedy refused to support the invasion.
    d. the CIA was not involved.

    ANS: A   DIF: Medium   REF: 780   OBJ: 31.2
    TOP: Kennedy's Presidency / Cuba

23. Kennedy's response to the civil war in Vietnam was to
    a. call for elections throughout the country.
    b. send in advisers to train the South Vietnamese army.
    c. support neutralist forces in South Vietnam.
    d. send in American combat troops to help the South Vietnamese.

    ANS: B   DIF: Medium   REF: 787   OBJ: 31.3
    TOP: Kennedy's Presidency / Vietnam

24. The test ban treaty of 1963
    a. banned all nuclear testing.
    b. was turned down by the United States Senate.
    c. permitted underground nuclear testing.
    d. applied only to the United States and the Soviet Union.

    ANS: C   DIF: Medium   REF: 786   OBJ: 31.3

25. In dealing with the Cuban missile crisis, Kennedy ordered
    a. an invasion of Cuba to seize the missiles.
    b. a naval quarantine to intercept military equipment shipped to Cuba.
    c. a grain embargo against the Soviet Union.
    d. a general air strike on targets in Cuba.

    ANS: B   DIF: Medium   REF: 785   OBJ: 31.3
    TOP: Kennedy's Presidency / Cuba

26. Kennedy decided to build more missiles because
    a. the Secretary of Defense advised him to do so.
    b. during the campaign, Nixon had accused him of being soft on the Soviets.
    c. he believed the Soviets could be deterred if the United States had enough missiles to survive a first strike attack.
    d. he wanted the United States to be the first country to land an astronaut on the moon.

    ANS: C   DIF: Medium   REF: 783   OBJ: 31.3
    TOP: Kennedy's Presidency / National Defense

27. Which of the following events occurred AFTER the Cuban missile crisis?
    a. The Bay of Pigs invasion failed.
    b. The Soviets sent Yuri Gagarin into space.
    c. The Soviets signed a test ban treaty.
    d. The Soviets built the Berlin Wall.

    ANS: C   DIF: Medium   REF: 785–786   OBJ: 31.3
    TOP: Nuclear Weapons / Soviet Union

28. Khrushchev ordered Soviet missiles to be removed from Cuba in return for an American pledge
    a. not to invade Cuba.
    b. to resume purchasing Cuban sugar.
    c. not to support the South Vietnamese.
    d. to sign the test ban treaty.

    ANS: A   DIF: Medium   REF: 786   OBJ: 31.3
    TOP: Kennedy's Presidency / Cuba

29. During Kennedy's presidency, the Soviet Union was ahead of the United States in
    a. nuclear weapons.   c. outer space exploration.
    b. per capita income.   d. industrial output.

    ANS: C   DIF: Medium   REF: 784   OBJ: 31.3
    TOP: Soviet Union Space Exploration

30. Which of the following Kennedy programs was passed by Congress?
    a. federal aid to education   c. tax cuts
    b. free medical care for the aged d. urban renewal

    ANS: D   DIF: Medium   REF: 788   OBJ: 31.4
    TOP: Kennedy's Presidency / Domestic Program's

31. Kennedy tried to control inflation by
    a. proposing wage-price guideposts.
    b. establishing price ceilings.
    c. asking Congress to reduce spending.
    d. asking Congress to lower the minimum wage.

    ANS: A   DIF: Medium   REF: 788–789   OBJ: 31.4
    TOP: Kennedy's Presidency / Economy

32. Freedom riders were successful in
    a. abolishing the poll tax.
    b. getting more African-Americans enrolled in southern colleges.
    c. integrating interstate bus terminals.
    d. bringing needed food and supplies into Appalachia.

    ANS: C   DIF: Medium   REF: 790   OBJ: 31.4
    TOP: Civil Rights Movement

33. The 1963 March on Washington, D.C. was organized to
    a. pressure Congress into passing a civil rights bill.
    b. integrate colleges in Washington, D.C.
    c. protest a bomb explosion that killed four African-American girls in a Birmingham church.
    d. demand free medical care for the elderly.

    ANS: A   DIF: Medium   REF: 791   OBJ: 31.4
    TOP: Civil Rights Movement

34. In 1979 a House Committee on the assassination concluded that
    a. Jack Ruby had acted alone in shooting Oswald.
    b. the findings of the Warren Commission were correct.
    c. more than one gunman had fired at Kennedy in Dallas.
    d. Oswald was a Soviet agent.

    ANS: C   DIF: Medium   REF: 792   OBJ: 31.5
    TOP: Kennedy's Assassination

35. President Kennedy was noted for
    a. trying to end the Cold War.
    b. his promises rather than his achievements.
    c. his inactivity as President.
    d. serving only 100 days of his second term.

    ANS: B   DIF: Medium   REF: 793   OBJ: 31.5
    TOP: Kennedy's Presidency

36. In the 1960 campaign, Kennedy claimed that the government had neglected the poor, the elderly, the young, and minorities. One may assume, therefore, that he would NOT support
    a. passing civil rights legislation.   c. giving more federal aid to education.
    b. reducing social security benefits.   d. increasing the minimum wage.

    ANS: B   DIF: Medium   REF: 775   OBJ: 31.1
    TOP: Presidential Elections

37. Since the Cuban refugee fighters who landed at the Bay of Pigs were not greeted by a popular uprising, it is reasonable to assume that
    a. the invaders missed their proper landing site.
    b. most Cubans opposed the Soviet Union.
    c. many Cubans supported the Castro government.
    d. the CIA was not involved in the invasion.

    ANS: C   DIF: Medium   REF: 780   OBJ: 31.2
    TOP: Cuban History / Bay of Pigs

38. Kennedy's belief that relieving poverty rather than military intervention was the most effective way to discourage Communist revolution is BEST illustrated by which of the following activities?
    a. creating the Peace Corps
    b. supporting the Bay of Pigs invasion
    c. sending advisers to South Vietnam
    d. encouraging a coalition government in Laos

    ANS: A   DIF: Medium   REF: 782   OBJ: 31.2
    TOP: Kennedy's Presidency / Communism

39. Which of the following is a CONSEQUENCE of the other three?
    a. the Cuban missile crisis
    b. American control of NATO's nuclear arsenal
    c. De Gaulle's decision to leave NATO
    d. Kennedy's desire for closer cooperation with the European Common Market

    ANS: C   DIF: Medium   REF: 785–786   OBJ: 31.3
    TOP: Kennedy's Presidency / Foreign Policy

40. Which of Kennedy's advisors was most directly concerned with civil rights issues?
    a. C. Douglas Dillon   c. Robert Kennedy
    b. Robert McNamara   d. Dean Rusk

    ANS: C   DIF: Medium   REF: 790   OBJ: 31.4
    TOP: Kennedy's Presidency / Civil Rights

• 41. Many southern states evaded the Fifteenth Amendment, which was designed to protect the right of African-Americans to vote, by having
    a. segregated schools.   c. "whites only" lunch counters.
    b. poll taxes.   d. ghettos.

    ANS: B   DIF: Medium   REF: 788   OBJ: 31.4
    TOP: Civil Rights / Voting

42. In which of the following groups would there have been the MOST dissatisfaction with the accomplishments of the New Frontier?
    a. public school teachers   c. southern whites
    b. southern African-Americans   d. urban slum dwellers

    ANS: C   DIF: Medium   REF: 788, 790–791
    OBJ: 31.5   TOP: Kennedy's Presidency / Domestic Programs

ESSAY

1. Identify the fallacy in the following argument. Write your answer on a separate sheet of paper and write a paragraph explaining why you chose it.

    The government of South Vietnam in the 1950s allowed more people to vote and lowered rents on land to 25 percent of what they had been. It was a progressive democratic government.
    A. single cause
    B. preceding event as cause
    C. stereotyping
    D. special pleading

    ANS:
    answer D Students' paragraphs should support their answer.

    DIF: Hard   OBJ: 31.0   TOP: Vietnam History

2. Describe two ways in which the thousand days of John F. Kennedy was "a time of hope and promise," and two ways in which they were "a time of frustration and fear."

    ANS:
    President Kennedy's 1000 days could be seen as a time of hope and promise in that he was a young, energetic President with a beautiful wife and young children, and he fostered a spirit of challenge and confidence in the American people. The resolve with which he assured Berliners that the U.S. would not leave them to be swallowed up by Russia, the courage with which he out-faced Krushchev over the missiles in Cuba, and the movement for justice and greater equality which he promoted in America were all solid reasons to be hopeful. The Alliance for Progress, the Peace Corps, the challenge of having a man on the moon by 1970, and the New Frontier proposals all held the same kind of hope. But the 1000 days was also a time of frustration and fear. American involvement in Southeast Asia and at the Bay of Pigs, and the possibility of conflict in Berlin, surely made U.S. citizens abroad fearful.

    DIF: Hard   REF: 778–792   OBJ: 31.0   TOP: Kennedy's Presidency

3. What role did television play in the election of 1960?

    ANS:
    Answers will vary but could include the following ideas: In the televised debates between Kennedy and Nixon, Kennedy showed up better, appearing handsome, poised, and alert. Since he was initially less well known than Nixon, Kennedy's performance swung crucially needed votes to his side in a close election.

    DIF: Hard   REF: 775–776   OBJ: 31.1   TOP: Presidential Elections

4. Why did the United States become involved in Laos, and how was Kennedy able to limit that involvement?

ANS:
Answers will vary but could include the following ideas: Kennedy became involved to prevent a Communist takeover of Laos. But instead of sending in American troops to bolster the country's pro-Western government, he agreed to participate in a British- sponsored conference, which established a neutral coalition government in Laos.

DIF: Hard   REF: 779–780   OBJ: 31.2
TOP: Kennedy's Presidency / Foreign Affairs

5. Kennedy's handling of the Cuban missile crisis led some observers to accuse him of "brinkmanship"—pushing a dangerous situation to the limit of safety. Do you agree or disagree? Could Kennedy have avoided a confrontation? Explain your answer.

ANS:
Answers will vary but could include the following ideas: While Kennedy rejected proposals to invade or bomb Cuba, he did risk war with the Soviets. It might also be suggested that the presence of Soviet missiles in Cuba was a negotiable issue; Khrushchev might have been willing to remove them had Kennedy agreed to make concessions on some other issues.

DIF: Hard   REF: 785–786   OBJ: 31.3
TOP: Kennedy's Presidency / Cuba

6. In what ways did Kennedy's defense policy move away from deterrence toward a "flexible response"?

ANS:
Answers will vary but could include the following ideas: By "flexible response," Kennedy meant building up armed forces capable of deploying various kinds and degrees of force around the world. Thus, the United States could challenge Soviet-supported forces in "wars of national liberation" without resorting to the threat of "massive retaliation."

DIF: Hard   REF: 782–784   OBJ: 31.3
TOP: Kennedy's Presidency / National Defense

7. In what ways were the policies of "flexible response," "massive retaliation," and "containment" similar?

ANS:
Answers will vary but could include the following ideas: American strategic planning—bases and huge naval fleets scattered around the globe, defensive alliances, military and economic aid, summit conferences, and the occasional use of troops in actual combat—remained the same. Moreover, all three policies were aimed at the same goal, containment of Communism.

DIF: Hard   REF: 782–785   OBJ: 31.3
TOP: Kennedy's Presidency / National Defense

8. Why did Kennedy have trouble getting his domestic programs passed?

ANS:
Answers will vary but could include the following ideas: Most of the New Frontier reforms were blocked by a conservative coalition in Congress of Republicans and southern Democrats. In addition, specific Kennedy programs aroused opposition from special interest groups. Thus, the Catholic Church helped kill an aid-to-education bill that did not include funds for parochial schools, and the American Medical Association stopped plans to use the Social Security system to provide medical care to the elderly.

DIF: Hard   REF: 788–789   OBJ: 31.4
TOP: Kennedy's Presidency / Domestic Programs

9. "The civil rights movement did not rely on Congress and the President, but took direct action to achieve its goals." Assess the validity of this generalization as it applies to the Kennedy years.

ANS:
Answers will vary but could include the following ideas: There were massive demonstrations, such as the March on Washington, and acts of civil disobedience, such as the lunch counter sit-ins and freedom rider demonstrations, which were the hallmark of the civil rights movement.

DIF: Hard   REF: 790–792   OBJ: 31.4
TOP: Kennedy's Presidency / Civil Rights Movement

10. "Kennedy was great not for what he did, but for what he was about to do." Assess the validity of this statement.

ANS:
Answers will vary but could include the following ideas: The brevity of Kennedy's presidency (1,000 days), his narrow victory in 1960, and the strength of his opponents are factors that prevented him from implementing an ambitious program of domestic reform. Much of the New Frontier was carried out under Kennedy's successors.

DIF: Hard   REF: 793–794   OBJ: 31.5   TOP: Kennedy's Presidency

(page intentionally left blank)

MATCHING

Match each item with the correct statement below.

a. William Westmoreland
b. Medicare
c. Pentagon Papers
d. Malcolm X
e. Thurgood Marshall

f. Robert Weaver
g. Ralph Nader
h. Martin Luther King
i. VISTA
j. Rachel Carson

1. First African-American appointed to the Supreme Court.
2. Commanded American forces in Vietnam.
3. Black Muslim leader who called for a separate black nation.
4. Wrote "Silent Spring," which made Americans aware of the danger of pesticides.
5. Medical insurance for the elderly financed by an increase in the Social Security payroll tax.
6. As Secretary of Housing and Urban Development, he was the first African-American in the Cabinet.
7. Led civil rights march from Selma to Montgomery, Alabama, in 1965.
8. A study of the United States role in Vietnam after World War II
9. Wrote "Unsafe at Any Speed," which made Americans aware of hazards of automobiles
10. A domestic Peace Corps created to help the poor in America.

1. ANS: E   DIF: Easy   REF: 807–808   OBJ: 32.0
   TOP: Supreme Court / African-Americans
2. ANS: A   DIF: Easy   REF: 812   OBJ: 32.0
   TOP: Vietnam War
3. ANS: D   DIF: Easy   REF: 806   OBJ: 32.0
   TOP: Black Leaders
4. ANS: J   DIF: Easy   REF: 802   OBJ: 32.0
   TOP: Ecology
5. ANS: B   DIF: Easy   REF: 801   OBJ: 32.0
   TOP: Johnson's Presidency / Federal Programs
6. ANS: F   DIF: Easy   REF: 802   OBJ: 32.0
   TOP: African-Americans in Government
7. ANS: H   DIF: Easy   REF: 806   OBJ: 32.0
   TOP: Civil Rights
8. ANS: C   DIF: Easy   REF: 812   OBJ: 32.0
   TOP: Vietnam
9. ANS: G   DIF: Easy   REF: 803   OBJ: 32.0
   TOP: Highway Safety Act
10. ANS: I   DIF: Easy   REF: 799   OBJ: 32.0
    TOP: Johnson's Presidency / Federal Programs

MULTIPLE CHOICE

1. To protect the employment rights of African-Americans, the 1964 Civil Rights Act created the
   a. Community Relations Service.
   b. National Labor Relations Board.
   c. Equal Employment Opportunity Commission.
   d. Job Corps.

   ANS: C   DIF: Medium   REF: 798–799   OBJ: 32.1
   TOP: Civil Rights

2. The War on Poverty included all of the following EXCEPT
   a. the Peace Corps.   c. VISTA.
   b. the Economic Opportunity Act.   d. the Community Action Program.

   ANS: A   DIF: Medium   REF: 799   OBJ: 32.1
   TOP: Johnson's Presidency / Federal Programs

3. Medicare provided
   a. federal grants to states that wanted to provide medical aid to the needy.
   b. medical care only for those elderly people not receiving Social Security payments.
   c. low-cost medical insurance for all elderly people.
   d. free medical care for all people over 65.

   ANS: C   DIF: Medium   REF: 801   OBJ: 32.2
   TOP: Johnson's Presidency / Federal Programs

4. The Immigration Act of 1965
   a. abolished the quota system.
   b. admitted thousands of Soviet Jewish refugees.
   c. reduced the quotas of all countries outside the Western Hemisphere.
   d. required visas of all foreign visitors to the United States.

   ANS: A   DIF: Medium   REF: 802   OBJ: 32.2
   TOP: Immigration

5. The term "counterculture" referred to
   a. a way of life different from that of most Americans.
   b. a concern with the relations between organisms and their environment.
   c. the civil rights movement.
   d. a community based on strict Christian principles.

   ANS: A   DIF: Medium   REF: 808   OBJ: 32.3
   TOP: Counterculture

6. In 1965 Martin Luther King began his drive to register southern African-American voters at
   a. Jackson, Mississippi.   c. Selma, Alabama.
   b. Montgomery, Alabama.   d. Memphis, Tennessee.

   ANS: C   DIF: Medium   REF: 805–806   OBJ: 32.3
   TOP: Civil Rights Movement

7. Which of the following organizations was part of the New Left?
   a. Communist Party
   b. Students for a Democratic Society
   c. League for Industrial Democracy
   d. Socialist Party

   ANS: B   DIF: Medium   REF: 808–809   OBJ: 32.3
   TOP: Social Awareness

8. The idea that if Vietnam fell to the Communists, so would all of Southeast Asia was known as
   a. the "credibility gap."
   b. "winding down" the war.
   c. the "domino theory."
   d. the "conspiracy theory."

   ANS: C   DIF: Medium   REF: 810   OBJ: 32.4
   TOP: Vietnam War / Communism

9. Members of the anti-war movement protested the Vietnam war by doing all of the following EXCEPT
   a. burning draft cards.
   b. holding teach-ins.
   c. joining the Viet Cong.
   d. holding mass marches.

   ANS: C   DIF: Medium   REF: 811–812   OBJ: 32.4
   TOP: Vietnam War

10. In 1964 Barry Goldwater campaigned on a program that was essentially
    a. very similar to Lyndon Johnson's.
    b. a repudiation of the Roosevelt-Truman-Kennedy welfare system.
    c. a plan to end the War in Vietnam through negotiations with the NLF.
    d. a revival of the liberal Republican tradition.

    ANS: B   DIF: Medium   REF: 800   OBJ: 32.1
    TOP: Presidential Elections

11. Race riots of the 1960s were a result of
    a. the assassination of African-American leaders.
    b. the failure of Congress to pass civil rights legislation.
    c. the disillusionment that African-Americans felt at the slowness of improvement.
    d. the assassination of African-American leaders AND the disillusionment that African-Americans felt at the slowness of improvement.

    ANS: D   DIF: Medium   REF: 804–807   OBJ: 32.0
    TOP: Civil Rights Movement

12. Laws were passed during Lyndon B. Johnson's administration to aid the
    a. poor.
    b. African-Americans.
    c. elderly.
    d. all of the above

    ANS: D   DIF: Medium   REF: 801–802   OBJ: 32.0
    TOP: Johnson's Presidency

13. The major reason the United States intervened in the Dominican Republic in 1965 was
    a. to prevent the establishment of a Communist government there.
    b. to protect American industries there.
    c. to establish American military bases.
    d. to remove a fascist leader from power.

    ANS: A   DIF: Medium   REF: 811   OBJ: 32.0
    TOP: U.S. Foreign Policy / Communism / Dominican Republic

14. All of the following describe Lyndon B. Johnson EXCEPT that he was a
    a. superb "horse trader" as a leader in Congress.
    b. former high school teacher.
    c. reluctant civil rights advocate.
    d. former senator from Texas.

    ANS: C   DIF: Medium   REF: 797–798   OBJ: 32.0
    TOP: Lyndon B. Johnson

15. All of the following took place during Johnson's administration EXCEPT
    a. the abolishing of the immigration quota system.
    b. increased federal aid to education.
    c. the balancing of the federal budget.
    d. the food-stamp program.

    ANS: C   DIF: Medium   REF: 799, 801–802
    OBJ: 32.0   TOP: Johnson's Presidency

16. Which of the following was NOT a provision of the Civil Rights Act of 1964?
    a. racial discrimination prohibited in places of public resort
    b. busing required to achieve racially integrated schools
    c. an Equal Opportunity Commission established
    d. court cases to speed up school desegregation authorized

    ANS: B   DIF: Medium   REF: 798–799   OBJ: 32.1
    TOP: Civil Rights Movement

17. In 1964 Congress passed legislation that did all of the following EXCEPT
    a. conserve wilderness land.
    b. provide loans to college students.
    c. provide money for mass transit systems.
    d. cut the food stamp program.

    ANS: D   DIF: Medium   REF: 799   OBJ: 32.1
    TOP: Johnson's Presidency / Federal Programs

18. Which of the following measures that were passed during Johnson's administration was NOT originally proposed by JFK?
    a. aid to education   c. income tax surcharge
    b. medical insurance for the aged d. civil rights legislation

    ANS: C   DIF: Medium   REF: 799   OBJ: 32.2
    TOP: Johnson's Presidency / Taxation

© Prentice-Hall, Inc.

19. Which of the following government departments was created during the Johnson years?
    a. Defense
    b. Housing and Urban Development
    c. Health, Education, and Welfare
    d. Interior

    ANS: B   DIF: Medium   REF: 802   OBJ: 32.2
    TOP: Johnson's Presidency / Federal Programs

20. Johnson sidestepped the Catholic Church's opposition to his aid to education program by
    a. prohibiting aid to parochial schools.
    b. banning prayers in public schools.
    c. offering aid to all schools according to the number of students from poor families.
    d. restricting aid to schools in which most students were Protestants.

    ANS: C   DIF: Medium   REF: 801   OBJ: 32.2
    TOP: Johnson's Presidency / Federal Programs

21. During the Johnson years, Congress passed laws reducing all of the following kinds of pollution
    EXCEPT
    a. radiation from atomic energy plants.
    b. chemicals dumped in lakes and rivers.
    c. junkyards and billboards.
    d. pesticides used in agriculture.

    ANS: A   DIF: Medium   REF: 803   OBJ: 32.2
    TOP: Johnson's Presidency / Pollution Laws

22. To help pay for the ever-higher cost of the Vietnam War, LBJ asked Congress to impose a (an)
    a. new tax on corporate profits.
    b. increase in Social Security taxes.
    c. surcharge on income taxes.
    d. increase in sales taxes.

    ANS: C   DIF: Medium   REF: 804   OBJ: 32.2
    TOP: Vietnam War / Cost

23. Which of the following did NOT contribute to inflation?
    a. increasing demand for goods
    b. government defense spending
    c. the tax cut
    d. urban and rural poverty

    ANS: D   DIF: Medium   REF: 804   OBJ: 32.2
    TOP: Economics

24. What did John F. Kennedy and Malcolm X have in common?
    a. Both were born in poverty.
    b. Both advocated racial integration.
    c. Both were assassinated.
    d. Both had served terms in Congress.

    ANS: C   DIF: Medium   REF: 792, 807   OBJ: 32.3
    TOP: Social Leaders

25. After the passage of the Voting Rights Act of 1965,
    a. few African-Americans took advantage of the opportunity to register.
    b. African-American voter registration went up by 50 percent.
    c. large numbers of African-Americans were elected to Congress.
    d. African-American voter registration went up by 50 percent AND large numbers of African-Americans were elected to Congress.

    ANS: B   DIF: Medium   REF: 806   OBJ: 32.3
    TOP: Civil Rights Movement

26. Which of the following happened LAST?
    a. the passage of the Voting Rights Act
    b. massive rioting in Detroit and Newark
    c. Martin Luther King, Jr., receiving the Nobel Peace Prize
    d. the march from Selma to Montgomery

    ANS: B   DIF: Medium   REF: 805–807   OBJ: 32.3
    TOP: Civil Rights Movement

27. The incident that prompted Congress to pass the Tonkin Gulf Resolution was
    a. an attack by North Vietnamese gunboats on two U.S. destroyers.
    b. the invasion of South Vietnam by the North.
    c. the assassination of Ngo Dinh Diem.
    d. the first American bombing raids against North Vietnam.

    ANS: A   DIF: Medium   REF: 809   OBJ: 32.4
    TOP: Vietnam War

28. There was a major shift in American public opinion against the Vietnam War as a result of
    a. the Tonkin Gulf Resolution.
    b. sending U.S. advisers to help the South Vietnamese army.
    c. the 1965 peace offensive.
    d. the 1968 Tet Offensive.

    ANS: D   DIF: Medium   REF: 812–813   OBJ: 32.4
    TOP: Vietnam War

29. Lyndon B. Johnson did not run for reelection in 1968 because of his
    a. poor showing in the primaries.
    b. poor health.
    c. desire to concentrate on ending the Vietnam War.
    d. poor showing in the primaries AND desire to concentrate on ending the Vietnam War.

    ANS: D   DIF: Medium   REF: 813–814   OBJ: 32.4
    TOP: Presidential Elections

© Prentice-Hall, Inc.

30. Which of the following events occurred LAST?
    a.   the Tet offensive
    b.   the 37-day pause in the bombing of North Vietnam
    c.   the 1964 election
    d.   the Tonkin Gulf Resolution

    ANS: A   DIF: Medium   REF: 800, 809, 812
    OBJ: 32.4   TOP: Vietnam War

31. In the 1960s, most African-Americans lived in poor, run-down urban neighborhoods and were
    denied good schools and highly paid jobs. Which of the following legislations was designed to
    help remedy this problem?
    a.   the Regional Development Act of 1964   c.   the Civil Rights Act of 1964
    b.   the Voting Rights Act of 1965   d.   Medicare

    ANS: C   DIF: Medium   REF: 798–799   OBJ: 32.1
    TOP: Civil Rights Movement

32. If you learned of the abolition of the quota system, saw an article about the book "Unsafe at Any
    Speed," and read about passage of the Medicare bill, you were probably reading a newspaper in
    a.   1964.   c.   1966.
    b.   1965.   d.   1967.

    ANS: B   DIF: Medium   REF: 801–803   OBJ: 32.2

33. In the early 1960s, the CHIEF cause of segregation in the North was
    a.   state regulations.   c.   habits and attitudes.
    b.   local ordinances.   d.   federal programs.

    ANS: C   DIF: Medium   REF: 804–805   OBJ: 32.3
    TOP: Civil Rights

34. Which of the following BEST illustrates the changing attitudes of the nation's young people
    during the 1960s?
    a.   the Atlantic City convention   c.   the National Youth Administration
    b.   events at Harvard and Berkeley   d.   the Stonewall, Texas ceremony

    ANS: B   DIF: Medium   REF: 808–809   OBJ: 32.3
    TOP: Social Awareness

35. During the early years of Johnson's administration, many Americans doubted the necessity of
    sending troops to Vietnam. Which of the following helped Johnson justify American
    intervention in Southeast Asia?
    a.   the Pentagon Papers   c.   the bombing of North Vietnam
    b.   the Gulf of Tonkin incident   d.   the credibility gap

    ANS: B   DIF: Medium   REF: 809–810   OBJ: 32.4
    TOP: Vietnam War

SHORT ANSWER

In one or two sentences, define and distinguish between the terms given below.

1. "Urban Renewal"

   ANS:
   "Urban Renewal" refers to the clearing of slums and rebuilding of cities. It was one of a host of projects of Johnson's Great Society.

   DIF: Hard   REF: 802   OBJ: 32.0
   TOP: Johnson's Presidency / Federal Programs

2. ecology

   ANS:
   Ecology is the science of the relationship between organisms and their environment.

   DIF: Hard   REF: 803   OBJ: 32.0   TOP: Ecology

3. domino theory

   ANS:
   The domino theory was a popular justification for U.S. involvement in Vietnam. Eisenhower and Johnson believed that if South Vietnam fell to communism, its neighbors would also fall.

   DIF: Hard   REF: 810   OBJ: 32.0   TOP: Communism

4. counterculture

   ANS:
   Counterculture is a name for a way of life different from that accepted by most of the people at that time. The hippies of the 1960s belonged to a counterculture.

   DIF: Hard   REF: 808   OBJ: 32.0   TOP: Counterculture

ESSAY

1. Which of the following statements is an example of the fallacy of stereotyping? Write your answer on a separate sheet of paper and support your answer with a paragraph explaining why you chose it.
   A. Most college students of the 1960s went about the business of getting an education and preparing for a future career.
   B. SNCC and SDS were born as reform movements but turned to anarchism and disruption.
   C. College students of the 1960s were "hippies" who used drugs, wore long hair and strange clothes, and rebelled against all of society.
   D. The "hippies" of the 1960s tried to show that they rejected the values of most Americans.

   ANS:
   answer C Students' paragraphs should support their answer.

   DIF: Hard   REF: 808–809   OBJ: 32.0   TOP: Counterculture

2. The 1960s have been called an "Age of Protest." Who protested, what were they protesting, and why? Organize your answer in terms of three major social movements of the times.

   ANS:
   Student answers will vary but could include these ideas: Three major social movements of the time were: 1) concern over environment and safety, 2) opposition to the Vietnam war, and 3) the struggle for civil rights. Rachel Carson and Ralph Nader led the country to a new awareness of pesticide pollution and other environmental damage as well as the need for more attention to safety in automobile design. Opposition to the war in Vietnam came from a variety of groups, especially those allied with what came to be known as the New Left. Protests over the civil rights issue also came from the New Left, from such groups as the SDS and SNCC, though these groups brought attention to other problems in American society as well.

   DIF: Hard   REF: 801–814   OBJ: 32.0
   TOP: Vietnam War / Civil Rights / Federal Programs

3. Much of the legislation passed during Lyndon Johnson's presidency had initially been proposed by John F. Kennedy but stalled in Congress. Explain why Johnson achieved greater success than Kennedy had.

   ANS:
   Answers will vary but could include the following ideas: JFK had only narrowly won the election and lacked broad support. Some of his civil rights legislation was opposed by southern Democrats whom he could not sway. Kennedy's assassination produced an emotional climate in the nation that called for passage of legislation in JFK's name. Also, LBJ was a more skilled manipulator of Congress, thanks to his long years there.

   DIF: Hard   REF: 797–800   OBJ: 32.1   TOP: Johnson's Presidency

4. Compare and contrast John F. Kennedy and Lyndon B. Johnson with respect to their goals, style of leadership, and political effectiveness.

ANS:
Answers will vary but could include the following ideas: Johnson's and Kennedy's legislative goals were quite similar; however, their styles were different. Johnson was an earthy, southern politician, while Kennedy projected an urbane image. Because of his political skills and because of his popular mandate during the 1964 election, Johnson was much more effective politically than Kennedy.

DIF: Hard   OBJ: 32.2   TOP: Kennedy / Johnson Presidencies

5. How did Ralph Nader and Rachel Carson influence Great Society legislation?

ANS:
Answers will vary but could include the following ideas: Carson's book, "Silent Spring," alerted the nation to the dangers of environmental pollution, prompting Congress to pass a series of laws to protect the environment. Nader's book, "Unsafe at Any Speed," highlighted structural defects in American automobiles that Congress sought to rectify with the Highway Safety Act.

DIF: Hard   REF: 802–804   OBJ: 32.2
TOP: Johnson's Presidency / Federal Programs

6. Summarize the philosophies of three African-American leaders of the 1960s. How did they differ? Which leaders had the most lasting influence? Explain your answer.

ANS:
Answers will vary but could include the following ideas: Martin Luther King, Jr.: African-Americans should stir the nation's con- science with nonviolent protest of injustice and win correction of injustice through new laws. Malcolm X: African-Americans should remain apart from white society and win power to run their own political and economic affairs. Stokely Carmichael: African-Americans should win political power through African-American control over the civil rights movement and their own institutions. King seems to have had the most influence; his philosophy was least troubling to whites who would have to share its consequences and its rewards.

DIF: Hard   REF: 805–808   OBJ: 32.3
TOP: Civil Rights Movement

7. Based on what you have read in the chapter, describe three areas in which Johnson's Great Society programs achieved important reforms.

ANS:
Answers will vary but could include the following ideas: Areas in which Johnson achieved significant reform were aid to education, civil rights, welfare, and environmental protection.

DIF: Hard   REF: 801–804   OBJ: 32.3
TOP: Johnson's Presidency / Federal Programs

8. What factors caused the urban riots of the 1960s?

    ANS:
    Answers will vary but could include the following ideas: African- Americans' frustration with the lack of change in their social and economic status, despite civil rights reforms, was the major cause of rioting.

    DIF: Hard   REF: 804–808   OBJ: 32.3
    TOP: Civil Rights Movement

9. How and why did U.S. involvement in Vietnam change in 1964–1965?

    ANS:
    Answers will vary but could include the following ideas: During the years 1964-1965, the United States became more deeply committed to involvement in Vietnam. American troops swelled from thousands to hundreds of thousands. Bombings and mining of offshore waters also increased. President Johnson and his supporters justified this escalation on the grounds that the nation had an obligation to defend the freedom and civil rights of peoples around the globe. Johnson also used the "domino theory" to explain his actions; that is, if Vietnam fell to the Communists, other Southeast Asian nations would soon follow.

    DIF: Hard   REF: 809–814   OBJ: 32.4   TOP: Vietnam War

10. "Congress betrayed its Constitutional responsibility by abdicating its war-declaring powers to the President under the Tonkin Gulf Resolution." Do you agree or disagree? Explain your answer.

    ANS:
    Answers will vary but could include the following ideas: Agree— The positions taken by Senators Wayne Morse and Ernest Gruening were correct; that is, that the Tonkin Gulf Resolution amounted to a "predated declaration of war." Disagree—Johnson's claim that he was acting as the nation's commander-in-chief justifies his stance. The examples of Truman in Korea and Kennedy in the Cuban missile crisis might be cited.

    DIF: Hard   REF: 809–810   OBJ: 32.4   TOP: Vietnam War

(page intentionally left blank)

MATCHING

Match each item with the correct statement below.

a.	J. Edgar Hoover	f.	Archibald Cox
b.	Warren Burger	g.	George Wallace
c.	Robert Kennedy	h.	Michael Collins
d.	John Mitchell	i.	Paris
e.	Spiro Agnew	j.	Chicago

1. American Independent party candidate for President in 1968 and former governor of Alabama.
2. After victory in the California primary, he was killed by Sirhan Sirhan.
3. Site of 1968 Democratic convention that was marked by violence and protest.
4. First special prosecutor in the Watergate affair—he insisted Nixon turn over the tapes.
5. Nixon's Attorney General who approved a plan to "bug" Watergate.
6. Nixon named him as Chief Justice when Earl Warren retired.
7. Site of Vietnam peace talks.
8. Nixon's Vice President who resigned after pleading "no contest" to income-tax evasion.
9. FBI head who would not approve Nixon's plans for spying on "enemies."
10. Armstrong, Aldrin, and he were on the first successful flight that landed on the moon.

1. ANS: G   DIF: Easy   REF: 819   OBJ: 33.0
   TOP: Presidential Elections

2. ANS: C   DIF: Easy   REF: 817   OBJ: 33.0
   TOP: Presidential Elections

3. ANS: J   DIF: Easy   REF: 818   OBJ: 33.0
   TOP: Presidential Elections

4. ANS: F   DIF: Easy   REF: 835   OBJ: 33.0
   TOP: Watergate

5. ANS: D   DIF: Easy   REF: 833   OBJ: 33.0
   TOP: Watergate

6. ANS: B   DIF: Easy   REF: 829   OBJ: 33.0
   TOP: Supreme Court

7. ANS: I   DIF: Easy   REF: 825   OBJ: 33.0
   TOP: Vietnam War

8. ANS: E   DIF: Easy   REF: 835   OBJ: 33.0
   TOP: Nixon's Presidency

9. ANS: A   DIF: Easy   REF: 831   OBJ: 33.0
   TOP: Watergate

10. ANS: H   DIF: Easy   REF: 822   OBJ: 33.0
   TOP: Space Exploration

MULTIPLE CHOICE

1. Chief Justice of the Supreme Court from 1953-1969, under whose leadership the court made landmark decisions in such cases as "Gideon v. Wainwright," "Escobedo," and "Miranda," he was
   a. Warren Burger.
   b. John Marshall.
   c. Thurgood Marshall.
   d. Earl Warren.

   ANS: D   DIF: Medium   REF: 819–820   OBJ: 33.1
   TOP: Supreme Court

2. Richard Nixon's visit to Russia in 1972 was a good example of the policy of
   a. collective security.
   b. executive privilege.
   c. detente.
   d. brinkmanship.

   ANS: C   DIF: Medium   REF: 828–829   OBJ: 33.2
   TOP: Nixon's Presidency / Foreign Policy

3. One of the clearest examples of the policy of detente between the Soviet Union and the United States was
   a. the SALT agreement.
   b. the Paris Accords on Vietnam.
   c. admission of the People's Republic of China to the UN.
   d. the Cambodian "incursion."

   ANS: A   DIF: Medium   REF: 828–829   OBJ: 33.2
   TOP: U.S. / Soviet Relations

4. Under President Nixon's policy of detente, the United States
   a. continued the Truman policy of containment.
   b. pitted the People's Republic of China against the Soviet Union.
   c. sought to ease tensions between Communist nations and the United States.
   d. accelerated the arms race to establish nuclear parity with the Soviets.

   ANS: C   DIF: Medium   REF: 828–829   OBJ: 33.2
   TOP: Nixon's Presidency / Communism

5. A special secret White House unit that was formed to stop the unauthorized release of government information to the public and the press was known as the
   a. "Yippies."
   b. "Plumbers."
   c. "Silent Majority."
   d. FCC.

   ANS: B   DIF: Medium   REF: 831   OBJ: 33.3
   TOP: Nixon's Presidency

6. Which of the following was Nixon's SECOND appointee as Special Prosecutor in the Watergate Affair?
   a. Archibald Cox
   b. Robert Bork
   c. Leon Jaworski
   d. Elliot Richardson

   ANS: C   DIF: Medium   REF: 836   OBJ: 33.3
   TOP: Watergate

7. Which of the following amendments extended the vote to people 18 to 21 years old?
   a. Twenty-fourth Amendment
   b. Twenty-fifth Amendment
   c. Twenty-sixth Amendment
   d. Twenty-seventh Amendment

   ANS: C   DIF: Medium   REF: 833   OBJ: 33.3
   TOP: U.S. Constitution

8. The term "Saturday Night Massacre" referred to
   a. the student deaths at Kent State.
   b. antiwar demonstrations in Chicago.
   c. Nixon's dismissal of key staff members during the Watergate hearings.
   d. the assassination of Robert F. Kennedy.

   ANS: C   DIF: Medium   REF: 835–836   OBJ: 33.3
   TOP: Watergate

9. The impeachment charges against Richard Nixon included all of the following EXCEPT
   a. obstruction of justice.
   b. abuse of presidential power.
   c. tax evasion.
   d. failure to abide by House subpoenas.

   ANS: C   DIF: Medium   REF: 837   OBJ: 33.3
   TOP: Watergate

10. Which of the following individuals was NOT a key adviser in the Nixon administration?
    a. Henry Kissinger
    b. H. R. Haldeman
    c. John D. Ehrlichman
    d. Elliot Richardson

    ANS: D   DIF: Medium   REF: 821   OBJ: 33.3
    TOP: Nixon's Presidency

11. George Wallace's major goal in running for President in 1968 was
    a. to throw the election into the House of Representatives in order to win support in Congress for his goals.
    b. to draw attention to his demands for a complete withdrawal from Vietnam.
    c. to establish a court system that would be more lenient to criminals.
    d. to become Vice President under Humphrey.

    ANS: A   DIF: Medium   REF: 819   OBJ: 33.0
    TOP: Presidential Elections

12. The 1973 Vietnam cease-fire
    a. required the withdrawal of both United States and Viet Cong troops from Vietnam.
    b. required the return of American prisoners of war.
    c. was a "one-sided" withdrawal of U.S. troops from Vietnam.
    d. required the return of American prisoners of war AND was a "one-sided" withdrawal of U.S. troops from Vietnam.

    ANS: D   DIF: Medium   REF: 825   OBJ: 33.0
    TOP: Vietnam War

13. Public and congressional distrust of President Nixon grew because he
    a. tried to end the war in Vietnam without victory.
    b. used government agencies to harass his political enemies.
    c. refused to release the Watergate tapes.
    d. used government agencies to harass his political enemies AND refused to release the Watergate tapes.

    ANS: D   DIF: Medium   REF: 835–837   OBJ: 33.0
    TOP: Watergate

14. As a result of the 1968 Democratic Convention in Chicago, the Democrats
    a. drew together behind Hubert Humphrey.
    b. were left badly divided and trailing Nixon at the polls.
    c. drew together behind Humphrey and ahead of Nixon at the polls.
    d. were left strongly united behind Eugene McCarthy.

    ANS: B   DIF: Medium   REF: 818   OBJ: 33.1
    TOP: Presidential Elections

15. The Supreme Court in the 1960s made decisions that favored all of the following EXCEPT
    a. integration of public facilities.   c. rights of the accused.
    b. separation of church and state.   d. capital punishment.

    ANS: D   DIF: Medium   REF: 819–820   OBJ: 33.1
    TOP: Supreme Court

16. Much of the violence at the 1968 Democratic Convention was related to
    a. the issue of law and order.
    b. Muskie's nomination for Vice President.
    c. the continuing war in Vietnam.
    d. Lyndon Johnson's refusal to seek another term.

    ANS: C   DIF: Medium   REF: 817–818   OBJ: 33.1
    TOP: Presidential Elections

17. All of the following developments occurred during the 1968 presidential campaign EXCEPT
    a. the assassination of Robert F. Kennedy.
    b. violent demonstrations in the streets of Chicago.
    c. the third-party challenge of George Wallace.
    d. publication of the "Pentagon Papers."

    ANS: D   DIF: Medium   REF: 817–819   OBJ: 33.1
    TOP: Presidential Elections

18. The Supreme Court decisions in "Gideon v. Wainwright" and "Miranda v. Arizona" (1966) dealt with
    a. integration.   c. election reform.
    b. rights of the accused.   d. religion in the schools.

    ANS: B   DIF: Medium   REF: 819–820   OBJ: 33.1
    TOP: Supreme Court

19. Critics of the Supreme Court under Chief Justice Earl Warren objected to Court decisions on all of the following grounds EXCEPT that they
    a. undermined the religious faith of the young.
    b. upset the principle of "one man, one vote."
    c. "pampered" criminals.
    d. intruded on the rights of states.

    ANS: B   DIF: Medium   REF: 819–820   OBJ: 33.1
    TOP: Supreme Court

20. Richard Nixon's 1968 election to the presidency marked the
    a. beginning of a political shift to the left.
    b. institution of new liberal social programs.
    c. beginning of a political shift to the right.
    d. end of the last programs of the New Deal.

    ANS: C   DIF: Medium   REF: 819–820   OBJ: 33.2
    TOP: Presidential Elections

21. The U.S. Senate repealed the Tonkin Gulf Resolution as a result of
    a. North Vietnam's invasion of South Vietnam.
    b. Nixon's removal of troops from South Vietnam.
    c. failure of the Paris peace talks.
    d. antiwar demonstrations in the United States.

    ANS: D   DIF: Medium   REF: 824   OBJ: 33.2
    TOP: Vietnam War

22. Nixon's domestic policies included all of the following EXCEPT
    a. checking inflation.   c. increasing social welfare programs.
    b. curbing unemployment.   d. reducing domestic conflicts.

    ANS: C   DIF: Medium   REF: 830   OBJ: 33.2
    TOP: Nixon's Presidency / Domestic Policy

23. The action by Nixon labeled "the boldest diplomatic move by an American President since Jefferson bought Louisiana" was
    a. the Cambodia "incursion."
    b. the reopening of diplomatic relations with the People's Republic of China.
    c. the SALT Treaty.
    d. American withdrawal from Vietnam.

    ANS: B   DIF: Medium   REF: 828   OBJ: 33.2
    TOP: Nixon's Presidency / Foreign Policy

24. In 1971 President Nixon cut the dollar loose from gold. In doing this, he hoped to
    a. keep the dollar inflated.   c. raise interest rates.
    b. reduce unemployment.   d. promote the sale of American goods.

    ANS: D   DIF: Medium   REF: 830   OBJ: 33.2
    TOP: Nixon's Presidency / Economic Policy

25. President Nixon's economic policies included all of the following EXCEPT a

    a.   mandatory wage-price freeze.   c.   balanced budget.

    b.   return to the gold standard.   d.   surcharge on foreign imports.

ANS: B   DIF: Medium   REF: 830   OBJ: 33.2
TOP: Nixon's Presidency / Economic Policy

26. Which of the following was NOT one of Richard Nixon's domestic policy goals?

    a.   reduced government costs

    b.   protection of states' rights

    c.   a balanced budget

    d.   increased busing to achieve integration

ANS: D   DIF: Medium   REF: 830   OBJ: 33.2
TOP: Nixon's Presidency / Domestic Policy

27. During the Watergate crisis, Richard Nixon

    a.   was impeached by the U.S. Senate.

    b.   appealed his impeachment to the Supreme Court.

    c.   resigned before impeachment by the House.

    d.   was found guilty by the Senate and forced to resign.

ANS: C   DIF: Medium   REF: 838   OBJ: 33.3
TOP: Watergate

28. Which of the following must happen before a President may be removed from office?

    a.   impeachment by both the House and the Senate

    b.   impeachment by the House and conviction by the Senate

    c.   impeachment by the House Judiciary Committee

    d.   trial by the Supreme Court

ANS: B   DIF: Medium   REF: 837   OBJ: 33.3
TOP: Presidential Impeachment

29. The Watergate Affair started when some of President Nixon's associates

    a.   accepted bribes for special favors.

    b.   "bugged" the political headquarters of their opponents.

    c.   leaked secrets about the Vietnam War to the press.

    d.   protested "dirty tricks" by the Democrats.

ANS: B   DIF: Medium   REF: 833   OBJ: 33.3
TOP: Watergate

30. What did Senator Hugh Scott call "a shabby, disgusting, immoral performance" in 1974?

    a.   Daniel Ellsberg's publication of the "Pentagon Papers"

    b.   the conduct of Richard Nixon as revealed by the White House tapes

    c.   actions of the antiwar demonstrators in Chicago

    d.   the Kent State shootings

ANS: B   DIF: Medium   REF: 837   OBJ: 33.3
TOP: Watergate

31. If you grieved over news of the assassination of Robert F. Kennedy, watched the "Yippies" demonstrate at the Democratic national convention in Chicago, and read reports of Nixon's nomination as the Republican candidate for President, you probably lived during the year
    a. 1968.
    b. 1970.
    c. 1972.
    d. 1974.

    ANS: A   DIF: Medium   REF: 817–819   OBJ: 33.1
    TOP: Presidential Elections

32. All of the following Supreme Court decisions upheld the rights of the accused EXCEPT
    a. "Brown v. Board of Education of Topeka."
    b. "Gideon v. Wainwright."
    c. "Escobedo v. Illinois."
    d. "Miranda v. Arizona."

    ANS: A   DIF: Medium   REF: 819–820   OBJ: 33.1
    TOP: Supreme Court

33. If you read newspaper reports about President Nixon's trip to China and watched the Watergate hearings on television, then you were probably living in the years
    a. 1968–1970.
    b. 1970–1972.
    c. 1972–1974.
    d. 1974–1976.

    ANS: C   DIF: Medium   REF: 828, 833–834
    OBJ: 33.2   TOP: Nixon's Presidency

34. The "Plumbers" would MOST likely have been concerned with which of the following?
    a. toxic spill at a chemical plant
    b. a newspaper "exclusive" about secret campaign funds
    c. water shortages in the Far West
    d. urban renewal programs

    ANS: B   DIF: Medium   REF: 831   OBJ: 33.2
    TOP: Nixon's Presidency

35. Which of the following events happened FIRST?
    a. George McGovern won the 1972 Democratic nomination.
    b. Congress repealed the Tonkin Gulf Resolution.
    c. President Nixon visited Peking, China.
    d. The Democratic National headquarters at the Watergate Hotel were broken into.

    ANS: B   DIF: Medium   REF: 824, 828, 832–833
    OBJ: 33.3   TOP: Vietnam War

36. Which of the following is INCORRECTLY paired?
    a. Henry Kissinger—Nixon's Secretary of State
    b. John Sirica—judge in the Watergate trial
    c. Archibald Cox—Nixon's Special Prosecutor
    d. John D. Ehrlichman—Nixon's Attorney General

    ANS: D   DIF: Medium   REF: 821   OBJ: 33.3
    TOP: Nixon's Presidency

SHORT ANSWER

In one or two sentences, define and distinguish between the terms given below.

1. detente

ANS:
Detente is a French word meaning "to relax or ease." It refers to Nixon's policy of easing tensions and reducing the risk of war with the Communist powers.

DIF: Hard   REF: 828–829   OBJ: 33.0
TOP: Nixon's Presidency / Communism

2. Watergate

ANS:
Watergate is a name of a building in Washington where Nixon's "Plumbers" were caught bugging the phones at the Democratic National Committee's haedquarters.

DIF: Hard   REF: 833   OBJ: 33.0   TOP: Watergate

3. The Saturday Night Massacre

ANS:
The Saturday Massacre refers to the resignations of Attorney General Richardson and his deputy when they refused to fire Watergate Special Prosecutor Archibald Cox, who wanted the Watergate tapes.

DIF: Hard   REF: 835–836   OBJ: 33.0   TOP: Watergate

ESSAY

1. What word in the following sentence makes a value judgment? Write your answer on a separate sheet of paper and support your answer with a paragraph explaining why you chose it. The Supreme Court under Chief Justice Earl Warren, in attempting to safeguard the constitutional rights of the individual against the power of the state, was actually pampering defendants.
   A. pampering
   B. rights
   C. Supreme
   D. power

ANS:
answer A Students' paragraphs should support their answer.

DIF: Hard   REF: 820   OBJ: 33.0   TOP: Supreme Court

2. The presidency of Richard Nixon produced an unprecedented crisis in the life of the nation. Explain that crisis in general terms and cite three specific long term consequences.

ANS:
The crisis was over the actions of the President. Did he have the authority to disregard the law in some situations? To promote his own reelection, did he have the right to act illegally? President Nixon had determined that he would use whatever tactics were necessary to win the race for the White House. So the break-in of the Democratic campaign headquarters in the Watergate Hotel in Washington was permissible, and when the "plumbers" were caught, it was natural enough to make efforts to cover up the connection to the President. Nixon ordered the cover-up then would not admit any wrong-doing or allow an effective investigation. Long-term consequences of this crisis include the negative idea that politics is a dirty arena patronized by base and dishonest people; the concept that even presidents are accountable to the people; and the office of the special prosecutor in cases involving government officials.

DIF: Hard   REF: 830–838   OBJ: 33.0   TOP: Watergate

3. Why have modern Presidents required large White House staffs? What problems might arise from this arrangement?

ANS:
Answers will vary but could include the following ideas: The complexity and size of the federal government has led modern-day Presidents to utilize a large administrative staff to help them manage the sprawling federal bureaucracy. Problems that might arise from this situation include (1) the increased cost of government, (2) the President's potential isolation from the vast government army that officiates over government, and (3) the difficulty of directing such a large and varied group of employees efficiently.

DIF: Hard   REF: 821   OBJ: 33.1
TOP: Government / Presidential Staff

4. A message often seen on bumper stickers and billboards in the late 1960s read, "Impeach Earl Warren." Explain what this message meant, and why people supported this statement.

ANS:
Answers will vary but could include the following ideas: The message was a clear call for Warren's removal from office. The demand for impeachment arose among those Americans who objected to rulings by the Warren Court on matters such as integration, separation of church and state, and the rights of the accused.

DIF: Hard   REF: 819–820   OBJ: 33.1   TOP: Supreme Court

5. Explain how violence affected the 1968 election campaign.

    ANS:
    Answers will vary but could include the following ideas: The violence at the 1968 Democratic national convention was dramatic. The scenes of outbursts by protestors and of police riots were televised for millions to see. This dark vision of politics cast a shadow over the Democratic party, and some Americans began to question whether the Democrats could solve the nation's problems.

    DIF: Hard   OBJ: 33.1   TOP: Presidential Elections

6. Why was U.S. recognition of the People's Republic of China a momentous event? Why was Nixon well-suited to bring about this change in policy?

    ANS:
    Answers will vary but could include the following ideas: The United States had refused to recognize the People's Republic of China for more than 22 years. Nixon's visit to Peking normalized relations and opened the way for Red China's membership in the UN. Nixon was able to make this bold move largely because of his long-standing credentials as a fighter against communism.

    DIF: Hard   REF: 828–829   OBJ: 33.2
    TOP: Nixon's Presidency / Foreign Policy

7. Based on what you have read in the chapter, identify the steps that Richard Nixon took to end the Vietnam War.

    ANS:
    Answers will vary but could include the following ideas: Nixon initially used secret large-scale bombings of suspected North Vietnamese and Viet Cong bases in Cambodia. Protest against the war grew louder, despite Nixon's gradual withdrawal of troops. Even after Congress repealed the Tonkin Gulf Resolution, Nixon continued to put pressure on North Vietnam by mining Haiphong Harbor. At the same time, he entered into secret peace talks between the United States and North Vietnam. These talks collapsed because of continued U.S. bombing raids. When Nixon called an end to these raids, North Vietnamese leaders agreed to a cease-fire.

    DIF: Hard   REF: 822–828   OBJ: 33.2
    TOP: Nixon's Presidency / Vietnam War

8. What were Nixon's goals for (a) the Supreme Court, (b) the economy, and (c) foreign policy? How successful was he in achieving his goals?

ANS:
Answers will vary but could include the following ideas: Nixon wanted to appoint judges to the Supreme Court who favored a strict (and more conservative) interpretation of the Constitution. He also hoped to halt the rapid inflation within the United States and to bring down the unemployment rate. His most important objectives, however, were in foreign policy. He sought to end the Vietnam War and prevent open conflict with the Communists. Nixon achieved his greatest victories in the area of foreign policy: by ending the Vietnam War and by opening talks with the Soviet Union and the People's Republic of China. In the domestic area, Nixon did manage to appoint a new Chief Justice of the Supreme Court, but the Court did not always rule the way in which he had anticipated. Nixon also failed to rein in the economy and move toward a balanced budget.

DIF: Hard   REF: 822–830, 835   OBJ: 33.2
TOP: Nixon's Presidency

9. Explain the important events and the implications of the Watergate Affair.

ANS:
Answers will vary but could include the following ideas: The important events in the Watergate Affair include the decision to use "dirty tricks," the bugging of Democratic headquarters, and the subsequent coverup. The outcome of the affair was what amounted to a Constitutional crisis for the nation. The fact that Congress and the American public refused to place a President above the law reaffirmed that the system could and did work.

DIF: Hard   REF: 830–838   OBJ: 33.3   TOP: Watergate

10. Opinion polls in 1975 and 1976 showed a sharp drop in people's trust in government. What may have been some other by-products of the Watergate Affair? Explain.

ANS:
Answers will vary but could include the following ideas: There were Constitutional implications as well as implications of curtailed presidential power. There was also the subsequent election of a little-known Democratic candidate (Carter) as President and the one-term Presidencies of both Ford and Carter that followed Nixon's resignation.

DIF: Hard   REF: 830–838   OBJ: 33.3
TOP: Watergate / Aftermath (Consequences of)

(page intentionally left blank)

MATCHING

Match each item with the correct statement below.

a. Puerto Ricans   d. Native Americans
b. African-Americans   e. women
c. Mexican-Americans   f. mentally and physically handicapped

1. "Brown Power"
2. busing
3. Forrest J. Gerrard
4. Betty Friedan
5. mainstreaming
6. Operation Bootstrap

1. ANS: C   DIF: Easy   REF: 865   OBJ: 34.0
     TOP: Equal Rights / Mexicans & Mexican Americans
2. ANS: B   DIF: Easy   REF: 850   OBJ: 34.0
     TOP: Integration
3. ANS: D   DIF: Easy   REF: 862   OBJ: 34.0
     TOP: Equal Rights / Native Americans
4. ANS: E   DIF: Easy   REF: 855–856   OBJ: 34.0
     TOP: Equal Rights / Women
5. ANS: F   DIF: Easy   REF: 872   OBJ: 34.0
     TOP: Equal Rights / Handicapped
6. ANS: A   DIF: Easy   REF: 866   OBJ: 34.0
     TOP: Puerto Rico

MULTIPLE CHOICE

1. The purpose of the quota system that grew out of the 1960s civil rights movement was to
   a. give new opportunities to members of minority groups.
   b. replace affirmative action programs.
   c. allow African-Americans to enter all federally funded programs.
   d. prevent women from holding too many managerial jobs.

   ANS: A   DIF: Medium   REF: 851   OBJ: 34.1
   TOP: Equal Rights / Minorities

2. All of the following groups were organized to discriminate against minority groups EXCEPT the
   a. Immigration Restriction League.   c. Ku Klux Klan.
   b. American Protective Association.   d. National Women's Suffrage Association.

   ANS: D   DIF: Medium   REF: 855   OBJ: 34.1
   TOP: Discrimination

3. In the late 1970s, the term "backlash" was commonly used to describe the reaction of
   a. African-Americans to confusion within the civil rights movement.
   b. women to continued job discrimination.
   c. some whites to government assistance programs for minorities.
   d. government officials to pressures exerted by special interest groups.

   ANS: C   DIF: Medium   REF: 851   OBJ: 34.2
   TOP: Discrimination

4. An outspoken supporter of the "Brown Power" movement was
   a. Thurgood Marshall.   c. James Hodgson.
   b. Reies Lopez Tijerina.   d. Luis Munoz Marin.

   ANS: B   DIF: Medium   REF: 865   OBJ: 34.4
   TOP: Equal Rights / Mexicans & MexAmericans

5. The person responsible for organizing migrant farm workers into a union was
   a. Cesar Chavez.   c. Senator Joseph Montoya.
   b. Reies Lopez Tijerina.   d. Leonal Costillo.

   ANS: A   DIF: Medium   REF: 864   OBJ: 34.4
   TOP: Equal Rights / Mexicans & Mexican Americans

6. The Immigration Reform and Control Act of 1986
   a. made legal all illegal aliens who had been in the country since 1970.
   b. closed the country's borders to all immigrants.
   c. brought about the removal of all illegal aliens out of the country in early 1986.
   d. made legal all illegal aliens who could prove that they had been in the United States
      since January 1, 1982.

   ANS: D   DIF: Medium   REF: 869   OBJ: 34.5
   TOP: Immigration

7. The goal of President Eisenhower's "termination plan" was to
   a. provide Native Americans with a better standard of living.
   b. give full tribal sovereignty back to Native Americans.
   c. appoint Native Americans to the Bureau of Indian Affairs.
   d. end all federal involvement with Native Americans.

   ANS: D   DIF: Medium   REF: 861   OBJ: 34.6
   TOP: Native Americans

8. The program aimed at giving preferences to women, blacks, and other minorities to correct past injustices is known as
   a. democratic education.   c. affirmative action.
   b. open admission.   d. equality in education.

   ANS: C   DIF: Medium   REF: 850–851   OBJ: 34.7
   TOP: Affirmative Action

9. Which statement about immigrants coming to the United States in the 1800s and early 1900s was TRUE?
   a. They were often treated as second-class citizens.
   b. Employers were eager to hire them.
   c. Existing laws protected their rights.
   d. Children of immigrants received equal educational opportunities.

   ANS: A   DIF: Medium   REF: 848   OBJ: 34.1
   TOP: Immigration

10. African-Americans have achieved the MOST success in gaining their goals through
    a. voting.
    b. reverse discrimination.
    c. moving their families to the North.
    d. joining the American Protection Association.

    ANS: A   DIF: Medium   REF: 850–855   OBJ: 34.2
    TOP: Equal Rights / Voting

11. Which of the following is an example of affirmative action?
    a. giving preference to African-Americans, women, or other minorities for jobs or college admissions
    b. "open admissions" programs in colleges that require no entry exams
    c. requiring students who compete in sports to maintain at least a "C" average
    d. placing a quota on the number of people allowed to immigrant to the United States

    ANS: A   DIF: Medium   REF: 850–851   OBJ: 34.2
    TOP: Affirmative Action

12. The Bakke decision reflected concern with what concept?
    a. feminism   c. mainstreaming
    b. natural aristocracy   d. reverse descrimination

    ANS: D   DIF: Medium   REF: 851   OBJ: 34.0
    TOP: Discrimination

13. Total equality has been MOST nearly achieved by minorities in the United States in the area of
    a. housing.   c. income.
    b. voting.   d. land ownership.

    ANS: B   DIF: Medium   OBJ: 34.2   TOP: Equal Rights / Voting

14. A "comfortable concentration camp" was the term used by a
    a. militant Native American to describe reservation life.
    b. Chicago African-American to describe a segregated public school.
    c. leading feminist to describe the home.
    d. bracero to describe a vineyard in California.

    ANS: C   DIF: Medium   REF: 856   OBJ: 34.3
    TOP: Equal Rights Movement

15. Which argument BEST supports passage of an Equal Rights Amendment?
    a. A woman's place is in the home.
    b. The average woman earns 59 cents for every dollar earned by a man.
    c. More women than men voted in the 1976 presidential election.
    d. More girls are involved in high school sports than ever before.

    ANS: B   DIF: Medium   REF: 857   OBJ: 34.3
    TOP: Equal Rights Movement

16. Which law included an amendment that barred job discrimination on the basis of sex and race?
    a. Snyder Act of 1924   c. Civil Rights Act of 1964
    b. Equal Rights Amendment   d. Equal Employment Opportunity Act

    ANS: C   DIF: Medium   REF: 857   OBJ: 34.3
    TOP: Equal Rights Movement

17. Which of the following statements BEST describes Betty Friedan's argument in "The Feminine Mystique"?
    a. Women only want to bear children and be housewives.
    b. Married women who work should earn less than married men.
    c. Women are equal to men in their ability to do all kinds of jobs.
    d. Women should fight for their full voting rights.

    ANS: C   DIF: Medium   REF: 855–856   OBJ: 34.3
    TOP: Equal Rights Movement

18. By the 1970s, the MOST important barrier(s) to full female equality was/were
    a. legal restrictions.
    b. customs and traditions.
    c. affirmative action programs.
    d. President Carter's opposition to the ERA.

    ANS: B   DIF: Medium   REF: 855–856   OBJ: 34.3
    TOP: Equal Rights Movement

19. In which state did most Cuban refugees settle?
    a. Florida   c. North Carolina
    b. New Jersey   d. California

    ANS: A   DIF: Medium   REF: 867   OBJ: 34.4
    TOP: Immigration / Cuba

20. Puerto Ricans are represented in the United States government
    a. by a bureau in the State Department.
    b. by a resident commissioner in Congress who has no vote.
    c. by voting in U.S. presidential elections.
    d. by a bureau in the State Department AND by a resident commissioner in Congress who has no vote.

    ANS: B   DIF: Medium   REF: 866   OBJ: 34.0
    TOP: Puerto Rico

21. The Equal Rights Amendment passed by Congress and sent to the states in 1972
    a. was the first such amendment ever introduced in Congress.
    b. was added to the Constitution in 1982.
    c. failed to win approval by the required three-fourths of the states.
    d. received overwhelming support from women and almost none from men.

    ANS: C   DIF: Medium   REF: 857   OBJ: 34.0
    TOP: Equal Rights Amendment

22. Which of the following has historically set Puerto Ricans apart from other Hispanics?
    a. Puerto Ricans are already American citizens.
    b. Most Puerto Ricans are migrant workers.
    c. Many Puerto Ricans fled their country because of a Communist takeover.
    d. Puerto Ricans are allowed to vote in national elections.

    ANS: A   DIF: Medium   REF: 866   OBJ: 34.4
    TOP: Puerto Rico

23. Which group makes up the largest Spanish-speaking population in the United States?
    a. Nicaraguans   c. Cubans
    b. Mexican-Americans   d. Puerto Ricans

    ANS: B   DIF: Medium   REF: 864   OBJ: 34.4
    TOP: Immigration / Mexico

24. Which of the following groups occupied offices in Washington, D.C. to demand greater Indian rights?
    a. Passamaquoddy Indians of Maine   c. Bureau of Indian Affairs
    b. American Indian Defense Association   d. American Indian Movement

    ANS: D   DIF: Medium   REF: 861   OBJ: 34.6
    TOP: Indian Rights Movement

25. As director of the American Indian Defense Association, John Collier attempted to
    a. offer jobs to Native Americans in urban areas.
    b. help Native Americans to preserve old ways and to participate fully in American life.
    c. end federally funded programs for Native Americans.
    d. register Native Americans to vote.

    ANS: B   DIF: Medium   REF: 861   OBJ: 34.6
    TOP: Indian Rights Movement

26. Which of the following events in the Indian rights movement occurred LAST?
    a. "termination" program
    b. Snyder Act
    c. Indian New Deal
    d. Indian Self-Determination and Education Assistance Act

    ANS: D   DIF: Medium   REF: 861–862   OBJ: 34.6
    TOP: Indian Rights Movement

27. The Rehabilitation Act and other laws for the handicapped in the 1970s provided for all of the following EXCEPT
    a. the redesign of public buildings.
    b. no discrimination in employment practices.
    c. mainstreaming in schools and colleges receiving federal funds.
    d. a 5 percent college admissions quota for the physically disabled.

    ANS: D   DIF: Medium   REF: 871–872   OBJ: 34.7
    TOP: Equal Rights / Physically Handicapped

28. Which of the following items does NOT belong in the list below?
    a. Civil Rights Act of 1964   c. Rehabilitation Act of 1973
    b. Equal Rights Amendment   d. Operation Bootstrap

    ANS: D   DIF: Medium   REF: 866   OBJ: 34.5
    TOP: Equal Rights

29. In recent years Native Americans have been most successful in advancing their own interests
    a. by using the courts to reclaim land and win more control over their lands.
    b. by demonstrations and violent actions.
    c. by voting and lobbying.
    d. by waging aggressive publicity campaigns.

    ANS: A   DIF: Medium   REF: 863   OBJ: 34.0
    TOP: Indian Rights Movement

30. A major flaw in the idea of a "natural aristocracy" is that
    a. social status and wealth affect an individual's ability to compete in life.
    b. different individuals have different abilities.
    c. the United States does not have an Old World aristocracy to set standards of behavior.
    d. the United States offers few opportunities for individuals to display their talents.

    ANS: A   DIF: Medium   REF: 846   OBJ: 34.1
    TOP: Social Class

31. In the Weber case, the Supreme Court found that giving minorities half of the openings in a special training program at Kaiser Aluminum was legal because it attempted to correct "patterns of social segregation and hierarchy." What did the Court mean by "patterns of social segregation and hierarchy"?
    a. legal barriers to the achievement of full equality by minorities
    b. reduced opportunities for minorities based on custom and informal discrimination
    c. the "Jim Crow" laws that prevailed throughout the North into the 1950s
    d. the unwillingness of minorities to be assimilated

    ANS: B   DIF: Medium   REF: 851   OBJ: 34.2
    TOP: Affirmative Action

32. Which of the following statements was the result of the other three?
    a. In 1972, Congress passed the Equal Rights Amendment.
    b. "The Feminine Mystique" was published.
    c. Full-time working women were paid only 59 percent of what men were earning.
    d. Employers often passed over qualified women for promotions.

    ANS: A   DIF: Medium   REF: 855–860   OBJ: 34.3
    TOP: Equal Rights Movement

33. Which of the following was NOT a result of the Immigration and Control Act of 1986?
    a. Anyone hiring illegal immigrants could be fined.
    b. The nation's borders would be more closely patrolled.
    c. Illegal immigrants who were in the country since 1982 were allowed to become legal residents.
    d. All illegal aliens who could prove that they were persecuted in their own country were granted political asylum.

    ANS: D   DIF: Medium   REF: 869   OBJ: 34.0
    TOP: Immigration

34. Which of the following was NOT a characteristic of the Indian rights movement during the 1970s?
    a. violent protests   c. relocation
    b. militant groups   d. demonstrations

    ANS: C   DIF: Medium   REF: 860–863   OBJ: 34.6
    TOP: Indian Rights Movement

35. Which of the following does NOT relate to the women's rights movement?
    a. Twenty-fourth Amendment   c. Civil Rights Act
    b. Nineteenth Amendment   d. Equal Employment Opportunity Act

    ANS: A   DIF: Medium   REF: 848   OBJ: 34.7
    TOP: Equal Rights Movement

SHORT ANSWER

In one or two sentences, define and distinguish between the terms given below.

1. racial balance—busing

   ANS:
   Racial balance is the concept in which local populations accurately reflect the percentages of minorities in the larger community. Busing was one method to bring minorities to schools at which they were underrepresented, and give these students an equal education.

   DIF: Hard   REF: 850   OBJ: 34.0   TOP: Integration

2. affirmative action—backlash

ANS:
Affirmative action was a federal policy to increase the representation of women and minorities, especially in jobs and higher education. A "backlash" occurred in which a new kind of prejudice against qualified white males was created by this attempt.

DIF: Hard   REF: 850–852   OBJ: 34.0   TOP: Affirmative Action

3. termination—relocation

ANS:
Termination was a federal program in which the government was to end all federal involvement with Native Americans and leave the states to deal with them. Another program was called "relocation." It offered jobs to induce Native Americans to relocate in cities.

DIF: Hard   REF: 861   OBJ: 34.0
TOP: Government Policy / Native Americans

ESSAY

1. Which of the following statements uses comparison reasoning? Write your answer on a separate sheet of paper and support your answer with a paragraph explaining why you chose it.
   A. The problem of discrimination was more complicated and more deeply rooted than it had seemed.
   B. Boston was scarred by its struggle with school busing, but schools in Buffalo, New York set an example of peaceful integration.
   C. Laws could not cure discrimination just as the Eigtheenth Amendment had not cured the social ills of drunkenness.
   D. Affirmative action gave new advantages to groups that had suffered from discrimination.

ANS:
answer C Students' paragraphs should support their answer.

DIF: Hard   REF: 850   OBJ: 34.0   TOP: Discrimination

2. In one paragraph each, point out progress made in the recent years by any two of the following groups of Americans: Hispanics, Native Americans, women, the handicapped.

ANS:
The rise of the Brown Power movement brought gains, as did the organizing of farm labor under such leaders as Cesar Chavez. In the late 1960s Congress voted over $500 million in Native American aid. Self-government on reservations followed, and Native Americans were appointed to key government positions. Congress passed the Indian Self Determination and Education Act in 1975, and a new post of Indian Affairs was created. The Civil Rights Act of 1964 forbade sex discrimination, and Congress approved the "Equal Rights" Amendment in 1972. In that year the government set goals and timetables for hiring women in some industries, and the Equal Employment Opportunity Act was passed. For the handicapped, recent improvements were the Rehabilitation Act of 1973 and laws preventing job discrimination. Federal regulations affecting design of buildings and sidewalks improved access. Raised letters and audible signals helped the blind.

DIF: Hard   REF: 850–874   OBJ: 34.0
TOP: Equal Rights / Minorities

3. How does a society benefit when its people engage in lively competition for income and social status? What are the costs of such competition?

ANS:
Answers will vary but could include the following ideas: Equal opportunity and competition are basic to the ideals of freedom in the Constitution. For example, competition allows people to strive for their fullest potential and to reap the greatest rewards possible. This situation exists in a free society. However, not everybody has equal talents and abilities. Therefore, one of the costs necessary for competition is that certain rules have to be established that allow everybody a chance at reaping the rewards of competition, even though everybody may not be an "equal winner."

DIF: Hard   OBJ: 34.1   TOP: Society

4. In the past, what were the two MOST important problems facing immigrants when they arrived in this country? Do immigrants face similar problems today? If not, why? If so, what action(s) might the federal government take to correct this situation?

ANS:
Answers will vary but could include the following ideas: Immigrant groups were discriminated against in many areas. The most important areas were housing, education, and job opportunities. At that time there was no civil rights legislation to protect them from unfair treatment. However, today there are laws to protect new immigrants. The descendants of the old immigrant groups can now be found in high political office as well as every socio-economic class. Nevertheless, new immigrants such as those from Mexico, Southeast Asia, and various Central American and Caribbean countries, still face discrimination.

DIF: Hard   REF: 848–849, 864–869   OBJ: 34.1
TOP: Immigration

5. Based on what you have read in the chapter, describe the progress made by African-Americans in winning their rights and advancing in American society during recent decades. In your opinion, has the issue of civil rights for African-Americans been resolved? Explain your answer.

ANS:
Answers will vary but could include the following ideas: The Twenty-fourth Amendment, the Voting Rights Act, the 1954 Supreme Court decision banning segregation in public schools, the use of busing to achieve "racial balance," the Civil Rights Act, and affirmative action programs are all advances won by African- Americans during recent years. Many argue, however, that barriers to progress still exist for African-Americans in America.

DIF: Hard   REF: 850–855   OBJ: 34.2
TOP: Equal Rights / African-Americans

6. Evaluate the gains and losses of the women's rights movement during the 1960s and 1970s. Which, if any, of the losses have been turned into victories during the past 20 years? Explain your answer and give specific examples to support your argument.

ANS:
Answers will vary but could include the following ideas: The Equal Employment Opportunity Act and the Civil Rights Act are only two of the achievements that women have helped bring about. With the help of this type of legislation, women have been able to make inroads into various professions and skilled craft trades in unprecedented numbers. Yet the women's movement still faces opposition. One need only note the defeat of the Equal Rights Amendment and the words of those who feel women should not break with their traditional roles.

DIF: Hard   REF: 855–860   OBJ: 34.3
TOP: Equal Rights Movement

7. Briefly describe the political relationship between Puerto Rico and the United States.

ANS:
Answers will vary but could include the following ideas: Puerto Rico is a Commonwealth country. That means Puerto Ricans are self-governing, but that its people are full citizens of the United States. Thus there are no restrictions on their travel to the United States. However, Puerto Ricans cannot vote in national elections, nor are they allowed a congressional delegation with voting power. On the other hand, they are not required to pay federal taxes. Though Puerto Rico has had the economic benefits of U.S.-sponsored programs such as Operation Bootstrap, there remain mixed feelings toward the United States. Those who advocate complete independence are still a minority.

DIF: Hard   REF: 866–867   OBJ: 34.4   TOP: Puerto Rico

8. Discuss the policies of the U.S. government since the Roosevelt Administration toward Native Americans. In your opinion, which policies have helped Native Americans make the greatest gains? What do you think our government's policies should be toward Native Americans today?

ANS:
Answers will vary but could include the following ideas: In retrospect, the "termination" and "relocation" programs can be viewed as the federal government's attempt to rid themselves of the so-called "Indian problem." Since the beginning of the Native Americans' "New Deal," Indians have exerted more and more determination to determine their own cultural destinies and be compensated for lost lands. Reflections of these efforts are such gains as the development of the American Indian Movement and the passage of the Indian Self-Determination and Educational Assistance Act of 1975.

DIF: Hard   REF: 861–863   OBJ: 34.6
TOP: Government Policy / Native Americans

9. Explain the ways in which legislative victories against discrimination in the United States have contributed to the extension of the rights of the physically handicapped?

ANS:
Answers will vary but could include the following ideas: Legislation such as the Civil Rights Act of 1964, the Equal Employment Opportunity Act, the Rehabilitation Act of 1973, and the Americans with Disabilities Act have paved the way for extending the rights of the handicapped. New legislation has lowered the structural barriers that prevented these citizens from having access to public transportation, buildings, education, and ultimately jobs. Many gains have been made toward rights for the mentally retarded; for example, the requirement that education be provided through age 21 for mentally retarded citizens.

DIF: Hard   REF: 871–873   OBJ: 34.5
TOP: Equal Rights / Physically Handicapped

(page intentionally left blank)

MATCHING

Match each item with the correct statement below.

a. Developing countries
b. shuttle diplomacy
c. Silicon Valley
d. EPA
e. PLO
f. trade deficit
g. Caspar Weinberger
h. Nelson Rockefeller
i. OPEC
j. Anwar Sadat

1. Poorer nations that were adversely affected by the oil crisis.
2. A former governor of New York and multimillionaire whom Ford chose as his Vice President.
3. Agency created in 1970 to bring together government programs dealing with pollution and other problems.
4. The group of nations that is organized to control oil output and prices.
5. Reagan's Secretary of Defense who advocated huge increases in federal defense spending.
6. The nickname of Secretary of State Kissinger's methods of reaching agreements with other countries.
7. A Middle East organization that used terrorism to try to abolish Israel and establish a homeland.
8. Boom area in California that produces computer chips.
9. Condition which arises when the U.S. purchases more from other nations than they are buying from us.
10. He was the first leader of an Arab country to visit the state of Isreal.

1. ANS: A   DIF: Easy   OBJ: 35.0   TOP: Oil Crisis
2. ANS: H   DIF: Easy   REF: 877   OBJ: 35.0
   TOP: Ford's Presidency
3. ANS: D   DIF: Easy   REF: 885   OBJ: 35.0
   TOP: Environmental Protection Agency
4. ANS: I   DIF: Easy   REF: 880   OBJ: 35.0
   TOP: OPEC
5. ANS: G   DIF: Easy   REF: 898   OBJ: 35.0
   TOP: Reagan's Presidency
6. ANS: B   DIF: Easy   REF: 889   OBJ: 35.0
   TOP: Henry Kissinger
7. ANS: E   DIF: Easy   REF: 893   OBJ: 35.0
   TOP: Mid-East Conflicts
8. ANS: C   DIF: Easy   REF: 901   OBJ: 35.0
   TOP: Computers
9. ANS: F   DIF: Easy   REF: 900   OBJ: 35.0
   TOP: Economics / Trades
10. ANS: J   DIF: Easy   REF: 893   OBJ: 35.0
    TOP: Mid-East Conflicts

MULTIPLE CHOICE

1. All of the following were examples of congressional efforts to limit the power of the Presidency EXCEPT the
   a. Intelligence Oversight Board.
   b. War Powers Act.
   c. Budget and Impoundment Act.
   d. Congressional Budget Office.

   ANS: A   DIF: Medium   REF: 879   OBJ: 35.1
   TOP: Government

2. President Ford's "clemency" program was directed at
   a. Vietnam era draft evaders and deserters.
   b. Richard Nixon and his White House staff.
   c. the Central Intelligence Agency.
   d. the Federal Bureau of Investigation.

   ANS: A   DIF: Medium   REF: 877–878   OBJ: 35.1
   TOP: Ford's Presidency

3. Which of the following executive departments was created under President Carter?
   a. Department of Housing and Urban Development
   b. Department of Energy
   c. Department of Education
   d. Department of Labor

   ANS: B   DIF: Medium   REF: 887   OBJ: 35.2
   TOP: Carter's Presidency

4. The term "Pathet Lao" refers to the
   a. capital of North Vietnam.
   b. rebel group that took over South Vietnam.
   c. Communist-backed group that took over Laos.
   d. deposed leader of Cambodia.

   ANS: C   DIF: Medium   REF: 890–891   OBJ: 35.3
   TOP: Communism / Laos

5. The Panama Canal treaties
   a. transferred control of the canal to Panama.
   b. were proposed by Ronald Reagan.
   c. were defeated by the Senate.
   d. damaged our relations with Latin America.

   ANS: A   DIF: Medium   REF: 892   OBJ: 35.4
   TOP: U.S. Foreign Policy / Panama Canal

6. Which of the following came to power after the 1979 revolution in Iran?
   a. Ayatollah Ruhollah Khomeini
   b. Nguyen van Thieu
   c. Lon Nol
   d. Anwar Sadat

   ANS: A   DIF: Medium   REF: 894   OBJ: 35.4
   TOP: Iran

7. In the 1970s, all of the following American-backed leaders fell from power EXCEPT
   a. Anastasio Somoza.
   b. Shah Mohammad Reza Pahlavi.
   c. Menachem Begin.
   d. Lon Nol.

   ANS: C   DIF: Medium   REF: 887, 889, 894
   OBJ: 35.4   TOP: Foreign Leaders

8. All of the following are examples of "entitlements" EXCEPT
   a. medicare payments.
   b. Social Security payments.
   c. income taxes.
   d. veterans' benefits.

   ANS: C   DIF: Medium   REF: 898   OBJ: 35.1
   TOP: Entitlements

9. Labor contracts that feature "give-backs" require that workers
   a. give up some benefits.
   b. give up union membership.
   c. lose seniority.
   d. gain more vacation time.

   ANS: A   DIF: Medium   REF: 903   OBJ: 35.2
   TOP: Labor Contracts

10. The reduction of government control of business and other activities was known as
    a. reindustrialization.
    b. deregulation.
    c. give-backs.
    d. payments-in-kind.

    ANS: B   DIF: Medium   REF: 902–903   OBJ: 35.2
    TOP: Deregulation

11. The Arab oil embargo of 1973–74 was triggered by
    a. U.S. aid to Israel during the Yom Kippur War.
    b. the revolution in Iran.
    c. a dispute about shipping rights in the Persian Gulf.
    d. the U.S. refusal to pay increased prices for Libyan oil.

    ANS: A   DIF: Medium   REF: 879   OBJ: 35.1
    TOP: U.S. Foreign Policy / Israel

12. Gerald Ford tried to control inflation by
    a. increasing Social Security taxes.
    b. limiting oil imports.
    c. increasing government spending.
    d. raising the prices of imports.

    ANS: C   DIF: Medium   REF: 880   OBJ: 35.1
    TOP: Ford's Presidency

13. President Ford lost the MOST public support by
    a. offering pardons to draft evaders.
    b. pulling U.S. troops out of Cambodia.
    c. offering a pardon to former President Nixon.
    d. imposing mandatory wage-and-price controls.

    ANS: C   DIF: Medium   REF: 877   OBJ: 35.1
    TOP: Ford's Presidency

14. What produced the second energy crisis in 1979?
    a. renewed conflict between Egypt and Israel
    b. a revolution in Iran
    c. strip mining
    d. a worldwide shortage of oil

    ANS: B   DIF: Medium   REF: 887   OBJ: 35.2
    TOP: Energy Crisis

15. All of the following contributed to a high rate of inflation in the 1970s EXCEPT
    a. rising oil prices.   c. unemployment
    b. a high minimum wage.   d. environmental regulations.

    ANS: D   DIF: Medium   OBJ: 35.2   TOP: Economics

16. President Carter tried to halt the steep rate of inflation by
    a. setting voluntary wage-and-price controls.
    b. lowering taxes.
    c. cutting environmental programs.
    d. rationing oil.

    ANS: A   DIF: Medium   REF: 884   OBJ: 35.2
    TOP: Carter's Presidency

17. The 1975 Helsinki Agreements included
    a. a condemnation of the Arab oil embargo.
    b. a focus on the issue of human rights.
    c. an outline of ways to stop high inflation and unemployment in Europe.
    d. a settlement of the dispute over fishing rights in the Atlantic.

    ANS: B   DIF: Medium   REF: 888–889   OBJ: 35.3
    TOP: Helsinki Agreements

18. All of the following took place after the U.S. withdrawal from Southeast Asia EXCEPT
    a. North Vietman's defeat of South Vietnam.
    b. a Communist takeover of Laos.
    c. free elections in Vietnam.
    d. Khmer Rouge killings in Cambodia.

    ANS: C   DIF: Medium   OBJ: 35.3
    TOP: U.S. Foreign Policy / S.E. Asia

19. All of the following occurred during Henry Kissinger's terms as Secretary of State EXCEPT
    a. opening relations with China.
    b. the Vietnam peace treaty.
    c. mutual recognition between East and West Germany.
    d. Panama Canal treaties approved by the senate.

    ANS: D   DIF: Medium   REF: 888   OBJ: 35.3
    TOP: Henry Kissinger

20. During the 1970s, the American view of world affairs was dominated by a concern with
    a. Soviet-American relations.
    b. the Third World.
    c. crises in the Middle East.
    d. resolution of the Vietnam War.

    ANS: A   DIF: Medium   REF: 828, 892   OBJ: 35.4
    TOP: Soviet Union Relations

21. Political problems in the Middle East included all of the following elements EXCEPT
    a. religious conflicts.
    b. concerns about the supply of coal.
    c. demands for a homeland for Palestinian refugees.
    d. terrorist activities.

    ANS: B   DIF: Medium   REF: 893   OBJ: 35.4
    TOP: Mid-East Conflicts

22. Which of the following was NOT responsible for the serious deficit in Reagan's first budget proposals?
    a. increased defense spending
    b. reduced revenues resulting from tax cuts
    c. the failure of the economy to perform as expected
    d. spending cuts in federal welfare programs

    ANS: D   DIF: Medium   REF: 897–898   OBJ: 35.1
    TOP: Reagan's Presidency

23. Supply-side economics
    a. favors running up of large federal deficits.
    b. is a theory developed by John Maynard Keynes.
    c. favors individual and business tax cuts to spur the economy.
    d. was supported by Jimmy Carter.

    ANS: C   DIF: Medium   REF: 897–898   OBJ: 35.5
    TOP: Economics

24. The Federal Reserve System controls all of the following EXCEPT
    a. issuance of money.
    b. financing of the national debt.
    c. interest on money loaned to member banks.
    d. money spent on national defense.

    ANS: D   DIF: Medium   REF: 898   OBJ: 35.5
    TOP: Federal Reserve System

25. Which is a TRUE statement about President Reagan's defense policy?
    a. He rejected spending on NATO defense.
    b. He rejected the proposal for a new B-1 bomber.
    c. He recommended a large increase in defense spending.
    d. He canceled plans to develop "Star Wars" weapons.

    ANS: C   DIF: Medium   REF: 898   OBJ: 35.5
    TOP: Reagan's Presidency

26. All of the following contributed to labor difficulties during the Reagan administration EXCEPT
    a. the decline of the smokestack industries.
    b. the deregulation of many industries.
    c. competition from abroad.
    d. the policies of the Department of the Interior.

    ANS: D   DIF: Medium   REF: 899–902   OBJ: 35.6
    TOP: Reagan's Presidency

27. As a result of the 1983 settlement, AT&T
    a. had to get rid of its local phone companies.
    b. could enter the computer industry.
    c. could raise its long distance rates.
    d. had to get rid of its local phone companies AND could enter the computer industry.

    ANS: D   DIF: Medium   REF: 903   OBJ: 35.6
    TOP: Deregulation

28. In the early 1980s, what area of technological development had the greatest impact on the daily lives of Americans?
    a. computers   c. solar energy
    b. the space shuttle program   d. robots

    ANS: A   DIF: Medium   REF: 900   OBJ: 35.6
    TOP: Computers

29. As President, Carter accomplished all of the following EXCEPT
    a. reform of the electoral college.
    b. establishment of a Department of Energy.
    c. a Panama Canal treaty.
    d. getting an increase in Social Security taxes to stave off collapse.

    ANS: A   DIF: Medium   REF: 882, 887, 892–893
    OBJ: 35.0   TOP: Carter's Presidency

30. In the late 1970s the United States
    a. used over 30 percent of the world's energy.
    b. had to import 80 percent of its energy needs.
    c. had 30 percent of the world's population.
    d. had a 50 percent inflation rate.

    ANS: A   DIF: Medium   REF: 885   OBJ: 35.0
    TOP: U.S. Energy Consumption

31. Carter's major weakness as President was that
    a. he had no prior political experience.
    b. he was unable to get along with Congress.
    c. he lacked a competent Cabinet.
    d. he was overly cautious in making proposals.

    ANS: B   DIF: Medium   REF: 884   OBJ: 35.0
    TOP: Carter's Presidency

32. Both the Freedom of Information Act and the Privacy Act
    a. limited private contributions to political candidates.
    b. expanded the powers of the CIA and the FBI.
    c. opened up government files to citizens.
    d. set up agencies to monitor the CIA.

    ANS: C   DIF: Medium   REF: 878   OBJ: 35.0
    TOP: U.S. Government

33. The accident at Three Mile Island raised concern about
    a. the safety of nuclear reactors.   c. environmental effects of strip mining.
    b. the problem of smog.   d. damage from acid rain.

    ANS: A   DIF: Medium   REF: 886–887   OBJ: 35.0
    TOP: Nuclear Power

34. President Carter negotiated the SALT II Agreements with the Soviets in order to
    a. outlaw the use of nuclear arms.
    b. limit the number of strategic weapons.
    c. propose a plan for new weapons.
    d. see surplus missiles and bombers.

    ANS: B   DIF: Medium   REF: 892   OBJ: 35.0
    TOP: Carter's Presidency / Foreign Policy

35. Political Action Committees (PACs) were formed by
    a. President Carter to reform the Social Security System.
    b. special interest groups to get candidates elected.
    c. Congress as part of an effort to monitor the Presidency.
    d. students to end American involvement in Vietnam.

    ANS: B   DIF: Medium   REF: 884   OBJ: 35.0
    TOP: Special Interest Groups

36. If you watched the Watergate hearings on television and waited in line for rationed gasoline, you were probably living in the years
    a. 1968–1969.   c. 1972–1974.
    b. 1970–1971.   d. 1975–1976.

    ANS: C   DIF: Medium   OBJ: 35.1
    TOP: U.S. History 1972-1974

37. Which of the following items is INCORRECTLY paired?
    a. Begin—Israel   c. Quaddafi—Libya
    b. Khomeini—Iran   d. Pahlavi—Egypt

    ANS: D   DIF: Medium   REF: 879, 887, 893
    OBJ: 35.2   TOP: Mid-East Leaders

38. Which of the following is an OPINION rather than a fact?
    a. Under Communist rule, many "boat people" fled from South Vietnam.
    b. Khmer Rouge policy in Cambodia led to millions of deaths.
    c. United States aid could have prevented Communist takeovers in Laos and Cambodia.
    d. From the start, there were violations of the 1973 cease-fire agreement in South Vietnam.

    ANS: C   DIF: Medium   OBJ: 35.3
    TOP: Communism / Laos & Cambodia

39. Presidents Nixon, Ford, and Carter had the following experiences in common EXCEPT
    a. the problem of rapid inflation.
    b. failure to win a second term as President.
    c. problems arising from energy shortages.
    d. lack of public confidence.

    ANS: D   DIF: Medium   REF: 838, 882, 896
    OBJ: 35.4   TOP: Presidential Elections

40. Which of the following would have been the MOST satisified with the accomplishments of the Reagan administration?
    a. conservationists   c. women
    b. African-Americans   d. defense contractors

    ANS: D   DIF: Medium   REF: 898   OBJ: 35.5
    TOP: Reagan's Presidency

SHORT ANSWER

In one or two sentences, define and distinguish between the terms given below.

1. pardon-clemency

   ANS:
   A pardon is forgiveness for a crime such as Ford's pardon of Nixon for Watergate. Clemency refers to mercy or leniency, such as when Ford announced that Vietnam draft evaders would not be punished if they swore allegience and two years of alternate service.

   DIF: Hard   REF: 877–878   OBJ: 35.0
   TOP: Ford's Presidency / Pardon / Clemency

2. recession-inflation

   ANS:
   Recession refers to a slowdown in the economy often characterized by high unemployment. Inflation refers to rising prices. A combination of the two conditions has been called "stagflation."

   DIF: Hard   REF: 884, 898   OBJ: 35.0   TOP: Economics

3. Khmer Rouge-Pathet Lao

ANS:
The Khmer Rouge were the Cambodian Communists who came to power in 1975. The Pathet Lao were the pro-Communists who seized power in Laos in 1975.

DIF: Hard   REF: 889–891   OBJ: 35.0
TOP: Communism / Laos & Cambodia

ESSAY

1. What is the fallacy in the following statement? Write your answer on a separate sheet of paper and write a paragraph explaining why you chose it.
    President Reagan's economic policies were the reason for the improvement in the economy from 1980 to 1984.
    A. single cause
    B. preceding event as cause
    C. stereotyping
    D. special pleading

    ANS:
    answer a Students' paragraphs should support their answers.

    DIF: Hard   REF: 896–900   OBJ: 35.0
    TOP: Reagan's Presidency / Economics

2. Explain three of the problems affecting the economy which plagued the presidencies of Ford and Carter.

    ANS:
    Three problems affecting the U.S.economy in the Ford and Carter years were inflation and recession, energy (oil) costs, and a trade deficit. These were all interconnected. In 1973 inflation was running 8.5 percent annually. By 1974 it had increased to 12 percent. President Ford viewed inflation as a number one problem for the country. He thought that government spending was the main cause and tried to prevent Congress from spending excessively. A large factor in the inflation was the rising price of energy, specifically oil. By 1973 the price of a barrel had quintupled. Due to the high energy costs, prices shot up and the nation suffered the worst recession since WWII. As American dollars poured out of the country to pay for oil, our trade deficit mounted. This was the amount of goods we sold abroad compared to what we bought abroad. So the purchasing power of the dollar overseas declined.

    DIF: Hard   REF: 879–880, 884–886, 896–901   OBJ: 35.0
    TOP: U.S. Economy / Ford / Carter

3. How did OPEC's increase in oil prices affect the United States?

ANS:
Answers will vary but could include the following ideas: The results of OPEC's increase in oil prices were the inflation that followed the price hike and the subsequent scramble to develop alternative energy sources.

DIF: Hard   REF: 880   OBJ: 35.1   TOP: Mid-East / Oil

4. Imported oil poses too many risks to be calmly accepted. . . . The United States should make a much greater attempt to stop the growth of its oil imports. But can the United States do this? There are four conventional sources of domestic energy: oil, natural gas, coal, and nuclear power. Briefly outline the advantages and disadvantages of each of these sources of power. What other methods might lessen U.S. dependence on foreign oil?

ANS:
Answers will vary but could include the following ideas: Conventional power sources such as natural gas and coal vary in availability. However, though they may not be scarce at this time, the consumption of these fuels creates air pollution and a deterioration of the ozone layer. Nuclear power provides a clearer source of energy, but the long-range effect of radioactive wastes remains in question. Oil, in short supply during the 1970s, provides an efficient source of energy but exposes the United States to reliance on foreign oil producers and subjects the nation to changes in world oil prices. As alternative energy sources, there are such possibilities as solar power, geothermal power, and waste-refuse plants.

DIF: Hard   REF: 886–887   OBJ: 35.2
TOP: Oil / Alternative Energy

5. In 1974 there were only 600 PACs. By 1984 the number had grown to over 4,000. What factors do you think contributed to this tremendous increase? Do you feel that PACs help or hurt the political system? Explain your answer.

ANS:
Answers will vary but could include the following ideas: There has been an enormous increase in the number of special interest groups competing for influence in Congress. This could be viewed in both a positive and negative light. While some might say that PACs and other lobbyists make it possible for Congress to know what the people want on a specific issue, others would say that it gives those with money an advantage over those who are less prosperous. The increased influence of special interest groups has coincided with the decline in party loyalty and the tendency for people to organize around issues rather than parties.

DIF: Hard   REF: 884   OBJ: 35.2
TOP: Special Interest Groups

6. Explain Carter's relations with the Soviet Union and the fate of the SALT II agreement.

ANS:
Answers will vary but could include the following ideas: In general, Carter's relationship with the Soviets was strained because of his open criticism of the human rights violations of the Soviets. The President particularly angered the Russians by praising their dissidents and abruptly proposing a sweeping plan for arms limitations. By the time Carter had ironed out some of the problems the Soviets had with the new plan, the Soviets had invaded Afghanistan. SALT II was not signed.

DIF: Hard   REF: 891–892   OBJ: 35.4
TOP: Carter's Presidency / Foreign Policy

7. Why did the United States sign a treaty on the Panama Canal in 1978? What were the treaty's provisions?

ANS:
Answers will vary but could include the following ideas: In the early 1900s, the United States had signed a treaty with the Republic of Panama that gave the United States, in essence, total control of the canal forever. Starting with the Johnson administration, there was a growing recognition that the treaty was unfair. (At the time of the signing, there was a feeling that Panama had no choice but to sign.) Carter also felt the treaty was unfair. That, in addition to a need to improve relations with other South American countries, motivated Carter to negotiate a new treaty. The new treaty gave the Republic of Panama complete control of the Canal at the end of 1999.

DIF: Hard   REF: 892–893   OBJ: 35.4
TOP: U.S. Foreign Policy / Panama Canal

8. Explain how the overthrow of the Shah of Iran affected the national interests of the United States.

ANS:
Answers will vary but could include the following ideas: The U.S. lost an ally in the Middle East. The overthrow of the Shah had an impact on the strategic defense of the Persian Gulf. Additionally, it cut off an important source of oil for the United States.

DIF: Hard   REF: 887–888   OBJ: 35.4   TOP: Mid-East Conflicts

9. Compare and contrast Keynesian economic theory with the ideas of "supply-side economics."
   How successful were Reagan's attempts at implementing a supply-side economic program?

   ANS:
   Answers will vary but could include the following ideas: While Keynesians and supply-siders
   shared the belief that government policy could strongly affect the nation's economic health,
   Keynesians favored intervention on the "demand" side, while supply-siders favored intervention
   on the "supply" side. Answers should examine the effects of supply-side economics on the
   recession and inflation of the early 1870s, the economic recovery of the mid-1980s, and the
   growing federal budget deficit.

   DIF: Hard   REF: 897–898   OBJ: 35.1
   TOP: Reagan's Candidacy / Economics

10. Explain what "deregulation" was and how it worked, giving specific examples of the policy in
    action.

    ANS:
    Answers will vary but could include the following ideas: Deregulation meant cutting back on
    federal control of many industries in order to increase marketplace competition and business
    efficiency and to return to free-market principles. Examples might include AT&T and the
    airlines.

    DIF: Hard   REF: 902–903   OBJ: 35.2   TOP: Deregulation

MATCHING

Match each item with the correct statement below.

a. Sandra Day O'Connor
b. Clarence Thomas
c. Tiananmen Square
d. Solidarity
e. Geraldine Ferraro

f. "Columbia"
g. Anwar el-Sadat
h. "velvet revolution"
i. NAFTA
j. Saddam Hussein

1. Site of an attack on unarmed, pro-democracy demonstrators by the Chinese army.
2. Bush appointment to the Supreme Court, accused of sexual harassment by Anita Hill.
3. Unofficial labor union formed in Poland in 1980.
4. Peaceful demonstrations leading to the collapse of the Communist government in Czechoslovakia.
5. Dictator who sent the armies of Iraq to seize Kuwait.
6. First woman appointed to the Supreme Court.
7. Egyptian leader who was assassinated in 1981.
8. America's first reusable space vehicle.
9. First woman nominated for Vice-President by a major party.
10. Eliminated tariffs and other barriers to trade with Canada and Mexico.

1. ANS: C   DIF: Easy   REF: 930   OBJ: 36.0
    TOP: China / Tiananmen Square
2. ANS: B   DIF: Easy   REF: 934   OBJ: 36.0
    TOP: Supreme Court
3. ANS: D   DIF: Easy   REF: 911   OBJ: 36.0
    TOP: Poland
4. ANS: H   DIF: Easy   REF: 927   OBJ: 36.0
    TOP: Communism / Czechoslovakia
5. ANS: J   DIF: Easy   REF: 931   OBJ: 36.0
    TOP: Middle East Conflicts
6. ANS: A   DIF: Easy   REF: 914   OBJ: 36.0
    TOP: Supreme Court
7. ANS: G   DIF: Easy   REF: 908   OBJ: 36.0
    TOP: Middle East Leaders
8. ANS: F   DIF: Easy   REF: 913   OBJ: 36.0
    TOP: Space Exploration
9. ANS: E   DIF: Easy   REF: 913   OBJ: 36.0
    TOP: Presidential Elections
10. ANS: I   DIF: Easy   REF: 939   OBJ: 36.0
    TOP: Clinton's Presidency / Foreign Trade Policy

MULTIPLE CHOICE

1. What was the name of the unofficial Polish labor union?
   a. PLO
   b. Solidarity
   c. NATO
   d. Sandinista

   ANS: B   DIF: Medium   REF: 911   OBJ: 36.3
   TOP: Poland

2. The SALT II treaty between the United States and the Soviet Union dealt with
   a. arms control.
   b. debts of the Third World.
   c. space exploration.
   d. "Star Wars."

   ANS: A   DIF: Medium   REF: 911   OBJ: 36.3
   TOP: Soviet Union Relations

3. The African-American candidate who made a strong showing in the 1984 bid for the Democratic nomination for President was
   a. Guion S. Bluford.
   b. Martin Luther King, Jr.
   c. Thurgood Marshall.
   d. Jesse Jackson.

   ANS: D   DIF: Medium   REF: 913   OBJ: 36.4
   TOP: Presidential Elections

4. Which of the following people did the Democrats nominate for President in 1984?
   a. Gary Hart
   b. John Anderson
   c. Walter Mondale
   d. Jimmy Carter

   ANS: C   DIF: Medium   REF: 913   OBJ: 36.4
   TOP: Presidential Elections

5. Bill Clinton's first two years in office included each of the following EXCEPT:
   a. a debate over health care.
   b. the passage of NAFTA.
   c. the appointment of Clarence Thomas to the Supreme Court.
   d. the signing of the Family Leave Act.

   ANS: C   DIF: Medium   REF: 939–940   OBJ: 36.5
   TOP: Clinton's Presidency

6. The system of "apartheid" in South Africa
   a. is based on the exploitation of the white majority.
   b. has been received with indifference throughout the world.
   c. is fought through the peaceful efforts of Bishop Tutu.
   d. has yet to be addressed by the United States Congress.

   ANS: C   DIF: Medium   REF: 922   OBJ: 36.5
   TOP: Apartheid

7. Which of the following was awarded the Nobel Peace Prize for his leadership in the struggle against apartheid?
   a. Jesse Jackson
   b. Desmond Tutu
   c. Mao Zedong
   d. George Bush

   ANS: B   DIF: Medium   REF: 922   OBJ: 36.4
   TOP: Apartheid

8. All of the following are Baltic states EXCEPT
   a. Latvia.
   b. Estonia.
   c. Lithuania.
   d. Kiev.

   ANS: D   DIF: Medium   REF: 929   OBJ: 36.5

9. Who was the Chinese leader during the Tiananmen Square Massacre?
   a. Mao Zedong
   b. Todor I. Zhikov
   c. Manuel Noriega
   d. Deng Xiaoping

   ANS: D   DIF: Medium   REF: 930   OBJ: 36.6
   TOP: China / Tiananmen Square

10. What was the code name for the military attack on Iraq?
    a. Operation Desert Storm
    b. Operation Just Cause
    c. Operation Bootstrap
    d. Operation Desert Shield

    ANS: A   DIF: Medium   REF: 933   OBJ: 36.6
    TOP: Persian Gulf War

11. President Reagan was referring to what country when he used the phrase "evil empire"?
    a. Cuba
    b. the Soviet Union
    c. Libya
    d. the People's Republic of China

    ANS: B   DIF: Medium   REF: 906   OBJ: 36.1
    TOP: U.S. / Soviet Relations

12. All of the following contributed to a deterioration of Soviet-American relations in the early 1980s EXCEPT
    a. concern over high oil prices.
    b. South Korean airline incident.
    c. institution of martial law in Poland.
    d. invasion of Afghanistan.

    ANS: A   DIF: Medium   REF: 910–911   OBJ: 36.1
    TOP: U.S. / Soviet Relations

13. A major reason for United States involvement in El Salvador and Nicaragua in 1980s is to
    a. protect United States investments there.
    b. stop communist aggression.
    c. protect American students who attend universities there.
    d. stop communist aggression AND protect American students who attend universities there.

    ANS: B   DIF: Medium   REF: 907–908   OBJ: 36.1
    TOP: U.S. Foreign Policy / El Salvador & Nicaragua

14. Each of the following is true about the Persian Gulf War EXCEPT:
    a. With the possession of Kuwait, Iraq held 20 percent of the world's oil.
    b. Saddam Hussein was forced from office.
    c. Iraq was defeated.
    d. Iraq fired missiles at Saudi Arabia and Israel.

    ANS: B   DIF: Medium   REF: 931–933   OBJ: 36.1
    TOP: Mid-East Conflicts

15. President Reagan's main concern about the political situation in El Salvador was that
    a. the country might become allied with Argentina.
    b. Marxists might gain control of the government.
    c. El Salvador might invade Nicaragua.
    d. Cuba might invade El Salvador.

    ANS: B   DIF: Medium   REF: 907   OBJ: 36.3
    TOP: U.S. Foreign Policy / El Salvador

16. A major aim of Reagan's foreign policy during his first term was to
    a. force the collection of debts from Third World nations.
    b. stop the spread of communism.
    c. make human rights a cornerstone of American foreign policy.
    d. negotiate a nuclear freeze agreement with the Soviets.

    ANS: B   DIF: Medium   REF: 907–911   OBJ: 36.3
    TOP: Reagan's Presidency / Foreign Policy

17. Which of the following did President Reagan support during his 1984 presidential campaign?
    a. the Equal Rights Amendment   c. busing
    b. affirmative action   d. voluntary school prayer

    ANS: D   DIF: Medium   REF: 912   OBJ: 36.4
    TOP: Reagan's Presidency

18. Gorbachev's policy of promoting a more open society was known as
    a. perestroika.   c. glasnost.
    b. "star wars."   d. "new thinking" about old problems.

    ANS: C   DIF: Medium   REF: 916   OBJ: 36.2
    TOP: Soviet Union

19. NASA originally designed vehicles like the "Columbia" to
    a. provide a cost-effective method to get satellites into orbit.
    b. explore the planets in our solar system.
    c. take a crew of astronauts to Mars.
    d. take part in Reagan's plan for "Star Wars."

    ANS: A   DIF: Medium   REF: 912–913   OBJ: 36.4
    TOP: Space Exploration

20. Each of the following is true about the 1992 presidential election EXCEPT:
    a. George Bush's reelection was hurt by divisions in the Republican party.
    b. Al Gore was Bill Clinton's running mate.
    c. Bill Clinton won the election.
    d. H. Ross Perot won a large number of electoral votes.

    ANS: D   DIF: Medium   REF: 936–938   OBJ: 36.3
    TOP: Presidential Elections

21. Which of the following people was NOT involved in the Iran-contra affair?
    a. Douglas Ginsburg   c. William Casey
    b. Oliver North   d. John Poindexter

    ANS: A   DIF: Medium   REF: 919   OBJ: 36.3
    TOP: Iran / Iraq War / Reagan Foreign Policy

22. Which area was of LEAST concern to the United States in the late 1980s?
    a. the Middle East   c. Latin America
    b. Central America   d. the Far East

    ANS: D   DIF: Medium   OBJ: 36.3   TOP: U.S. Foreign Relations

23. President Reagan ordered the invasion of Grenada for all of the following reasons EXCEPT to
    a. overthrow the radical government.
    b. stop the island from becoming a communist base.
    c. protect Americans living on the island.
    d. test the legality of the War Powers Act.

    ANS: D   DIF: Medium   REF: 909–910   OBJ: 36.1
    TOP: Reagan's Presidency / Grenada

24. Reagan called for constitutional amendments
    a. requiring a balanced federal budget.
    b. allowing voluntary prayer in public schools.
    c. abolishing capital punishment.
    d. requiring a balanced federal budget AND allowing voluntary prayer in public schools.

    ANS: D   DIF: Medium   REF: 912   OBJ: 36.2
    TOP: Reagan's Presidency

25. In the 1984 presidential election, Reagan won by
    a. a landslide.
    b. only two states.
    c. a small percentage of the popular vote.
    d. a narrow margin of electoral votes.

    ANS: A   DIF: Medium   REF: 913   OBJ: 36.4
    TOP: Presidential Elections

26. Which of the following factors did NOT contribute to the Savings and Loan crisis?
    a. high-risk loans made by savings banks
    b. low interest rates
    c. dishonest bankers
    d. an increase in government insurance on deposits

    ANS: B   DIF: Medium   REF: 924   OBJ: 36.4
    TOP: Economics / Savings & Loan Crisis

27. Which of the following was determined to be the PRIMARY cause of the stock market crash in 1987?
    a. buying on margin
    b. computer trading programs
    c. the dissolution of the Securities and Exchange Commission
    d. inaccuracy of the Dow Jones average

    ANS: B   DIF: Medium   REF: 920   OBJ: 36.4
    TOP: Economics / '87 Stock Market Crash

28. Which of the following was NOT a problem faced by the Bush Administration?
    a. Republican control of the Senate   c. the national debt
    b. the Savings and Loan crisis   d. pollution at nuclear weapons plants

    ANS: A   DIF: Medium   REF: 924   OBJ: 36.4
    TOP: Bush Presidency

29. The stock market crash of 1987
    a. was caused by new computer trading programs.
    b. was not as bad as the crash of October 1929.
    c. was expected to take place after a strong "bull market."
    d. was not felt around the world until months later.

    ANS: A   DIF: Medium   REF: 919–920   OBJ: 36.5
    TOP: Economics / '87 Stock Market Crash

30. Which of the following was NOT a problem in the Soviet Union during the late 1980s?
    a. a weak communist party   c. ethnic unrest
    b. food shortages   d. a weak central government

    ANS: A   DIF: Medium   REF: 928–930   OBJ: 36.5
    TOP: Soviet Union

31. Each of the following were of concern to middle-class Americans in the early 1990s EXCEPT:
    a. unemployment.   c. drugs.
    b. war in Russia.   d. gangs and crime.

    ANS: B   DIF: Medium   REF: 936   OBJ: 36.5
    TOP: Life in America

32. The first elected president of Poland was
    a. Lech Walesa.
    c. Wojciech Jaruzelski.
    b. Erich Honecker.
    d. Helmut Kohl.

    ANS: C   DIF: Medium   REF: 925   OBJ: 36.5
    TOP: Poland

33. The "velvet revolution" occurred in
    a. Hungary.
    c. Czechoslovakia.
    b. Poland.
    d. Romania.

    ANS: C   DIF: Medium   REF: 927   OBJ: 36.5
    TOP: Communism / Czechoslovakia

34. The United States intervened in Haiti in 1994 in order to
    a. stop the spread of communism.
    b. restore the democratically-elected president to power.
    c. end drug trafficking there.
    d. protect American business interests.

    ANS: B   DIF: Medium   REF: 944   OBJ: 36.5
    TOP: U.S. Foreign Policy / Haiti

35. Which of the following was not a response to Iraq's seizure of Kuwait?
    a. the deployment of U.S. troops to Saudi Arabia
    b. an economic blockade
    c. the execution of Iraqi hostages
    d. a U.N. resolution to use force if Iraq did not withdraw from Kuwait

    ANS: C   DIF: Medium   REF: 931–933   OBJ: 36.6
    TOP: Iran / Iraq War

36. Which of the following countries provided troops to defend Saudi Arabia?
    a. Iran
    c. Eqypt
    b. Soviet Union
    d. Panama

    ANS: C   DIF: Medium   REF: 931   OBJ: 36.6
    TOP: Mid-East Conflicts

37. The goal of "Operation Just Cause" was to
    a. liberate Kuwait from Iraqi control.
    b. topple the regime of Manuel Noriega.
    c. punish Deng Xiaoping for the Tiananmen Square massacre.
    d. take over Panama.

    ANS: B   DIF: Medium   REF: 931   OBJ: 36.6
    TOP: U.S. Foreign Policy / Panama

38. The U.S. missiles used to destroy Iraqi scud missiles were known as
    a. cruise missiles.
    c. anti-ballistic missiles.
    b. patriot missiles.
    d. H-bombs.

    ANS: B   DIF: Medium   REF: 933   OBJ: 36.6
    TOP: Iran / Iraq War

39. Which of the following is a CONSEQUENCE of the other three?
    a. The economy went into a recession in 1990.
    b. Oil prices rose.
    c. The cold war ended and defense spending was cut.
    d. Taxpayers paid for the costs of failed Savings and Loans.

    ANS: A   DIF: Medium   REF: 934   OBJ: 36.3
    TOP: Bush's Presidency / Economics

40. Which of the following is a CONSEQUENCE of the other three?
    a. Israel invaded Lebanon.
    b. Congress invoked the War Powers Act.
    c. United States marines joined an international peace-keeping force in Lebanon.
    d. Lebanese Christians massacred Palestinians in Beirut.

    ANS: B   DIF: Medium   REF: 908–910   OBJ: 36.3
    TOP: Mid-East Conflicts

41. Which of the following is an OPINION rather than a fact?
    a. The fact that he chose a woman as his running mate was the chief reason Walter
       Mondale lost the 1984 election.
    b. Reagan called space "our next frontier."
    c. In 1982 a monument was dedicated in Washington, D.C., honoring Americans who had
       died in Vietnam.
    d. Reagan's financial policies became known as "supply-side economics."

    ANS: A   DIF: Medium   REF: 913   OBJ: 36.4
    TOP: Presidential Elections

42. All of the following are Supreme Court Justices EXCEPT
    a. Antonin Scalia.   c. Anthony M. Kennedy.
    b. William H. Rehnquist.   d. Robert Bork.

    ANS: D   DIF: Medium   REF: 914–915   OBJ: 36.5
    TOP: Supreme Court

43. All of the following helped protect the U.S. from another depression following the stock market
    crash of 1987 EXCEPT
    a. federal insurance on bank accounts.
    b. the Securities and Exchange Commission.
    c. a revised Federal Reserve System.
    d. the Dow Jones stock average.

    ANS: D   DIF: Medium   REF: 920   OBJ: 36.4
    TOP: Economics / Stock Market

44. Which of the following did NOT inhibit George Bush's efforts to win reelection?
    a. his handling of the Gulf War   c. H. Ross Perot's candidacy
    b. the economy   d. divisions in the Republican party

    ANS: A   DIF: Medium   REF: 936–938   OBJ: 36.6
    TOP: Presidential Elections

ESSAY

1. Which of the following is a CONSEQUENCE of the other three? Write your answer on a separate sheet of paper and support your answer with a paragraph explaining why you chose it.
   A. The Soviet Union ends its support of the Warsaw Pact country.
   B. The Soviet Union promises not to intercede in Poland.
   C. Communist regimes in Eastern Europe collapse.
   D. The Soviet Union economy is a ruin.

   ANS:
   answer C Students' paragraphs should support their answers.

   DIF: Hard   REF: 928–929   OBJ: 36.0   TOP: Soviet Union

2. Some critics of Reagan's Central American policies and Clinton's intervention in Haiti contended that they didn't want "another Vietnam." Explain what is meant by this statement. What do you think U.S. policy toward Central America and the Caribbean should be? Support your position with information from your text and current news stories.

   ANS:
   Student answers will vary but could include these ideas: Critics felt that increasing support of the anti-government contras in Nicaragua and the anti-communist government in El Salvador would tend to lead the United States toward the use of American military personnel in direct military intervention.The similarity to the early Vietnam conflict is striking: The U.S. sent aid to the group fighting the Communists, then began sending advisors, and finally sent armies of soldiers. Was this beginning to happen in Central America? Opinions as to what U.S. policy should be in Central America and the Carribean will vary, but could include some mention of Communist rebels in El Salvador, the Marxist government in Nicaragua, and news stories regarding the current status of the conflicts.

   DIF: Hard   REF: 944   OBJ: 36.0
   TOP: U.S. Foreign Policy / South America / Caribbean

3. How did Reagan attempt to counter Soviet influence in Europe?

   ANS:
   Answers will vary but could include the following ideas: Reagan planned to put new medium-range missiles in Western Europe as part of NATO's defense system in order to counter Soviet influence and the perceived threat of a Soviet nuclear attack.

   DIF: Hard   REF: 910–911   OBJ: 36.3   TOP: U.S. / Soviet Relations

4. Explain the role played by the United States in the affairs of El Salvador and in the affairs of Nicaragua.

ANS:
Answers will vary but could include the following ideas: Through the CIA, and without the knowledge and consent of Congress, the Reagan administration funded and trained anti-Sandinista guerrillas and helped plant mines in Nicaraguan harbors. The United States also held large-scale military maneuvers in Honduras and in El Salvador to indicate its ability and readiness to support anti-Marxist movements and governments in neighboring Nicaragua and El Salvador.

DIF: Hard   REF: 907–908, 918–919, 921–922   OBJ: 36.3
TOP: U.S. Foreign Policy / El Salvador & Nicaragua

5. Explain the threat posed to the financial stability of the world by the buildup of foreign debts among Third World countries.

ANS:
Answers will vary but could include the following ideas: During the years of high inflation during the 1970s, borrowing money from banks of industrial nations seemed cheap. However, by 1983, Third World countries could not even pay the interest on their enormous debts. Their problems were created by high oil prices and a worldwide recession. Such massive, unpaid debts eventually began to threaten the economies of the entire world.

DIF: Hard   REF: 910–911   OBJ: 36.3
TOP: Economics / Foreign Debt

6. Explain how the Democratic presidential race of 1984 reflected the major changes that had taken place in the party and in the nation since the 1950s.

ANS:
Answers will vary but could include the following ideas: Both the strong campaign of Jesse Jackson and the nomination of Geraldine Ferraro would have been almost unthinkable 30 years before. In the 1960s, African-Americans suffered severe discrimination in their attempts to exercise their right to vote. Neither were women expected to play prominent roles in national politics.

DIF: Hard   REF: 913   OBJ: 36.4   TOP: Presidential Elections

7. Identify the justices appointed to the Supreme Court during the Reagan administration. How might the appointment of conservative judges affect future Supreme Court decisions?

ANS:
Answers will vary but could include the following ideas: Reagan appointed Justices Sandra O'Connor, Antonin Scalia, and Anthony Kennedy to the Supreme Court. He also named William Rehnquist to be Chief Justice. A more conservative Supreme Court might overturn some of the more liberal decisions made by the Court in the past, such as in the case of "Roe v. Wade."

DIF: Hard   REF: 914–915   OBJ: 36.3   TOP: Supreme Court

8. Explain the positions that the President and Congress held concerning sanctions against South Africa. What arguments might each side offer?

ANS:
Answers will vary but could include the following ideas: The President felt that sanctions would hurt the economy and cause a loss of jobs for the African-American work force. Congress believed the sanctions would force the South African government into reforming.

DIF: Hard   REF: 922   OBJ: 36.4   TOP: Aparthied

9. Explain the impact that the end of the cold war could have on the United States.

ANS:
Answers will vary but could include the following ideas: The end of the cold war could bring about reduced defense spending and more spending on public services. The end of the cold war could bring greater opportunity for resolving regional disputes without violence. The end of the cold war could bring about greater economic cooperation.

DIF: Hard   REF: 924–930   OBJ: 36.5   TOP: Cold War

10. Identify the purpose of the U.S. invasion of Panama. Do you think the actions of the United States were justified? Explain.

ANS:
Answers will vary but could include the following ideas: The purpose of the U.S. invasion of Panama, "Operation Just Cause," was to remove Manuel Noriega from power. The U.S. was trying to help the Panamanians overthrow a corrupt dictator whom they had voted against in the election. Some students, however, may question the United States' right to become militarily involved in another nation's political disputes.

DIF: Hard   REF: 931   OBJ: 36.6
TOP: U.S. Foreign Policy / Panama

(page intentionally left blank)